PRACTICAL ELECTRICAL WIRING

PRACTICAL
ELECTRICAL WIRING
Residential, Farm, and Industrial

BASED ON THE 1965
NATIONAL ELECTRICAL CODE

H. P. RICHTER

*Member, International Association of Electrical Inspectors
and National Fire Protection Association*

SEVENTH EDITION

McGRAW-HILL BOOK COMPANY

New York   San Francisco   Toronto

London   Sydney

PRACTICAL ELECTRICAL WIRING

Library of Congress Catalog Card Number 66-15839

52384

56–COCO–754321069

PREFACE

In preparing this book it has been the author's aim to make it simple enough for the beginner, yet complete enough so that it will be of value also to those already engaged in electrical work. It is intended to be, not a manual that merely recites the methods used in wiring buildings for the use of electricity, but rather a book that explains the subject in such fashion that the reader will learn both the *way* things are done and *why* they are done in that particular way. Only in this manner can the student master the subject so that he can solve his own problems as they arise in actual practice, for no book can possibly cover all the different problems that are likely to arise.

Since this book is not intended to include the subject of electrical engineering, only so many basic engineering data as are essential have been included, and these so far as possible have been boiled down to ABC proportions.

All methods shown are in strict accordance with the National Electrical Code, but no attempt has been made to include a detailed explanation of *all* subjects covered by the Code. The Code is written to include any and all cases that might arise in wiring every type of structure from the smallest cottage to the largest skyscraper; it covers ordinary wiring as well as those things that come up only very rarely. The scope of this book has been limited to the wiring of structures of limited size and at ordinary voltages, under 600 volts. Skyscrapers and steel mills and projects of similar size involve problems that the student will not meet until long after he has mastered the contents of this book.

The book consists of three parts:

Part 1 presents the fundamentals of electrical work; terminology; basic principles; the theory behind general practices. Part 2 deals with the actual wiring of residential buildings and

farms.   Part 3 covers the actual wiring of nonresidential buildings, such as stores, factories, schools, and similar structures.

The science or principles of electricity do not change; the art
or method of application does change.   That portion of this book,
having to do with *principles* has in this seventh edition been
revised and amplified to present such principles more clearly.
That portion concerned with *methods* has been revised or rewritten as required by Code changes, to describe new materials
and methods, and to outline the methods more clearly.

The author will welcome practical suggestions for the improvement of the content or the presentation of this book.

H. P. RICHTER

CONTENTS

Contents

PRACTICAL ELECTRICAL WIRING

Part 1

THEORY AND BASIC PRINCIPLES

Part 1 of this book is the introduction to practical electrical work, the ABC of the science and the art of electrical wiring. In order to master the art, naturally you must clearly understand the science or the principles involved. The terms used in the measurement of electricity, the names of the devices used in wiring, must be at your finger tips.

For that reason a considerable portion of the material presented in Part 1 of this book emphasizes the "why" more than the "how." If you understand the "why," the "how" becomes obvious. Master both, and Parts 2 and 3 of this book will be relatively simple.

Chapter 1

UNDERWRITERS AND CODES

This book will deal with the electrical materials that are installed in a building so that electric power can be safely used for all intended purposes.   It will also deal with *how* these materials are installed and *why* they are installed in a certain way.

In any discussion of electrical work you will often see the phrase "Approved by Underwriters" and also references to the "Code."   You must understand clearly who the Underwriters are and what the Code is.

Electricity is a powerful force.   Under control, it safely performs an endless variety of work for us; uncontrolled, it can lead to great harm and damage.   It is under control when the right kinds of materials are installed in the right way.   It becomes uncontrolled when the wrong kinds of materials are used or when the right kinds of materials are wrongly installed.

Uncontrolled electric power can cause fires, can kill people, and can lead to a multitude of other costly results.   When these things happen, individuals are the greatest sufferers.   Insurance companies also suffer losses, which can result only in higher insurance rates which individuals are called upon to pay. It is then only natural that insurance companies have led the way in work which leads to the setting up of minimum standards of quality in electrical materials, as well as uniform methods of installation—standards and methods that experiment and experience have shown lead to a maximum of usefulness with the least amount of danger.

Underwriters' Laboratories.   The American Insurance Association has established a testing organization known as Underwriters' Laboratories, Inc., with testing stations in Chicago and several other locations. Manufacturers who wish to do so submit samples of their product to these laboratories before going into production. In the laboratories the product is given exhaustive tests in accordance with established standards, and if it in every way comes up to the minimum requirements, it is listed in the Underwriters' official published list and is then known as "Listed by Underwriters' Laboratories, Inc."

It should be interesting to know that the tests by the Underwriters, and frequently also the tests that the manufacturers are required to make, are many times more severe than any conditions that are likely to be imposed upon the merchandise in actual use. For example, consider the tests required of the manufacturers by the Underwriters for ordinary wire used in residential wiring. The manufacturers have several choices of procedure, but, as a minimum, 10% of all the wire must be submerged in a tank of water for 12 hr and then tested at 1,500 to 3,500 volts (depending on the size of the wire) against breakdown while still submerged. Only after the wire meets this test is it labeled with the Underwriters' label, which indicates that the wire is suitable for use at not over 600 volts.

An example of the extreme severity of tests at the Underwriters' Laboratories is that applied to all plug fuses when submitted by manufacturers for listing. Such fuses are never rated at more than 30 amp. In the laboratory test, the fuse is short-circuited across a circuit capable of delivering 10,000 amp. The fuse will naturally blow, but it must cause no damage external to itself. See Fig. 1-1, which shows two fuses after test. The one shown at the bottom of the picture has blown, but it is still otherwise intact, and the fuseholder is not damaged; it was listed. The one shown at the top of the picture also has blown, but in the process it demolished both itself and the fuseholder; it was not listed. Used in a home, such a fuse could easily start a fire or cause an injury.

In order that the product may remain listed, the safety level must remain at least as high as the Underwriters' minimum specifications. To make sure that it does, the Underwriters send traveling inspectors to the factory from time to time to see that the required factory tests are made and that every effort is made to preserve adequate safety. Inspectors are more or less permanently stationed at some of the larger factories. The Underwriters also regularly buy samples in the open market from

Fig. 1-1. After testing both fuses, the Underwriters approved the one at the bottom. The fuse at the top did not have a chance of becoming a listed item. (*Underwriters' Laboratories, Inc.*)

merchants stocking the item, and repeat the original test. If the safety level is not maintained, listing is withdrawn. There are two basic types of follow-up service by the Underwriters: reexamination and label.

Reexamination Service. This type of service is used when it is relatively simple to maintain the safety of the original sample of the product. Many devices fall into this classification: sockets, receptacles, outlet boxes, porcelain insulators, most appliances, etc.   On such merchandise it is not necessary to test and inspect a large percentage of merchandise manufactured.

Fig. 1-2. The markers above on merchandise indicate that the material is approved by Underwriters.   (*Underwriters' Laboratories, Inc.*)

It is not essential that items falling into the reexamination classification be individually labeled to the effect that they are listed, although practically all manufacturers are eager to state this fact so that the purchasing public will not overlook it.   For this purpose the uniform markers shown in Fig. 1-2 have been

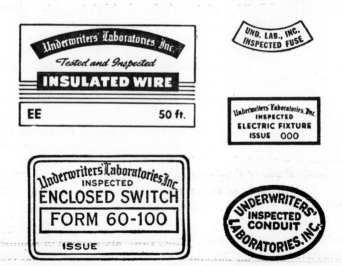

Fig. 1-3. Many items have an individual label on each piece of merchandise. Above are shown a few examples.   (*Underwriters' Laboratories, Inc.*)

developed and are in general use, both on the merchandise and on containers.

Label Service. This type of service is applicable to products where each piece of merchandise is individually labeled with a label that reads "Underwriters' Laboratories, Inc. Listed" or an abbreviation like "Und. Lab., Inc. List." Under the label service, representatives of the Underwriters' Laboratories make frequent inspections at the factory to examine and test samples of the labeled product. Into this classification fall wire and cable of all kinds, conduit, switches of all kinds, lighting fixtures, and similar devices. Examples of the labels used on the merchandise are seen in Fig. 1-3.

Flexible cords receive a special label which is applied in bracelet fashion every 5 ft on the cord, so that, when it is sold over the counter, the purchaser definitely knows that he is buying safe, sound merchandise (see Fig. 1-4). The bracelet label like-

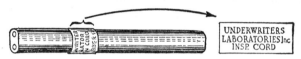

Fɪɢ. 1-4. Approved flexible cords bear the bracelet label shown above, every 5 ft.

wise is of great value when devices such as floor lamps, for example, are sold. The presence of the label on the cord means that the cord was made under label service follow-up.

The presence of such a bracelet label on the cord used in an assembly (such as an appliance cord or extension cord) indicates only that the cord used in the assembly is listed; the devices on the ends of the cord may or may not be listed. Today every cord *assembly*, if it is listed, must bear one of the two types of labels illustrated in Fig. 1-5, indicating that the complete assembly is listed. The bracelet of Fig. 1-4 is used mostly on flexible cords sold by the foot over the counter.

In certain classes of devices, such as, for example, toggle switches, the words "Und. Lab., Inc. List." are molded or stamped or otherwise made an integral part of the merchandise and constitute the label. Look for these words molded or stamped into bakelite, steel, or porcelain parts of such devices.

How Underwriters Are Supported. Underwriters' Laboratories is a nonprofit organization, and its cost of operation is absorbed by the manufacturers who submit merchandise. There is a fee for testing merchandise, and when a manufacturer buys

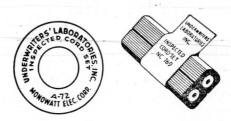

Fig. 1-5. Cord assemblies if approved have one of the above two types of labels.

the labels for his product from the Underwriters, he pays more than the bare cost of the label, the difference being a service charge which pays for the inspectors' expenses in checking at the factories, and which also supports the laboratories in general.

What "Listed by Underwriters" Means. Listing assures the public that the manufacturer of the listed item has submitted samples to the Underwriters, who have tested them and found that they meet the required minimum *safety* standards. The presumption is that the manufacturer in his future production will maintain that quality. The public is assured that the listed item probably meets minimum safety standards; the manufacturer knows his competitors are not skimping; insurance companies suffer smaller losses than would be the case if substandard materials were used. This is a happy arrangement whereby everybody benefits.

Listing does not mean that all listed items are of equal quality, or indeed that a listed item is necessarily of good quality for its purpose; it merely means that the listed item meets the minimum *safety* requirements of the Underwriters. For example, one listed switch may outlast another by five times, but both meet the minimum safety requirements. Exercise the same judgment in buying listed merchandise that you would in buying other kinds of merchandise with which Underwriters are not concerned.

An automobile tire designed for a passenger car will no doubt be suitable when used for that purpose but would be totally unsafe if used on a 3-ton truck. So also with electrical materials, "Listed by Underwriters" implies that the part or material in question is safe when used for the purpose for which it was designed. For example, armored cable is suitable for use only in dry locations, for which reason the electrical inspector will not give approval for its use in wet locations such as barns. It isn't suitable for that purpose and can't be used even if it is listed by Underwriters. Flexible cord is listed for use in connecting floor lamps, clocks, and similar devices, but may not be used for the wiring of circuits in a house, even if the cord is listed by Underwriters.

Identification. In any event, regardless of whether a product is listed under reexamination or label service, it must always be identified by the manufacturer's name or trademark, by a number that has been assigned by the Underwriters, or by some arbitrary symbol, and in addition by a type or catalogue description or by a "listed" label, so that it can be recognized as listed merchandise.

How to Recognize Listed Merchandise. How do you recognize listed merchandise when you see it? If the merchandise is labeled "Underwriters' Laboratories, Inc.," or with an abbreviation indicating the same, it is listed. If the merchandise or its carton bears the UL insignia of Fig. 1-2, it is listed. If it does not bear the manufacturer's marking or other designation which will identify it, it is not a listed item. Reference to the Underwriters' list of listed devices will establish in any event whether the merchandise is listed. The Underwriters' list contains tabulations showing manufacturers' names as well as catalogue numbers, thus making it easy to check any device. The safest policy is to buy electrical merchandise only from concerns that have a reputation to maintain and that cannot afford to jeopardize it by selling unlisted products.

It does not follow that just because an item is not listed it cannot be good merchandise, for some manufacturers have an exaggerated idea of the cost of having an item inspected and listed, and others just do not care; for these reasons they do not submit their products for listing. The presumption, however, is against merchandise that is not listed.

In fairness it must be stated that the Underwriters do not concern themselves at all with certain devices on which it is a simple matter to maintain good quality or which present no hazard whatever. In this class are, for example, low-voltage devices, such as doorbell wires and doorbells (but doorbell transformers *are* listed). Strangely, electric motors, except those of the explosion-proof type, are not listed.

National Electrical Code. If approved electrical devices of high quality are used, but installed in a haphazard fashion and with no regard to the relation of one device to the other or the total load they may be called upon to carry, the complete installation may still be dangerous. It is necessary therefore that standardized methods be set up which have been found in practice to be safe.

These standardized methods that experiment and experience have shown to be correct are set down in a form which has come to be known as the National Electrical Code. Whenever in this book the word "Code" is used it refers to this National Electrical Code, abbreviated NEC. The purposes of the Code are outlined in the following quotation from the Introduction of the Code:

a. The purpose of this Code is the practical safeguarding of persons and of buildings and their contents from hazards arising from the use of electricity for light, heat, power, radio, signaling, and for other purposes.

b. This Code contains basic minimum provisions considered necessary for safety. Compliance therewith and proper maintenance will result in an installation essentially free from hazard, but not necessarily efficient, convenient, or adequate for good service or future expansion of electrical use.

c. This Code is not intended as a design specification or an instruction manual for untrained persons.

From the above you can readily understand that the chief objective of the Code is to promote *safety* in electrical installations. Moreover, its specifications are the *minimum* requirements, again for safety. An electrical installation made in strict accordance with the Code will be safe, but it might still be impractical from many standpoints. As the quotation above from the Code points out, the installation might not be efficient,

convenient, or adequate for good service. Aside from comply-
ing with the Code requirements, the designer of an installation
and those who do the actual work must still use their own good
judgment and skill to produce an installation that will be completely satisfactory to the occupant of the building.

Do note also that the Code is "not an instruction manual for
untrained persons." Study of the Code is very necessary to
learn the science and art of wiring, but the Code alone is not
sufficient.

The Code is revised from time to time but not necessarily at
regular intervals. Once a new Code is issued, interim amendments appear that modify the original issue. In due course of
time, a new Code appears, incorporating all the amendments and
other new material. Usually the Code is reissued every two or
three years.

The Code is not written by one man or by a group of just a
few people. Each phase of the work is handled by those people
in the industry who are most competent to handle it. These
people are members of permanent committees established for
the purpose. There is a Correlating Committee of about a dozen
members, plus 17 subcommittees called "Code Making Panels,"
each with 6 to 12 members. To these committees falls the
tedious responsibility of listening to endless suggestions for re-
visions of the Code, debating the merits of the suggestions, and
finally revising the Code as seems desirable.

The Code consists of several dozen "Articles" each covering
one major division of the over-all subject, each subdivided into
as many "Sections" as required. Since each new Code contains
many changes and additions which must be "sandwiched" in
among the numbered portions of the previous Code, a major
editorial problem always exists. As a matter of fact, the 1956
Code had become quite a hodgepodge editorially; related details
were sometimes separated instead of following each other logically. As a result, the 1959 Code was reedited as far as numbering of the various articles and sections is concerned. For
example, Art. 250 covers the subject of grounding in both the
1956 and the 1959 Codes. In the 1956 Code this article was
broken down into Sec. 2501, 2502, and so on, all the way to
2632. In the 1959 Code the sections were numbered 250-1, 250-2,

and so on as far as necessary: 250-132. In other words, under the 1956 Code the first two digits of the section number indicated the article number, but in the case of the subject of grounding (Art. 250) the sections had beginning digits of both 25- and 26-, which is not possible under the arrangement adopted for the 1959 and subsequent Codes, where all are prefixed 250-.

The 1959 Code also was considerably rewritten editorially, so that, while the substance was not changed, the intent was restated in simpler words, easier to understand. These changes as well as the revised numbering scheme were of course carried forward to later Codes.

Each new Code of course carries changes in the rules as compared with the previous Code. Thus new Sections or even new Articles are added from time to time.

History of the Code. The first National Electrical Code was adopted in 1897. Before that time there were many other collections of rules or codes, not national in scope. For example, there was the 1890 "Rules and Requirements of the Michigan Inspection Bureau for Electric Lighting." Be thankful that today you have no such rule as one contained in that 1890 code: "All circuits shall be tested at least twice a day with a suitable magneto or other approved device, in order to discover any escapes to ground that may exist."

Enforcement of the Code. By this time you should logically be asking, "What jurisdiction do insurance companies or their laboratories or a group of manufacturers have over me—why can't I use such merchandise as I please and in such ways as I please?" The answer is that these bodies have no jurisdiction over you whatsoever; as far as they are concerned, you may do as you please. However, you are still obligated to obey the laws of your state or city or other municipality; with few exceptions these lawmaking bodies pass laws or ordinances which require that the provisions of the National Electrical Code must be observed in the territory involved. Another important consideration is that fire-insurance companies may refuse to issue policies to cover buildings that are not properly wired.

Aside from all legal considerations, common sense suggests that you and I take advantage of the experience of those who know more about the subject than we do. The experience of such experts collectively has resulted in the National Electrical Code, which then becomes a guide for all.

Local Codes. The National Electrical Code defines in a broad way what may and may not be done in the line of wiring, the different methods that are permitted, and so on. Frequently local ordinances limit the National Code, so that only a portion of what it permits is then permitted locally. For example, the National Code specifies that under certain conditions a conduit system, an armored-cable system, a nonmetallic system, or one of several other systems may be used in wiring a house. The local code or ordinance may specify that all these systems may be used locally except armored cable. It is therefore important that you be familiar not only with the National Electrical Code[1] but also with the local codes or ordinances that apply in your locality.

Permits. In many places it is necessary to get a permit from city, county, or state authorities before a wiring job can be started. The fees charged for permits generally are used to pay the expenses of electrical inspectors, whose work leads to safe, properly installed jobs. Power companies usually will not furnish power until an inspection certificate has been turned in.

Licenses. Many cities and states have laws which require that no one may engage in the *business* of electrical wiring without being properly licensed. The author knows of no place, however, where an individual may not wire *his own* premises without a license; the permit, if required, must, of course, still be obtained. Before applying for the permit, be sure you understand completely all problems in connection with your job, so that your wiring will in every way meet Code and local requirements. If it does not, the inspector will be required to turn down your job until the mistakes are corrected.

---

[1] A copy of the National Electrical Code can be obtained by sending $2 to the National Fire Protection Association, 60 Batterymarch St., Boston, Mass. 02110.

Chapter 2

ELECTRICITY: BASIC PRINCIPLES AND MEASUREMENTS

In the study of electricity you will meet the many different terms that have to do with measurement: "volts," "amperes," "watts," and others. It will be much easier to learn how one is related to the other than to get an idea of the absolute value of each. That is because electric power is measured in units which cannot be compared directly with feet, pounds, quarts, or any other measure familiar to you. If you consult your dictionary, you will find definitions like these:

Volt: the pressure required to force one ampere through a resistance of one ohm.
Ampere: the electric current which will flow through one ohm under a pressure of one volt.
Ohm: the resistance through which one volt will force one ampere.

Those definitions show a clear interrelationship between the three terms but give you little idea of the value of any one term. You are as badly off as you would be if you suddenly found yourself in India, trying to use Indian money which consists of pies, annas, and rupees. You can discover from a reference book that 12 pies make one anna and 16 annas make one rupee, but what is the value of a rupee in terms of the American money with which you are familiar? After you used the Indian money for a while, you would discover some relationship between rupees and dollars. So also in electrical work— after a while you will begin to see some relationship among the various electrical units such as volts, amperes, ohms, and others.

Unfortunately in electrical work, there is no way of translating an ampere, a volt, or an ohm into something that is familiar to you. Therefore we shall have to compare these terms with other measures which behave something like electrical measures. The best of comparisons or analogies are not very good, but they are better than none.

Gallons of Water. We can measure water in pounds or cubic feet or acre-feet or in many other ways. The measure known to most people is no doubt the gallon. A gallon of water is a specific *quantity* of water.

Coulombs of Electricity. When we come to measure electric power, the term that corresponds directly to the gallon in the case of water is the "coulomb." Ask all the people you know in the electrical business, "How much is a coulomb of electric power?" and 99% or more will answer, "Coulomb? I vaguely remember the term from way back when, but I don't know what a coulomb is." That being the case, why should we talk about it here? The only answer is that, while very few people indeed remember the definition of the term, it is nevertheless very helpful in getting to understand other electrical terms. We shall use it as a temporary tool, just as a child learns how to ride a tricycle before he learns how to ride a bicycle. Just accept it as a fact that a coulomb is a very definite *quantity* of electric power; do not bother trying to understand how big that quantity is.

Water in Motion. Gallons of water standing in a tank are just quantities of water. But if there is a small hose connected to the tank, water will flow out of it. If there is a big hose, water will flow out of it faster than out of the small hose. If we want to talk about how much faster it flows out of the big hose than out of the small one, we must use some measure to denote the *rate* of flow, so usually we talk about "gallons per minute." This phrase tells us about the quantity (gallons) and the time (per minute) and collectively indicates what we call the rate of flow.

Electric Power in Motion. Instead of a tank of water, let us now consider a battery, a generator, or other source of electric power. Instead of a hose connected to the tank, let us think of wire through which electric power will flow. Coulombs of electric power will flow through that wire, just as gallons of water flowed through the hose. And just as in the case of water we talk about "gallons per minute," so in the case of electric power we can talk about "coulombs per minute." Only in the case of electric power, it has become the custom to talk about "coulombs per second." Instead of saying that water flowed at the rate of "10 gallons per minute," we shall be talking about electric power flowing at the rate of "10 coulombs per second." But instead of using an awkward, long phrase "10 coulombs per second," we say "10 amperes," because an ampere[1] long ago was defined as a flow of one coulomb per second.

You must never say that current is flowing at 10 amperes *per minute*, for that would be the same as saying that it is flowing at the rate of 10 coulombs *per second per minute*, which does not make sense. Just remember that a coulomb is a *quantity*, an ampere a *rate*. Once you clearly understand that amperes measure the rate of flow, you can forget the coulomb completely and think in terms of amperes.[2]

Water under Pressure. A gallon of water standing in a tank is an inert, static quantity. Water dribbling out of your not-quite-shut-off garden hose at a gallon per minute is just a nuisance. Water coming out of your sprinkler on the lawn at a gallon per minute waters your lawn nicely and can be a delight-

---

[1] The ampere is named after André Marie Ampère (1775–1836), one of the great scientists of the early nineteenth century, who discovered many of the fundamental laws concerning the flow of electric current.

[2] In these days of electronics and atom bombs, a word may be in order to those who are interested in the purely scientific aspect of the subject. A flow of one ampere (one coulomb per second) is equivalent to a flow of 6,280,000,000,000,000,000 electrons per second past a given point. However, it is entirely safe to forget all about coulombs and electrons per second, except for those who intend to delve very thoroughly into basic electrical engineering, and even for those the exact figure is of more academic than practical interest. For those who are interested in comparing numbers as such, it may be interesting to note that the big number shown above, representing the number of electrons moving past a given point every second when a current of one ampere flows, is approximately two million times greater than the number that represents the number of seconds that have elapsed in the more than 1,900 years since the beginning of the Christian era.

ful shower for children playing under it. The same gallon-per-minute flow coming out of the same hose in the form of one tiny stream and directed at one of those same children who a moment ago thought it was fun will be considered painful because it seems to hurt. The same gallon-per-minute flow coming out of a high-pressure hose can cause real discomfort or perhaps even injury.

Suppose there are three water tanks located 10, 20, and 100 ft above ground level. A pipe runs from each tank to the ground level, and a pressure gauge is connected at the ground level. The gauges on the three tanks will show pressures of 4.3, 8.6, and 43 lb per sq in. (This disregards such things as, for example, pipe friction; let us not complicate the problem by going into details that are for the finished engineer, details that theoretically should be taken into consideration but which may be overlooked for the sake of simplification.) If a tank were located 1,000 ft above ground level, the pressure would be 430 lb per sq in.

One gallon per minute running out of the first tank would be a nuisance; a gallon per minute out of the last tank at 430 lb per sq in. could do a lot of damage. The difference lies in the difference in pressure between the two. The difference is measured in pounds per square inch, and the various pressures spell the difference between nuisance, convenience, and danger.

Electric Power under Pressure. Electric power is also under pressure, but instead of being measured in pounds per square inch, it is measured in volts. One volt[3] is a very low pressure; in commercial work higher pressures or voltages are used.

An ordinary flashlight cell or dry-cell battery (regardless of size) will if fresh develop approximately 1½ volts. Four of them connected in series, as in the so-called "hot-shot" battery, will develop $4 \times 1\frac{1}{2}$, or 6 volts. Connect 30 of them in series, as in the B battery used in some portable radios, and you have $30 \times 1\frac{1}{2}$, or 45 volts. A single cell of a storage battery develops

[3] The volt is named after Count Alessandro Volta (1745–1827), one of the great pioneer scientists who had much to do with the early research in electricity. For example, he discovered that when two dissimilar metals are immersed in an acid, an electric current will flow through a wire connecting the two metals. In other words, he discovered the principle underlying batteries of all kinds.

about 2 volts when fully charged; the six cells of an automobile battery develop 6×2, or 12 volts. An ordinary house-lighting circuit operates at about 115 or 230 volts. The high-voltage lines feeding the transformers found in alleys of city streets operate at 2,300 or 4,600 volts.

Refer back to footnote 2 on page 16. The number of electrons flowing past a given point in one second define the number of amperes flowing. The *speed* with which they move defines the voltage. Compare the electrons with rifle bullets: If I toss one of them against you, no harm is done because the speed is so slow (the voltage is low). If one is fired at you from a rifle, it will kill you because the speed is high (the voltage is high).

Water Once More. Suppose that each of the water tanks we have talked about has a capacity of 100 gal and that each tank is empty. You must fill each tank using a hand pump (pumping out of a source of water at pump level, just to simplify the problem). You will not have to work very hard to fill the tank located 10 ft above ground level in, say 5 min. You will have to work twice as hard to fill the one located 20 ft above ground level *in the same time*. To fill the one located 100 ft above ground level in the same 5 min, you will have to be "Superman"; to fill the one located 1,000 ft above ground level would be a fantastic job to do by hand.

It takes you 5 min to fill the 100-gal tank located 10 ft above ground level. Then to fill a tank ten times as large (1,000 gal) located at the same level should take you ten times as long, or 50 min. Then by like token, to fill the original 100-gal tank but now located ten times as high (100 ft) should take you ten times as long, also 50 min. In other words, it should take you 50 min to fill a 1,000-gal tank located 10 ft above ground level or a 100-gal tank located 100 ft above ground level. All this is probably easier to grasp in tabular form:

Capacity of tank, gallons	Height above ground, feet	Approximate pressure, pounds per square inch	Time to fill, minutes
100	10	4.3	5
1,000	10	4.3	50
100	100	43.0	50

From this discussion it is easy to see that neither gallons nor gallons per minute determines how much work is involved in filling the tank; pressure alone does not determine it; the two in combination with each other do determine it. In other words, gallons per minute times pressure per square inch measures the amount of work done in pumping.

Watts. In measuring electric power, neither the rate (amperes) nor the pressure (volts) tells us the energy flowing in a circuit. A combination of the two does tell us the answer very simply, for amperes × volts = watts. Watts measure the total energy flowing in a circuit at any given moment, just as horsepower measures the power developed by an engine at any given moment. Indeed, horsepower and watts are merely two different ways of measuring or expressing rate of work or power; 746 watts are always equal to 1 hp.

If a lamp consumes 746 watts, you would be entirely correct if you called it a 1-hp lamp, although that method of designating lamps is never used. Likewise you would be entirely correct if you said that a 1-hp motor is a 746-watt[4] motor, although that method of designating power of motors is not used (except in the case of "flea-power" motors which are sometimes rated, for example, "approximately 1½ watts output," instead of being rated as "$\frac{1}{500}$ hp").

Again note that the electrical term is just "watts," not "watts *per hour*." You would not say that the engine in your automobile delivers 250 hp *per hour;* at any given moment it delivers 250 hp, the power that 250 horses would or could deliver at any one moment if working simultaneously. Both watts and horsepower denote a *rate* at which work is being done, not a *quantity of work* being done in a given time.

From the above you can see that a given wattage may be a combination of any voltage whatsoever and the correspondingly correct amperage. For example:

---

[4] Note, however, that a motor which delivers 1 hp or 746 watts of power actually consumes more nearly 1,000 watts from the power line. The difference between the 1,000 watts consumed and the 746 watts delivered as useful power is consumed as heat in the motor, to overcome bearing friction, to overcome air resistance of the moving parts, and similar factors.

$$3 \text{ volts} \times 120 \text{ amp} = 360 \text{ watts}$$
$$6 \text{ volts} \times \ 60 \text{ amp} = 360 \text{ watts}$$
$$12 \text{ volts} \times \ 30 \text{ amp} = 360 \text{ watts}$$
$$60 \text{ volts} \times \ \ 6 \text{ amp} = 360 \text{ watts}$$
$$120 \text{ volts} \times \ \ 3 \text{ amp} = 360 \text{ watts}$$
$$360 \text{ volts} \times \ \ 1 \text{ amp} = 360 \text{ watts}$$

Carrying the illustration further, a lamp in an automobile headlight consuming 5 amp from a 12-volt battery consumes a total of 5×12, or 60 watts; a lamp consuming ½ amp from a 120-volt lighting circuit in a home consumes a total of $½ \times 120$, also 60 watts. The voltages and the amperages differ widely, but the wattages of the two lamps are the same.

This simple formula is not correct under all circumstances; the exceptions will be covered in a later chapter.

Kilo-, Mega-, Milli-, Micro-. A watt is a very small amount of energy; it is only $\frac{1}{746}$ hp. The Greek word "kilo" means thousand, so when we say "one kilowatt," it is just another way of saying "1,000 watts." The abbreviation is "kw," and 25 kw then means 25,000 watts. In the spoken word, the two letters of the abbreviation are usually pronounced (25 kay-double-u) instead of the words they stand for. By like token 20 kilovolts (20 kay-vee) means 20,000 volts, and so on.

Other prefixes that you will meet from time to time are the following:

Mega-: a million. Examples: megawatts, megacycles. Thus 25 megacycles means 25,000,000 cycles.

Milli-: one-thousandth. Examples: milliamperes, milliwatts. Thus 25 milliamperes means 25/1,000 amp.

Micro-: one-millionth. Examples: microvolts, microamperes. Thus 25 microvolts means 25/1,000,000 volt.

Watthours. The watt merely indicates the total amount of electrical energy that is flowing at a given moment; it tells us nothing about the total quantity of electrical energy that has flowed during a period of time, just as the fact that a man earns $2.25 per hour tells us nothing about his earnings per year unless we know how many hours he works. Multiplying the watts flowing at one time by the number of hours during which this number of watts flowed gives us *watthours*, which definitely measure the total amount of electrical energy consumed or flowing during a given time. For example:

$$10 \text{ watts} \times 1{,}000 \text{ hr} = 10{,}000 \text{ watthours}$$
$$100 \text{ watts} \times 100 \text{ hr} = 10{,}000 \text{ watthours}$$
$$1{,}000 \text{ watts} \times 10 \text{ hr} = 10{,}000 \text{ watthours}$$
$$5{,}000 \text{ watts} \times 2 \text{ hr} = 10{,}000 \text{ watthours}$$
$$20{,}000 \text{ watts} \times \tfrac{1}{2} \text{ hr} = 10{,}000 \text{ watthours}$$

Kilowatthours. One kilowatthour (kwhr) is 1,000 watthours, 20 kilowatthours is 20,000 watthours, etc. Power is paid for by the kilowatthour.

Reading Meters. Reading meters of the type shown in Fig. 2-1 needs no explanation. Some modern kilowatthour meters have a cyclometer dial, as shown in Fig. 2-2, and they are the

Fig. 2-1. Meters of this type are simple to read. (*Weston Electrical Instrument Corp.*)

Fig. 2-2. This type of register is found on some kilowatthour meters. (*Westinghouse Electric Corp.*)

most easily read. Other meters, like that shown in Fig. 2-3, have a register, shown in approximately full size in Figs. 2-4 and 2-5, with two different readings. There are four dials, on two of which the figures read from left to right in clockwise fashion, on the other two in counterclockwise fashion. Simply write down the last number the pointer has *passed* on each dial, considering the direction in which the pointer moves.

Refer to Fig. 2-4, and write down the proper numbers, as indicated by the pointers. The first (left-hand) pointer is between 2 and 3, so write down 2; the second is between 7 and

8, so write down 7; the third is between 4 and 5, so write down
4; the last is between 6 and 7, so write down 6. That makes

FIG. 2-3. The ordinary meter is a little harder to read. (*Westinghouse Electric Corp.*)

2,746 and indicates that 2,746 kwhr of energy have been used
since the meter was installed.

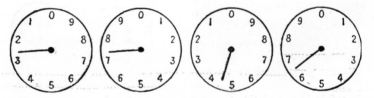

FIG. 2-4. Enlarged register of a kilowatthour meter. Read the figure the
pointer has passed. The reading above is 2,746 kwhr.

Now write down the readings in Fig. 2-5, which represents
the same meter a month later. The first pointer presents no

FIG. 2-5. The meter now reads 3,207 kwhr.

problem; write down 3. The second pointer, however, points directly at 2. Should you write down 1 or 2? If your watch had no minute hand but only an hour hand and that pointed to 2, how would you know whether the time was 1:58 or 2:02? You would have no way of knowing. However, the watch does have a minute hand, and if it points to 2 min before 12, you know it is 1:58, but if it points to 2 min after 12, you know it is 2:02. In other words, the minute hand tells you whether the hour hand has not quite reached 2 or has just passed 2. So also on the kilowatthour meter, look at the pointer on the dial to the right of the one that points directly to a figure.

If it has not reached 0, the pointer to the left has not reached the figure to which it *apparently points.* In this particular case, the second pointer points directly at 2, but since the third pointer is between 0 and 1, the second one must point a little after the 2, so we write down 2, not 1. The third and fourth pointers present no problem; write down 0, 7, making 3,207 kwhr. The difference between 3,207 and 2,746, or 461, naturally represents the number of kilowatthours used since the previous reading.

Some meters used for measuring very large quantities of power may have a notation on the register "×10," "×100," "multiply by 10," or some similar words. In that case the indicated kilowatthours must be multiplied by the "multiplier" to arrive at the correct reading.

Power Consumed by Various Devices. It will be well for you to know the approximate power consumed by everyday devices used in homes. The wattages are as follows:

		Watts	
Lamps:			
Incandescent	10	upward	
Fluorescent	15	to	60
Clock	2	to	3
Radio	40	to	150
Television	200	to	400
Sun lamp (ultraviolet)	275	to	400
Heat lamp (infrared)	—		250
Heating pad	50	to	75
Blanket, electric	150	to	200
Razor	8	to	12

Heater:

  Portable, household type............................. 1,000 to 1,500

  Wall type, permanently installed..................... 1,000 to 2,300

Fan, portable... 50 to 200

Air conditioner, room type............................ 800 to 1,500

Sewing machine.. 60 to 90

Vacuum cleaner.. 250 to 800

Refrigerator, household............................... 150 to 300

Freezer, household.................................... 300 to 500

Iron, hand (steam or dry)............................. 660 to 1,100

Hot plate, per burner................................. 600 to 1,000

Range (all burners and oven "on")..................... 8,000 to 14,000

Range top (separate).................................. 4,000 to 6,000

Range oven (separate)................................. 4,000 to 5,000

Toaster... 500 to 1,200

Coffee maker (percolator)............................. 500 to 1,000

Waffle iron... 600 to 1,000

Roaster... 1,200 to 1,650

Rotisserie (broiler).................................. 1,200 to 1,650

Fryer, deep fat....................................... 1,200 to 1,650

Frying pan.. 1,000 to 1,200

Food mixer.. 120 to 250

Dishwasher.. 600 to 1,000

Garbage-disposal unit................................. 200 to 400

Washing machine....................................... 350 to 550

Washer, automatic..................................... 600 to 800

Dryer, clothes.. 4,000 to 5,000

Water heaters... 2,000 to 5,000

Motors:

  ¼ hp.. 300 to 400

  ½ hp.. 450 to 600

  Over ½ hp, per hp................................... 950 to 1,100

Figuring an Electric Bill. The cost of electricity varies a great deal between localities and also with the amount used per month. For residential and farm use it seldom falls below 1 cent and very rarely reaches 10 cents per kilowatthour. Usually there is a step rate; the more power you use per month, the lower the cost per kilowatthour. For example, a typical rate is as follows:

First 60 kwhr............. 6¢ per kwhr

Next 40 kwhr............. 3¢ per kwhr

Over 100 kwhr........... 2¢ per kwhr

Assuming a monthly consumption of 461 kwhr, the total bill
would be:

```
60 kwhr @ 6¢...................   $ 3.60
40 kwhr @ 3¢...................     1.20
361 kwhr @ 2¢..................     7.22
    Total 461 kwhr..............   $12.02
    Average per kilowatthour.......      2⁷⁄₁₀¢ (approx)
```

To determine the cost of operating any electrical device for
1 hr multiply the watts consumed by the rate in cents per kilowatthour and point off five decimal places, giving the cost directly
in dollars per hour. For example, assume a 1,000-watt flatiron
at a rate of 5 cents. Multiplying 1,000 × 5 = 5,000; pointing off
five decimals gives 0.05000, or 5 cents per hour. For a 40-watt
lamp the figures are 40 × 5 = 200; pointing off five places gives
0.00200, or ²⁄₁₀ cent per hour, 5 hr for 1 cent. The oven on a
range may consume 3,600 watts, and at 2 cents per kilowatthour
the figures are 3,600 × 2 = 7,200; pointing off five decimal places
gives 0.07200, or a little over 7 cents per hour.

To determine the number of hours any device can be operated while consuming 1 kwhr, simply divide 1,000 by the wattage
of the device. Obviously a 1,000 watt lamp can be used just
1 hr; a 50-watt lamp, 20 hr; a large motor consuming 2,000 watts,
½ hr; and so on.

**Conductors and Nonconduc-
tors.** When you connect a lamp
through a piece of wire across the
two terminals of a dry cell, as
shown in Fig. 2-6, current flows
for the lamp lights. Yet no current flows through the wax that
is poured over the top of the dry
cell, nor does it flow through the
paper carton that makes contact
with the terminals of the cell during shipment. If a material will
permit current to flow through it,

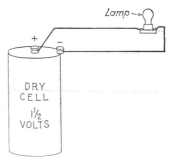

Fig. 2-6. Dry cells, no matter
how large or small, develop 1½
volts when new.

it is known as a "conductor"; if it will not permit current to flow,
it is an "insulator." There is no perfect conductor, nor is there
a perfect insulator.

Resistance. Number 10 copper wire has a diameter of 0.1019 in. Experiment shows that, if the two ends of a piece of this wire 1,000 ft long are connected to a source of electricity developing exactly 1 volt, 1 amp will flow through the wire.

If, however, you substitute aluminum wire of exactly the same diameter and length, only about $6/10$ amp flows. Still using aluminum wire of the same diameter but reducing the length from 1,000 to about 600 ft, 1 amp again flows.

If you substitute iron wire of exactly the same diameter and the same 1,000-ft length, only about $\frac{1}{6}$ amp flows. If the length of the wire is reduced from 1,000 to about 167 ft, 1 amp will again flow.

If you substitute a column of mercury of the same diameter and the same 1,000-ft length, only about $\frac{1}{60}$ amp flows. Reduce the column to about 17 ft, and 1 amp will again flow.

In these examples you will note that different metals under otherwise identical conditions permit different amperages to flow; stating it in another way, different metals resist the flow of current to different degrees. Resistance is measured in ohms. A given length of conductor is said to have a resistance of one ohm[5] if it permits exactly one ampere to flow when connected to a source of electricity delivering exactly one volt.

In these examples, the 1,000 ft of No. 10 copper wire and the shorter lengths of other metals each have a resistance of 1 ohm. The precise resistance depends on details such as the temperature, the chemical purity of the metal, and many other factors.

Ohm's Law. In the preceding paragraph it was shown that 1 volt forces exactly 1 amp to flow through different lengths of wire each made of a different material but each with exactly 1 ohm of resistance. Further experiment will show you that, if the voltage is doubled, 2 amp will flow; if it is 5 volts instead of 1 volt, 5 amp will flow. *As long as other conditions remain constant, the amperage is in direct proportion to the voltage.*

Still further experiment will show you that, if the voltage remains constant and the material in the wire is not changed but

---

[5] The ohm is named after George Simon Ohm, a German scientist of the early nineteenth century, who discovered the basic laws concerning resistance.

its cross-sectional area (not its diameter) is doubled, twice the amperage will flow. If the wire is increased to five times its original cross-sectional area, five times the amperage will flow. *As long as other conditions remain constant, the amperage is in direct proportion to the cross-sectional area of the wire.* Remembering that doubling the diameter of a circle increases its area four times, tripling the diameter increases the area nine times, it is evident that, as long as other conditions do not change, doubling the diameter of a wire increases the amperage four times, increasing the diameter three times increases the amperage nine times, etc. The reason should be obvious: Increasing the area of a wire by four times reduces its resistance to one-fourth of what it was, and so on.

The data given above pertain only when the wire in question is connected directly across a source of electricity. The conclusion should not be reached that doubling the cross-sectional area of the wire used to connect a motor, for example, will double the amperage flowing through the motor. The wire used for connections is only a small portion of the total wire in the circuit; the wire inside the motor must also be taken into consideration.

The basic principles and definitions outlined in the preceding paragraphs make it easy to recreate the well-known formula, known as Ohm's law, for calculating resistance, voltage, and amperage. If two of these factors are known, it is easy to calculate the missing one. The formula is

$$\frac{\text{Volts}}{\text{Amperes}} = \text{ohms}$$

For brevity, it is customary to use the standard symbols for these three factors:

> **E** for voltage
> **I** for amperes
> **R** for ohms

The same formula then becomes **E/I = R**. If by measurement the voltage is 10 and the amperage is 2, the resistance must be 5 ohms. Likewise, if the voltage is 110 and the amperage is 22, the resistance is 5 ohms.

The formula can be transposed easily so that instead of

$$\frac{E}{I} = R$$

it becomes

$$\frac{E}{R} = I$$

or the third form

$$E = I \times R$$

Divide the voltage by the amperes to find the ohms. Divide the voltage by the ohms to find the amperes. Multiply the amperes by the ohms to find the volts.

Careful inspection of the formula will confirm the facts pointed out in the previous paragraphs:

Voltage being constant, reduce resistance (increase size of wire) to increase the amperage.

Resistance (size and length of wire) being constant, increase voltage to increase amperage.

Amperage being constant, reduce resistance (increase size of wire) to permit lower voltage to be used.

Other Equations Derived from Ohm's Law. If we introduce watts into the formula (using the abbreviation W), the formula can be transposed into many forms. The 12 usual equations follow:

$W =$	EI	I^2R	$\dfrac{E^2}{R}$			
$E =$		IR		$\sqrt{WR}$		$\dfrac{W}{I}$
$I =$			$\dfrac{E}{R}$	$\sqrt{\dfrac{W}{R}}$	$\dfrac{W}{E}$	
$R =$	$\dfrac{E}{I}$				$\dfrac{E^2}{W}$	$\dfrac{W}{I^2}$

I = current, amperes E = voltage
R = resistance, ohms W = watts

Dangerous Voltages. Whether any given voltage is dangerous to human life depends on a great many factors. Sometimes a voltage as low as 115 is fatal, yet at other times individuals come in contact with much higher voltages and survive. The sensible course to follow is *safety first*—assume that any voltage of 115 and upward is dangerous. In specific cases, everything depends on such factors as the health of the individual, whether he is in contact with a grounded object, the amperage available along with the voltage, and many other factors. For example, the voltage involved when you touch a spark plug in a car is of the order of several thousand volts yet results only in an unpleasant shock. It is a very brief shock; if the current were continued, it would perhaps be fatal for at least some individuals.

Voltage Drop. All conductors have resistance; it requires energy to force a current through them. Assume a motor connected through a *long* length of wire to a source of electricity. Connecting a voltmeter directly across the start of the circuit of Fig. 2-7 will indicate the full voltage, probably 115 volts. The

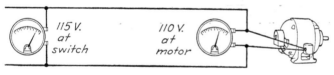

Fig. 2-7. This circuit illustrates voltage drop.

same meter connected directly across the motor will indicate a lower figure, probably 110 volts. The difference of 5 volts has been consumed in forcing the current through the wire.

The voltage that is lost in forcing current through the wire is known as "voltage drop." It is wasted power as far as useful purpose is concerned; it merely heats the wires. Excessive voltage drop also is responsible for many other bad effects, which will be discussed in Chap. 7.

Voltage drop is like lost pressure in a water hose. If a short hose is attached to a water faucet at the side of a house, you can squirt water, say, 50 ft. If a much longer length of hose is attached to the same faucet, you can squirt only a lesser distance, say, 35 ft. A pressure gauge might indicate 35 lb pressure at the faucet but 20 lb pressure at the end of the hose. The difference is expended in forcing water through the hose, and it corresponds to voltage drop in a wire.

The actual amount of voltage drop is easily calculated if the resistance of the wire and the amperage are known, using Ohm's law, $E = I \times R$. For example, if the amperage is $7\frac{1}{2}$ and the resistance is 2 ohms, the drop is $7\frac{1}{2}$ (amp) $\times$ 2 (ohms), or 15 volts.

From this it is equally simple to calculate the amount of power wasted. Remembering that watts = volts $\times$ amperes, the loss in the example of the previous paragraph is 15 (volts) $\times 7\frac{1}{2}$ (amp) or $112\frac{1}{2}$ watts.

Assume now that in the same example the amperage is doubled so that 15 amp flows instead of $7\frac{1}{2}$ amp. The voltage drop now is 15 (amp) $\times$ 2 (ohms), or 30 volts. *Doubling the amperage doubled the voltage drop.* Calculating the wattage loss involved, 30 (volts) $\times$ 15 (amp) gives 450 watts, instead of $112\frac{1}{2}$ watts at $7\frac{1}{2}$ amp. *Doubling the amperage increased the wattage loss four times.* The wattage loss in a circuit is proportional to the *square*[6] of the amperage. Current cannot be made to pass through a wire without some loss; but doubling the amperage of the load without increasing the wire size (which is the same as doubling the wattage so long as the starting voltage does not change) increases the wasted watts by four times; tripling the amperage increases the wasted watts by nine times; etc.

The formula for wattage loss has already been given as

$$\text{Wattage loss} = \text{amperes} \times \text{voltage drop}$$

However, since voltage drop = amperes $\times$ ohms, substituting "amperes $\times$ ohms" for "voltage drop" in the first formula gives this new formula:

$$\text{Wattage loss} = \text{amperes} \times \text{amperes} \times \text{ohms} = I^2R$$

This merely puts into formula form the statement of the previous paragraph that the wattage loss is proportional to the *square* of

---

[6] The square of a number is that number multiplied by itself. Thus 16 is the square of 4 ($4 \times 4 = 16$).

the amperage. All this concerns wattage loss in a given circuit with a given size of wire.

Operating Voltage. Previous paragraphs explained the fact that the greater the amperage in a wire, the greater the voltage drop and the greater the wattage lost in the form of heat. From this it should be obvious that, in order to carry high amperages without undue loss, large sizes of wire are required. The greater the distance, the heavier the wire must be. Therefore it is distinctly advantageous to keep amperages as low as is practical.

This, at least in theory, is simple, for any given wattage may consist of a low voltage with high amperage or of a high voltage with low amperage. Therefore relatively high voltages must be used, automatically giving correspondingly low amperages.

In practice, the actual voltage depends on the amount of power to be transmitted and the distance. In an automobile, while the wattage is fairly heavy at times, a battery of only 6 or 12 volts is used, even if the amperage flowing through the starting motor when it is cranking the engine is often over 250 amp; this is practical only because the distance is so short.

On a farm lighting plant usually a battery of 32 volts is used. The distances are seldom over a few hundred feet, and the amperages are reasonable.

For ordinary residential lighting the voltage is usually 115,[7] while for ranges and water heaters it is 230 volts. For industrial purposes, where the wattages are great, 460 and 575 volts are usually used.

The distribution lines that run down the city alleys are usually 2,300 volts, but the main distribution lines are at still higher voltages, until, for long-distance cross-country distribution, the voltages are well over 100,000 volts.

Since it is advantageous to keep amperages as low as possible in order to reduce voltage and wattage losses in the wires and to do away with the necessity of buying large size wire when a smaller size will do, and since this can be done by making the

[7] The voltage is often referred to as "110 volts" although today actually it is usually either 115 or 120 volts, with the trend toward 120 volts. Throughout this book, whenever the terms "115 volts" and "230 volts" are used, they will mean the common voltages, whether they happen to be 110 and 220, 115 and 230, or 120 and 240. In many foreign countries the standard voltage is 230.

voltage higher, it would appear entirely logical to use a high voltage for all purposes. You might well ask: "Why not use, for ordinary house wiring, 230 volts or 500 volts or higher?"

First of all, the higher voltages require heavier insulation, so that wire becomes more expensive; the higher voltages are more dangerous in case of accidental contact. Another important consideration is the fact that in the manufacture of devices consuming relatively low wattage, under 100 watts, the wire used inside the device is often of almost microscopic dimensions, even when the device is for a voltage as low as 115 volts. For example, the tungsten wire in the filament of a 60-watt 115-volt lamp as manufactured today is only 0.0018 in. in diameter; in a 3-watt lamp it is about 0.00033 in.[8] in diameter. If the device were for 230-volt use or for an even higher voltage, the wire would have to be still smaller, making factory production and uniformity decidedly difficult. The device would also be more fragile, and it would burn out more easily. The present common level of 115 volts is a compromise for lowest overall cost of installation, operation, and purchase of devices to be operated.

However, since the same home usually has small devices consuming from 5 to 500 watts, also appliances like electric ranges which may consume over 10,000 watts, it would be desirable to have available two different voltages, one relatively low for the low-wattage devices and one relatively high for the high-wattage devices. Fortunately this is practical.

Three-wire Systems. The 3-wire system in common use in homes today provides both 115 and 230 volts. Only three incoming wires are used and only a single meter. The 3-wire 115/230-volt system constitutes the ordinary system as installed in practically all houses and farms. The higher voltage is usually used for any single device consuming 1,650 watts or more.

Figure 2-8 shows two generators,[9] each delivering 115 volts; the two combined deliver 230 volts. Any device connected to either wires A and B (or wires B and C) will be connected to

---

[8] To cover a space of 1 in., 3,000 such filaments would have to be laid side by side.

[9] Two generators are not actually used. This will become clear in a later chapter concerning transformers.

115 volts. Any device connected to wires *A* and *C* will be connected to 230 volts. In actual wiring the central or *neutral* wire *B* is white; the outer two or "hot" wires are black. Connect any device operating on 115 volts to one black and one white wire, and any device operating on 230 volts to the two black wires. (These colors are correct only on grounded-neutral systems; this will be explained in the chapter on grounding. Practically all installations today have a grounded neutral.)

Effects of Electricity. The endless assortment of things that electricity does can, in great part, be broken down into forms or combinations of three basic effects: thermal, magnetic, chemical.

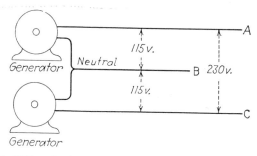

FIG. 2-8. With only three wires, two separate voltages are available.

The thermal effect of electricity is simply heat. A current cannot flow without causing some heat. Sometimes heat is not desired, as, for example, in the case of the unavoidable wattage loss referred to in the examples in this chapter. In an ordinary lamp over 90% of the current is wasted as heat, and less than 10% is converted into light, but the light is not possible without the heat. In a toaster or flatiron the heat only is desired.

The magnetic effect can be stated very simply. When a current flows through a wire, the wire is surrounded by a magnetic field—the area immediately around the wire becomes magnetized. Bring a small compass near a wire that is carrying current and the needle will move just as it will when you bring it near an ordinary horseshoe magnet. Wrap a wire a number of times around a piece of soft iron that is not in the least magnetic; during the time that a current flows through the wire, the soft iron becomes a magnet, weak or powerful depending upon such factors as the number of turns of wire and the number of amperes flowing. The moment the current stops flowing, the iron ceases to be magnetic. It is this magnetic effect that causes doorbells to ring, motors to run, and telephones and radio loudspeakers to operate.

The chemical effects are of great variety, including the electroplating of metals, the charging of storage batteries, and the electrolytic refinement of metals. In a dry-cell battery we have the reverse effect: a chemical action produces an electric current.

Chapter 3

AC AND DC; POWER FACTOR; TRANSFORMERS

As you read about electrical subjects, you will frequently meet the words "direct current" and "alternating current," also "cycles"; you will read about "single-phase," "2-phase," "3-phase," and "polyphase." These terms, while at first formidable and not at all understood by many people, really are fairly simple and easily understood if only you pay close attention to their explanation.

Direct Current. If an ordinary direct-current voltmeter (such as is used for testing dry cells or radio B batteries) is connected to a battery, the pointer will swing either to the right or to the left, depending on how the two terminals on the meter are connected to the corresponding terminals of the battery. Inspection will show that the two terminals of the meter are marked "+" and "−," "P" and "N," or "pos." and "neg.," all indicating positive and negative; the battery terminals are similarly marked. Only when the positive terminal of the meter is connected to the positive terminal of the battery will the pointer swing in the right direction. If on any source of electricity, whether battery or generator or other device, one terminal is positive, the other negative, *and they never change,* the current is known as "direct current," or "DC." Current from any type of battery is *always* direct current.

Alternating Current. Instead of an ordinary voltmeter which has the zero at one end of the scale, a zero-center voltmeter of the type shown in Fig. 3-1 may be used. This meter is the same as the first except that the terminals are not marked "pos." and "neg." Connect the terminals of this meter to the two terminals of a battery and note which way the needle swings. Then reverse the two leads to the battery, and the needle will swing in the opposite direction. The meter is equally easy to read whether the pointer swings to the right or to the left, and it provides the additional convenience that it is not necessary, before connection is made, to investigate carefully which is the positive and which is the negative terminal.

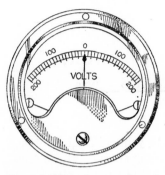

FIG. 3-1. The voltmeter above is of the same type as that in Fig. 2-1, except that the zero is in the center of the scale.

We are now ready to perform an experiment using this voltmeter with the zero in the center. Its two terminals are connected to a source of electricity, the nature of which is unknown to us. The pointer of the voltmeter performs in a peculiar fashion. It never comes to rest, but keeps on swinging from one end of the scale to the other, and back again, with great regularity. Let us watch that pointer carefully, starting from the zero in the center.

It starts swinging toward the *right,* first rapidly, then more slowly, until it reaches a maximum of about 162½ volts in exactly 15 sec. Then it starts dropping back toward 0, first slowly, then rapidly, until in 15 sec more it is back at 0. It does not stay there but keeps on swinging toward the *left,* and in 15 sec more it reaches the extreme left at 162½ volts, the same relative position as it originally had at the right. Again it swings back toward the right, and in 15 sec more, 1 min from the starting point, it is back where it started from—the zero.

It repeats this same procedure indefinitely, every minute. From observing the pointer it is evident that each wire is first positive, then negative, then positive, then negative, and so on, alternating between positive and negative continuously. The voltage is never constant, is always changing from 0 to a maximum of 162½ volts, first on the positive side, then on the negative. Current in which any given wire regularly changes from positive to negative, not suddenly but gradually as outlined above, is known as "alternating current," or "AC." If the data just observed are plotted, the actual voltage against the time, they will produce a chart such as is shown in Fig. 3-2. This portrays one cycle of alternating current.

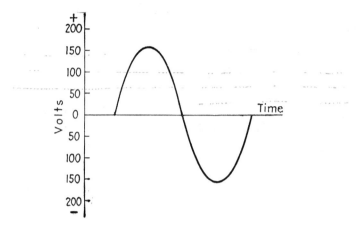

FIG. 3-2. This represents one cycle of alternating current. The voltage fluctuates regularly and continuously from zero to maximum to zero, and each wire alternates regularly between positive and negative.

Alternating current if considered *at any fixed moment,* rather than over an interval of time, is still direct current. *Alternating current may be defined as a current of regularly fluctuating voltage and regularly reversing polarity.*

Frequency. Alternating current which takes a full minute to go through the entire cycle (from no voltage to maximum voltage on the positive side, back to 0, to maximum voltage on the negative side, back to 0) would be known as "1 cycle *per minute.*" There is no such current in actual practice; actually in ordinary 60-cycle alternating current, as used in over 99% of all wired American homes and industrial establishments, all this change takes place at the rate of 60 times *per second,* much too fast to be observed by an ordinary voltmeter. Such current is then said to have a "frequency" of 60 cycles, the "per second" being understood. In the United States, practically all current is 60 cycle, and the few remaining 25-, 40-, and 50-cycle installations are rapidly being changed over to 60 cycle.

In foreign countries, most installations are of the 50-cycle type, but various other frequencies are also in commercial use, some as high as 133 cycles. In the United States, 180-cycle current is in common use in a few industries, and fluorescent-lighting installations operating at frequencies from 400 to 800 cycles are coming into use. Military equipment is often operated on frequencies of 400, 500, and 800 cycles per second. Metal-hardening equipment operating at 9,600 cycles is in use. The advantages of the higher frequencies lie chiefly in the fact that motors and transformers of any given output become smaller and smaller in size as the frequency increases.

It may be well to remember here that "kilo" means "thousand"; when your radio receiver is tuned to a station operating at 1,250 kilocycles (abbr. kc), it means that the signal coming into the receiver is alternating current of 1,250,000 cycles per second. If the receiver is tuned to a short-wave station operating at 40 megacycles ("mega" is a Greek word which has been adopted to designate "million"), it means that the signal is alternating current of 40,000,000 cycles per second.

Voltage of Alternating Current. In the curve of Fig. 3-2 the voltages range between 0 and 162½ volts. If a lamp rated at 115 volts is connected to a circuit of such varying voltage (1 cycle *per minute*), it will burn far more brightly than normal while the voltage is above 115 volts, less brightly than normal while the voltage is under 115, and part of the time the lamp will not light at all, because the voltage is very low, even zero twice during the cycle. Flickering would be extreme and unendurable. However, in the case of the ordinary 60-cycle alternating current, all this change of voltage takes place twice per cycle, 120 times *every second*. The filament of a lamp does not have time to cool off during the very short periods of time when no voltage is impressed on it, which is the chief reason for lack of observable flicker. In the case of very small lamps which have very thin filaments that can cool off quickly, operated on 25-cycle current which is still found in a few localities, a noticeable and annoying flicker is present.

The rated voltage of an alternating-current circuit is a value between 0 and the peak voltage and in the case under discussion is 115 volts.[1]   An alternating-current voltmeter connected to the circuit will read 115 volts.   A 115-volt alternating-current source will light a 115-volt lamp to the same brilliancy as a 115-volt direct-current source.

Alternating Current and Motors.   Alternating current as discussed up to this point is "single-phase" alternating current. In foreign countries it is frequently designated "monophasic" current.   When applied to a motor, remember that it magnetizes the steel poles of the motor every time it builds up from zero to peak voltage, or in other words 120 times per second, as shown in Fig. 3-3, which shows three consecutive cycles of 60-cycle cur-

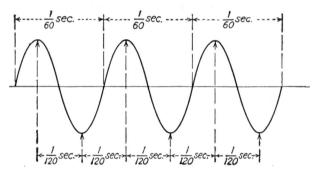

Fig. 3-3. Three cycles of 60-cycle alternating current.   All the changes shown take place in 3/60 or 1/20 sec.

rent.   At the top is indicated the time between cycles, or $\frac{1}{60}$ sec.   At the bottom is indicated the time between alternations, or $\frac{1}{120}$ sec.   One might say that the motor is given a push 120 times a second, just as a gasoline engine is given a push every time there is an explosion in the cylinder.   Offhand, 120 times per second may seem fast enough for any purpose, but remember that an ordinary motor runs at 1,800 rpm, which means that the rotor (the rotating part) makes 30 revolutions every second.   In turn this means that the 120 pushes per second become only 4 pushes per revolution; if the motor is a large one, the rotor or armature may

---

[1] The rated voltage is 0.707 of the peak voltage; the student will recognize 0.707 as $\frac{1}{2} \sqrt{2}$.   From this it is evident that the peak voltage is rated voltage times $\sqrt{2}$.

be 12 in. in diameter, over 36 in. in circumference, which in turn means that a point on the rotor has to turn about 9 in. between pushes. Do not imagine that these pushes are abrupt sudden impacts. They are gradual pushes that start slowly and build

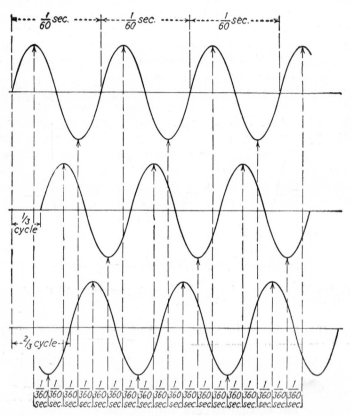

FIG. 3-4. Three separate single-phase currents combine to form 3-phase current.

up to a maximum as the voltage builds up to a maximum value.

In an ordinary 1-cylinder 4-cycle gasoline engine, running at 1,800 rpm, there is an explosion in the cylinder every other revolution, or 900 times every minute, or 15 times every second. The crankshaft gets a push 15 times every second. If more pushes are needed every second to secure smoother operation, or more power, it is simply done by using more cylinders: two or four or as many as needed. How is this to be done in the case of an electric motor? Fortunately it is rather simple.

Three-phase Alternating Current. It can be done by putting into the motor three separate windings not connected to each other in any way, but each connected to one of three separate sources of single-phase alternating current. The three separate sources of current must be so designed that the peak voltage of one does not coincide with the peak voltage of another. The voltages in the three sources come to their peaks in very regular fashion, one after the other. Then the motor receives three times as many pushes as before. Figure 3-4 shows the voltage curves of the three separate sources. At the top is indicated the time between cycles *in each separate source:* $\frac{1}{60}$ sec. At the bottom is indicated the time between pushes *from the three separate sources combined:* $\frac{1}{360}$ sec. That is 3-phase current, and it is nothing more or less than three separate sources of single-phase alternating current so arranged that the peaks of voltage follow each other in a regular, repeating pattern.

Do note that for each phase, the duration of a cycle is $\frac{1}{60}$ sec, but there are two pushes per cycle, so that the time between pushes is $\frac{1}{120}$ sec. But look at the bottom of the diagram and you will see that the pushes from the three phases combined are only $\frac{1}{360}$ sec apart. The pushes are imparted by each of the three windings in turn, as shown by the dotted lines from the peaks to the bottom of the diagram.

Figure 3-5 shows this diagrammatically: generator A and (inside the motor) winding A, also generator B and winding B, also generator C and winding C. In practice it would

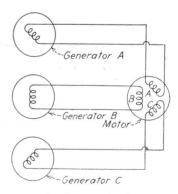

Fig. 3-5. Three single-phase generators form a 3-phase circuit, connected to a 3-phase motor.

be impossible to make three separate generators run in such precisely uniform fashion that the peaks of voltage would come at precisely the right time, and it would also be a most uneconomical method. A single generator is used with three separate windings so that the peak and the zero voltage of each winding come at precisely the right time. This is shown in Fig. 3-6, which also shows how the six wires shown in Fig. 3-5 become only three wires in actual practice.

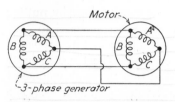

FIG. 3-6. The three separate single-phase generators of Fig. 3-5 have now been combined into one 3-phase generator. Only three wires are used instead of six.

Two-phase Alternating Current. Instead of three phases, 2-phase power operating on the same principle can also be used. However, this system is used in so few localities that it does not warrant space in this book.

Polyphase Current. When a current is either 2 phase or 3 phase, it is known as "polyphase" current (from the Greek word *poly* meaning "many"). It is also known as "multiphasic" current. With a few rare exceptions, polyphase current is never found in homes but is the general type of current employed for commercial and industrial uses for operating motors and similar devices. Even in those establishments, single-phase current is also found for lighting purposes and operating small miscellaneous devices.

Abbreviation. The word "phase" is usually abbreviated ϕ, the Greek letter *phi*.

Volt-amperes. The previous chapter contained the formula volts × amperes = watts. That formula is always correct in connection with direct current, but in connection with alternating current it is not correct because of power factor, which will be discussed in the next paragraph. Before that can be discussed, it is necessary that the term "volt-amperes" be understood.

In *single-phase work:*

$$\textbf{Volt-amperes} = \textbf{volts} \times \textbf{amperes}$$

In 3-*phase work:*

$$\textbf{Volt-amperes} = \textbf{1.73} \times \textbf{volts} \times \textbf{amperes}$$

In 3-phase work you will frequently meet the multiplier 1.73. Note that $1.73 = \sqrt{3}$.

Kilovolt-amperes.   One thousand volt-amperes is one kilovolt-ampere, abbreviated kva.   If the power factor of the load happens to be 100%, then and only then is one kilovolt-ampere the same as one kilowatt (kw).

Power Factor.   To explain just what power factor is must be left to any good book on electrical engineernig.   An explanation of how to measure it and a general idea of its importance are simple enough to be covered here.

In a direct-current circuit consisting of the load, together with an ammeter, a voltmeter, and a wattmeter, the product of the volts and the amperes is *without exception* equal to the reading of the wattmeter.   If, however, the same experiment is made on an alternating-current circuit, sometimes the same is true, sometimes not.

In an alternating-current circuit, whenever measurements show that the product of the volts and the amperes *is exactly equal* to the wattmeter reading, the device that constitutes the load is said to have a power factor of 100%.   Into this classification fall lamps, most appliances that generate only heat, and in general all noninductive devices, that is, those that do not involve windings of wire around a steel core.

If the product of volts times amperes *is greater than* the reading of the wattmeter, then the power factor is less than 100%.

Power factor is abbreviated PF; it is referred to also as "cos θ." [2] It is defined as the proportion between the real or measured watts (also known as "effective power") and the volt-amperes (also known as "apparent watts").   The formula is simply

$$\text{Power factor} = \frac{\text{watts}}{\text{volt-amperes}}$$

Measuring Power Factor.   To measure power factor we need only a voltmeter, ammeter, and wattmeter.   Assume a small single-phase motor on a circuit of 115 volts, consuming 5 amp as indicated by the ammeter and 345 watts as indicated by the wattmeter.   The formula then becomes

$$\text{Power factor} = \frac{345}{5 \times 115} \text{ or } \frac{345}{575} \text{ or } 60\%$$

[2] Cosine theta.

In the case of a 3-phase 230-volt motor consuming 12 amp. the volt-amperes are $1.73 \times 230 \times 12$, or 4,775. If the wattage as indicated by the wattmeter is 3,950,

$$\text{Power factor} = \frac{3,950}{4,775} \text{ or } 82.3\%$$

Generally speaking, the power factor of a motor improves (increases in percentage) with the increase in horsepower of the motor and also varies considerably with the type and quality of the motor in question. It may be as low as 50% for small fractional-horsepower motors, and over 90% for a 25-hp motor.

Watts in Alternating-current Work. The correct formula for use in connection with alternating-current work is

Watts = volt-amperes × power factor

In using this formula do not overlook the fact that, if the power is 3 phase, the product of the voltmeter and ammeter readings must be multiplied by 1.73.

Desirability of High Power Factor. Assume that a factory is using 100 amp of single-phase power at 230 volts, a total of 23,000 volt-amp, or 23 kva. If the power factor is 100%, this is equivalent to 23 kw. At 5 cents per kilowatthour, the power company receives $1.15 per hour for the total power.

Now assume a second factory also using 100 amp at 230 volts, but with a power factor of only 50%. That is still 23 kva but only 11.5 kw, and at 5 cents per kilowatthour the power company now receives only 57½ cents per hour.

Since it is the kilovolt-ampere load that determines wire size, transformer and generator size, and similar factors, and since each factory uses the same 23 kva, the power company must furnish wires just as big for the factory where they are paid 57½ cents per hour as for the one where they are paid $1.15 per hour; they tie up just as much transformer capacity, generator capacity, and all other equipment for the one as they do for the other.

It is natural, therefore, that power companies, when furnishing power to establishments where the power factor is low, not only charge for the kilowatthours consumed but also make an extra charge based on the kilovolt-amperes used during the month or period in question, as compared with the kilowatthours used. Since with a constant load in watts the volt-amperes decrease as the power factor increases, it is definitely in order to watch the power factor very carefully. Few installations attain 100% power factor, and rarely does one fall as low as 50%. The over-all power factor in an industrial establishment is generally determined by the electric motors in use, although other devices also contribute their share.

Power-factor Correction. The theory covering power-factor correction is entirely beyond the scope of this book but can be found in any good book on electrical engineering. The actual correction is accomplished by means of capacitors or synchronous motors; the required calculations should be made by one thoroughly familiar with the subject. Correcting the power factor not only reduces the charges for power consumed but carries with it many other advantages, including higher efficiency of electrical machinery because of reduced voltage drop.

Transformers. When it is necessary to transmit thousands of kilowatts of electrical energy over a considerable distance, wire large enough to transmit it at 115 or even 230 volts would have to be so big that the cost would be entirely prohibitive. If a relatively small wire and a much higher voltage are used, the voltage will be so high as to be dangerous in the final consumption and there will be many other disadvantages.

It would be most convenient, therefore, to have a way of changing current from one voltage to another as required. In the case of direct current there is no simple, efficient device available, but for alternating current there is fortunately a simple and efficient device that does just that—the transformer.

If an electric current flows through a wire that is wrapped around a soft iron rod or core, the core becomes a magnet as long as the current flows. The experiment can be simply made by wrapping a couple of dozen turns of insulated wire around an iron bolt; connect a dry cell to the two ends of the wire, and the bolt becomes a magnet as long as the dry cell is connected (see Fig. 3-7). Magnetic lines of force surround the wire and build up in the iron core. The moment the dry cell is disconnected, the bolt loses practically all its magnetism.

With a good galvanometer (which is a *very* sensitive direct-

current voltmeter), this next experiment is simply made.   Dis-
card the dry cell, and connect the two ends of a coil with at
least several hundred turns of wire to the two terminals of the
galvanometer (see Fig. 3-8).   Push the iron bolt suddenly into

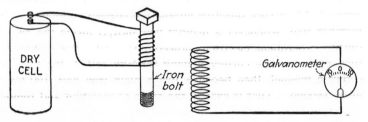

FIG.   3-7. When   current   flows   FIG. 3-8. Pushing a magnet into the
through a wire wrapped around an   coil generates a current indicated
iron bolt, the bolt becomes a mag-   by the voltmeter.   This is the sim-
net, but only as long as the current plest possible electrical generator.
flows.

the coil or pull it suddenly out; nothing happens.   Then use a
permanent magnet of any type; a 10-cent horseshoe magnet will
serve the purpose.   The more powerful the magnet, the easier
it will be to make this demonstration.   Push one leg of the magnet suddenly into the coil, and the needle on the galvanometer,
if sufficiently sensitive, will move, then drop back to zero.   As
long as the magnet is stationary inside the coil, nothing happens.
Pull the magnet out suddenly, and the galvanometer needle will
again move, but in a direction opposite to that taken when the
magnet was pushed into the coil.   The more turns of wire in the
coil, the easier it will be to perform this experiment.

This demonstrates that, whenever there is a *change* in the
magnetism in the space occupied by a coil of wire, electricity
flows in the wire; if magnetism of a constant nature is there,
nothing happens.

Consider now what will happen if 60-cycle alternating current
is connected to the two ends of the coil of wire around the
bolt.   The voltage in the alternating current applied to the coil
changes 120 times every second from zero to maximum to zero.
Therefore 120 times every second the bolt becomes a magnet, and
120 times every second it loses its magnetic power, as the voltage
in the circuit builds up from zero to maximum and then drops

back to zero. Consider now a contraption like that in Fig. 3-9, where again an iron bolt is used and on it two coils of wire, *A* and *B*, not connected to each other in any way. To coil *A* is connected a source delivering 60-cycle alternating current; a lamp is connected in series with it to limit the current. The other coil is connected to a very sensitive *alternating-current* voltmeter. Remember that, whenever a magnet was moved inside the coil in the first experiment, electricity flowed in the coil. Remember also that, with 60-cycle current flowing through coil *A*, the bolt becomes a magnet, then becomes just a plain iron bolt, 120 times every second. That is exactly the same as inserting and remov-

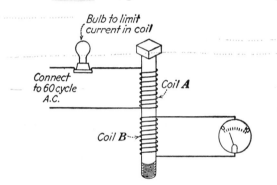

Fig. 3-9. A very crude transformer.

ing a magnet into coil *B* 60 times per second; accordingly, alternating current will flow in coil *B*, and the voltmeter, if it is sensitive enough, will show it. The device is a transformer, which transfers current from one coil to another coil not connected to it.

The device described is exceedingly crude. If a longer bolt is used and bent into the form of a complete circle, as shown in Fig. 3-10, it will be much more efficient and more current will flow in coil *B*.

In commercial use, solid cores like the bolt would be impractical because solid cores heat excessively. Instead, thin sheets of a special grade of steel are used, cut in U sections, which can later be stacked into a core, usually of rectangular shape, generally with the two coils over opposite legs. Many variations are possible, but for showing the principle, the type shown in

Fig. 3-11 will serve the purpose. The coil to which the power is applied is called the "primary"; the other coil from which the power is taken is called the "secondary."

An interesting demonstration transformer is described in the

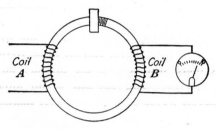

ᴌ ɪɢ. 3-10. Still a crude transformer, but much more efficient than the one shown in Fig. 3-9.

June, 1946, issue of *Electricity on the Farm* magazine, and illustrated in Fig. 3-12. Wind 150 turns of insulated bell wire or similar wire, about No. 18 in size, around one end of a heavy iron bar or bolt. This is the secondary; connect the ends of

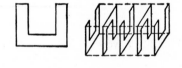

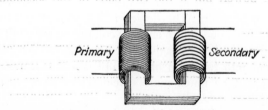

Fɪɢ. 3-11. This shows the general construction of transformers.

this winding to an ordinary flashlight bulb. On the other end of the bar, wind 50 turns of the same wire, this constituting the primary. Connect one end of the primary to a coarse file, the other end to one terminal of an ordinary dry cell. Connect a length of wire to the other terminal of the dry cell, and bare the opposite end of the wire but do not connect it to anything. Rub the bared end of this wire rapidly along the file.

The flashlight bulb will light, even if there is no connection between the two coils of wire. The dry cell is direct current, and direct current cannot ordinarily be used to operate transformers. However, rubbing the bare end of the wire along the teeth of the file causes the direct current to be frequently interrupted, so that there will flow in the primary an interrupted direct current, approximating one-half of an alternating current. Such a circuit would be impractical for handling any substantial amount of power, but it does demonstrate the principle of the transformer.

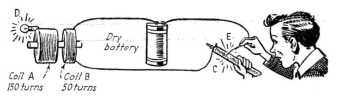

Coil A — 150 turns
Coil B — 50 turns

Fig. 3-12. This circuit demonstrates further the principle of the transformer.

Transformer Ratios. If the primary of a properly designed transformer is connected to a source of alternating current (of the voltage for which the primary was designed) and of practically unlimited power, but if the two ends of the secondary winding are *not* connected to anything or to each other, practically no current will flow in the primary. If, however, a load (lamps, appliances, motors, etc.) is connected to the secondary, then just as much current will flow in the primary as is required to deliver the required wattage to the secondary, but no more (assuming, of course, that the capacity of the transformer is adequate to the load connected to it).

Experiment shows that, if the primary has as many turns of wire as the secondary, the voltage and the amperage that can be made to flow in the secondary will be exactly the same as the voltage and the amperage in the primary, minus a small percentage because a transformer is not 100% efficient. It would be more correct to say that the voltage of the primary and the secondary will be the same, and the amperage flowing in the primary from the power line adjusts itself to the amperage demanded in the secondary by the nature of the particular load connected to it.

If the secondary has twice as many turns as the primary, the voltage in the secondary will be twice that of the primary but the amperage will be only half as great. If the secondary has ten times as many turns as the primary, the voltage in the secondary will be ten times that of the primary but the amperage will be only one-tenth as great. By reversing the proportions and having fewer turns in the secondary than in the primary, it is equally simple to step the voltage down, instead of up; the amperage, of course, will go up as the voltage goes down. The volt-amperes in the secondary are always equal to the volt-amperes in the primary minus a few per cent, depending on the efficiency of the transformer.

The minimum number of turns must be kept within the limits that experiment has shown lead to the greatest efficiency, and wire sizes in both primary and secondary must be chosen to carry the amperages involved. The smallest transformer usually found is the ordinary doorbell type, which steps 115-volt alternating current down to about 8 volts for operating doorbells and similar equipment; the largest are so big that there is difficulty finding railway cars sturdy enough to transport them.

Well-built transformers are very efficient, and, generally speaking, the larger the transformer, the greater the efficiency. In very large transformers it is possible to recover from the secondary over 99% of the power applied to the primary.

Practical Use of Transformers. In a large generating station, power is generated at, say, 2,300 volts. Then it is fed through transformers and stepped up to, say, 23,000 volts for transmission over a distance. At the point where it is to be distributed it is again fed through a transformer and stepped down to a more reasonable figure, often 2,300 volts, which is usually the voltage at which it is transmitted in the lines running down city alleys. At strategic points it is stepped down by another transformer to 115/230 volts, at which figure it is used (see Fig. 3-13). Actually the voltage at which the power is generated varies a great deal, as does the maximum voltage to which it is stepped up, this depending upon the amount of power involved and the distance over which it is to be transmitted. Voltages considerably in excess of 100,000 volts are ordinary; 500,000-volt lines are in use; 750,000-volt lines are "around the corner."

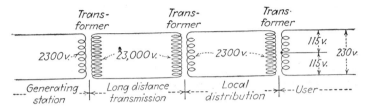

Fig. 3-13. Power is generated at a reasonable voltage, stepped up to a higher voltage for transmission over a distance, and then stepped down to the working voltage.

Series-parallel Connections. It is the usual practice in power and lighting transformers to have both the primary and the secondary consist each of two separate coils. When the two primary coils are connected in series, as shown in *A* of Fig. 3-14,

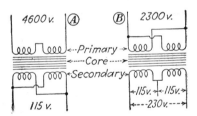

Fig. 3-14. By connecting the windings of transformers in series or parallel, the same transformer serves for two different voltages.

the primary will be suitable for connection to a 4,600-volt line; reconnected in parallel, as shown in *B*, the transformer becomes suitable for 2,300 volts. Likewise, the two secondary sections can be connected in parallel to deliver 115 volts, as shown in *A*, or in series to deliver 230 volts. More usually the secondary coils are connected in series, with a tap at the mid-point, forming the common 3-wire 115/230-volt system, as shown in *B*. Any given transformer, when the secondaries are connected in parallel to deliver 115 volts, will deliver twice the amperage that it will on 230 volts.

Use on Alternating Current Only.   Considering the discussion in the first paragraphs on the subject, it should be superfluous to state this, but let it be repeated: A transformer operates only on alternating current.

Three-phase Transformers.   A 3-phase transformer bank consists of three separate single-phase transformers.   The secondaries of these transformers, one for each phase, may be connected in a variety of ways.   The delta scheme shown in Fig. 3-15 formerly was the most common; frequently one of the wires is grounded. In new power lines today the star or Y scheme, as shown in Fig. 3-16, is more frequently used; usually there is a fourth wire,

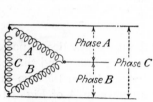

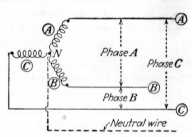

Fig. 3-15. Delta method of connecting 3-phase transformers.

Fig. 3-16. Star or Y method of connecting 3-phase transformers.

the grounded neutral as shown in dotted lines.   This system has many advantages, the detailed discussion of which belongs in a textbook of electrical engineering.

There is one point of comparison that should be noted.   First of all, in any 3-phase system, single-phase current is available by simply connecting across any two wires.   In the delta system, if the 3-phase voltage is 230, the single-phase voltage is also 230. If a fourth wire is led back to the mid-point of that transformer secondary which serves the two wires to be used for single-phase current, 115-volt single-phase is also made available.   However, the middle one of the three wires of such a 115/230-volt system is usually grounded.   Sometimes in a 3-wire 3-phase system one of the wires of the system is already grounded.   If there is one grounded wire at the *end* of one of the transformer secondaries and the fourth wire which leads to the *mid-point* of the same transformer secondary is also grounded, one-half of that secondary is short-circuited.   A delta system providing both 3-phase and single-phase power may therefore provide a distinct grounding problem. Consult the power company or your inspector in case of doubt.

In the star or Y system already described, and shown in Fig. 3-16, the 3-phase voltage instead of being 230 volts is usually 208 volts. The single-phase current available across any two of the wires (not including the neutral wire) is also 208 volts. However, the single-phase voltage between the neutral wire and any of the other three wires is 120 volts.

At first glance this may seem all wrong for, if the voltage between wires A and B in Fig. 3-16 is 208 volts, the voltage between the neutral wire and either A or B might be expected to be one-half of 208, or 104 volts, instead of 120 volts as previously stated. Remember, however, that in 3-phase current, the voltage comes to a peak or maximum at a different time in each phase. At the instant that the voltage in secondary A is 120 volts, that in B is 88 volts, so that across wires A and B there is a voltage of 120 + 88, or 208 volts. The system therefore has the advantage of making it possible to transmit over only four wires (including a grounded neutral) 3-phase power at 208 volts, single-phase power at 208 volts, and single-phase power at 120 volts. Occasionally in a home, instead of providing the usual 115/230-volt 3-wire system, three wires of the star-connected system (the neutral and any other two wires of Fig. 3-16) are provided, thus furnishing 120 volts for lighting and 208 volts (instead of the usual 230 volts) for water heaters and similar large loads.

Instead of 120/208 volts, newer installations in commercial and industrial establishments provide power at 277/480 volts. More will be said about this later.

Autotransformers. An autotransformer can be defined as a transformer in which a portion of the turns are common to both primary and secondary (see Fig. 3-17). Let there be a tap at the mid-point of the coil so that, although there are, for example, 1,000 turns of wire between A and C, there are only 500 between B and C. The

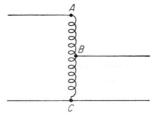

Fig. 3-17. In an autotransformer some of the turns are common to both primary and secondary.

entire coil A and C may then be considered the primary, those turns from B to C the secondary. Whatever the voltage across A to C, the voltage across B to C will be exactly half. The tap may be at any point in the coil. The voltage across B to C, as compared with the total voltage across A to C, will always be proportional to the number of turns from B to C, as compared with the total number of turns from A to C. This type of construction is somewhat less expensive than the usual two-coil type, but is rarely employed, as its use in general is prohibited by the Code with certain exceptions, notably in connection with motor-starting devices.

Chapter 4

BASIC DEVICES AND CIRCUITS

In order properly and intelligently to assemble the great number of available electrical devices to form a complete wiring system, you must understand the basic principles regarding electrical devices and electrical circuits.

If the electric current is to produce an effect, it is not enough
that the current merely flow up to the device that is to be operated; the current must flow *through* it. In other words, there
must be two wires from the starting point (the source of power)
to the device. The electric current can be compared with a
series of messengers who start from some given point (the generator of an electrical system), make a trip to their destination (the
device to be operated), and return to the starting point before
their errand is completed. The wires can be considered the
streets over which they travel, only they must be considered one-
way streets; the messengers must go out on one, return over a
different street (wire), because there are millions of them. As a
matter of fact, an electric current can be considered as consisting
of many millions of billions of such messengers per second for
every ampere flowing.[1]

Lamps. The most common electrical device is probably the
"light bulb." The correct name is "lamp"; the glass part of the
lamp is the bulb. The lamp consists essentially of a filament
which is a wire made of tungsten, a metal having a very high
resistance and a very high melting point. This makes it possible
to heat the wire to a very high temperature (over 4,000°F in
ordinary lamps) without it burning out. The filament is sus-

[1] See footnote 2, p. 16.

pended on supports inside the lamp, from which the air has been exhausted and into which, in most sizes, usually some inert gas like argon has been introduced to prolong the life. The ends of the filament are brought out to a convenient base, which makes replacement simple. In the base the center contact is insulated from the outer brass part of the base, thus providing two terminals for the two wires leading up to the lamp. The cross section of a lamp shown in Fig. 4-1 should make this clear. This pic-

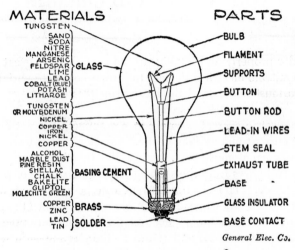

General Elec. Co.

FIG. 4-1. Cross section of a typical lamp.

ture also shows the wide variety of materials used in making lamps.

Lamps are held in sockets, the simplest being the screw-shell receptacle shown in Fig. 4-2; Fig. 4-3 shows a cross section of it. One terminal A is connected to the center contact corresponding to the center contact on the lamp base; the other terminal B is connected to the screw-shell terminal (which is carefully insulated from the center contact and terminal A), corresponding to the outer shell of the base on the lamp. When a lamp is screwed into such a socket, the current will flow in at one terminal, through the filament, and out again at the other terminal.

Circuits. Used in a general sense, as it will be in this chapter, a circuit is any combination of wires and devices which will permit electric power to do its work. Perhaps the words "hookup" or "wiring diagram" would be more descriptive. Only the basic devices necessary to make the combination of devices work will be included in this chapter; the supplementary devices such as conduit, outlet boxes, switch plates will be deferred to a later chapter.

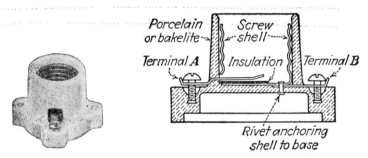

FIG. 4-2. A "cleat receptacle"—the simplest form of socket. (*General Electric Co.*)

FIG. 4-3. Cross section of the cleat receptacle shown in Fig. 4-2.

Outlets. Every point where electric power is taken from the wires *and consumed* is an outlet. Receptacle (plug-in) outlets in themselves use no current, but since current-consuming devices like radios and lamps are plugged into them, they are considered outlets. A switch uses no current; therefore it is not an outlet. Sometimes the term "outlet" is loosely and improperly used to indicate also any point where a device such as a *switch* (which *consumes* no current) is connected to the wires, this being commonly done in contracting work, when estimating the cost of a job on a "per-outlet" basis.

Source. In all the diagrams in this book where the word SOURCE appears, it will mean the generator, the battery, or wherever the current comes from—the SOURCE of supply. Actually, it may be the point where the wires enter the building or the point where the particular circuit under discussion begins.

Basic Circuit. Figure 4-4 shows a wire running from SOURCE to the socket with the lamp and another wire from the socket back to SOURCE. The current flows outward through one wire, through the lamp, and back through the other wire. This makes a complete circuit, and as long as SOURCE furnishes power, the lamp will light. It is not at all a practical circuit, since it is necessary to disconnect one of the wires from the socket or to cut a wire whenever the light is to be turned off. Such a circuit would not be very sensible, so a switch must be included. This

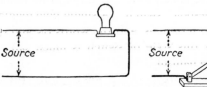
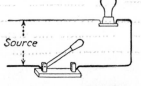

FIG. 4-4. The most simple circuit. There is no way of turning the lamp on or off.

FIG. 4-5. A switch has been added to the circuit at the left to control the lamp.

has been done in Fig. 4-5, the switch being the open porcelain-base type. Opening the blade is the same as disconnecting or cutting a wire, or, comparing it with the one-way street, it is the same as opening a drawbridge in the street and thus allowing no way of going ahead on that street until the bridge is again closed.

FIG. 4-6. The switch shown opens one wire.

FIG. 4-7. A toggle switch. The mechanism is completely enclosed. It does exactly what the switch shown in Fig. 4-6 does—it opens one wire. (*General Electric Co.*)

Toggle Switches. In actual wiring we would not use a clumsy porcelain-base switch of the type shown in Fig. 4-6. Instead, we use a neat toggle switch of the type shown in Fig. 4-7, concealed in the wall, with only the handle showing. It has two terminals just like the knife switch shown in Fig. 4-6. The mechanism is small and compact, but it does exactly what the knife switch does; in one position of the handle the switch is open, in the other position it is closed. Any switch that merely opens one wire is known as a "single-pole" switch. A single-pole toggle switch is identified by its two terminals, and the words ON and OFF on the handle. Obviously this style of switch is much safer than one with an exposed mechanism.

Series Wiring. The circuit of Fig. 4-5 controls only one lamp; often one switch must control two or more lamps. In drawing a diagram for this, most beginners will connect several sockets as shown in Fig. 4-8. The current can be traced from the SOURCE

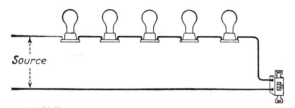

FIG. 4-8. This type of wiring is known as "series" wiring.

along the one-way street (wire) to the first lamp, to the second, to the third, to the fourth, to the fifth, and then along the other one-way street (wire) back through the switch to the SOURCE; consequently the lamps should light. They will light if the correct sizes are used. However, assume that each lamp is a different size; since all the current that flows through one must also flow through the other, the smallest lamps will carry more current than they should and will burn more brightly than normal. The biggest ones will carry less current than they should and will burn less brightly than normal. Medium-size lamps may burn at normal brilliancy. So far the scheme does not seem very practical. Burning out one lamp or removing it from its socket, as shown in Fig. 4-9, is equivalent to opening a switch in the circuit. All the lamps go out. This type of wiring is known as "series" wiring and is impractical for ordinary purposes.[2]

[2] The series circuit is used on old-style Christmas-tree lighting outfits, where eight identical lamps are used and consequently all burn at the same

Instead of a picture of a lamp in a socket being used as in past diagrams, from this point onward the arbitrary symbol of Fig.

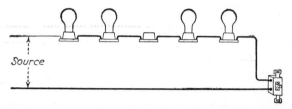

FIG. 4-9.   In series wiring, when one lamp goes out, all go out.

4-10 will be used to denote a lamp and its socket.   Note also the diagrams of Fig. 4-11, indicating whether wires that cross each other in diagrams are connected to each other or not.

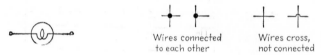

Wires connected
to each other

Wires cross,
not connected

FIG. 4-10. In illustrations from this point onward the symbol above will indicate a lamp with its socket.

FIG. 4-11. Note carefully the designations above, which show whether crossing wires are connected to each other or not.

Parallel Wiring.   The scheme used in ordinary wiring is known as "parallel" or "multiple" wiring, shown in Fig. 4-12.   When one lamp burns out or is removed, the current can still be traced from

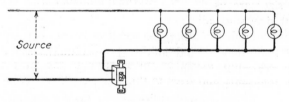

FIG. 4-12. One switch here controls five lamps.

the SOURCE directly to *each* of the lamps whether there are five as shown, or a dozen or more.   From the other terminal of each

brilliancy. Each lamp is rated at 15 volts; they can be used on a 115-volt circuit because each receives one-eighth of the total of 115 volts, or roughly 15 volts.

lamp the current can be traced back along the wire through the switch to the SOURCE. Try it; cover one or more of the lamps with a narrow strip of paper, leaving the wires exposed; the circuit will operate, regardless of the number of lamps in place, and the switch will always turn all the lamps on and off. This is the way the sockets in a five-light fixture are wired, operated by a single switch in the wall.

Using Several Switches. The circuits covered up to this point might serve well in a one-room summer cottage or an outbuilding on a farm, but all the lights in an entire house would never be controlled by one single switch. It is equally simple to wire a number of sockets with separate switches. Figure 4-13 will be

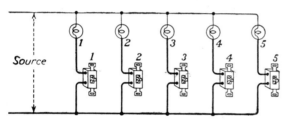

FIG. 4-13. Now each lamp is controlled by a separate switch.

recognized as the same as Fig. 4-12, except that in place of one switch there are now five switches; these have been numbered 1, 2, 3, 4, and 5, and likewise the lamps have been numbered 1, 2, 3, 4, and 5. Cover with a piece of paper both lamps and switches 2, 3, 4, and 5, leaving 1 exposed; immediately it becomes the simple circuit of Fig. 4-5. Cover lamps and switches 1, 2, 3, and 4, and again it becomes Fig. 4-5. Cover *any* four switches and lamps, and it becomes Fig. 4-5. Trace the current from the SOURCE to *any* lamp; it can be traced through the lamp to the switch for that lamp and back to the SOURCE. This can be done whether one or two or all the switches are on; each one is independent of the others.

Turn now to Fig. 4-14, where a *group* of lamps has been substituted for each single lamp, so that there are now five *groups* of lamps and five switches, numbered 1, 2, 3, 4, and 5. Cover with a piece of paper groups 2, 3, 4, and 5 with their switches, and immediately the simple circuit of Fig. 4-12 appears—five lamps controlled by a single switch. Cover any four groups, and in each case the current can be traced from SOURCE to any one of the lamps and through the switches controlling the group (if switches are turned on) back to SOURCE.

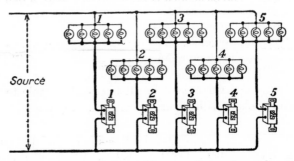

FIG. 4-14. This is the same as Fig. 4-13 except that each switch controls five lamps.

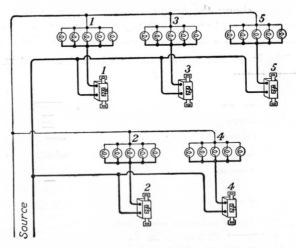

FIG. 4-15. Same as Fig. 4-14 but rearranged.

Figure 4-14 is the basic wiring diagram for a five-room house with a five-light fixture in each room, controlled by one switch for each room. Actually the wires would run more as shown in Fig. 4-15, which is more pictorial, with wires coming into the basement, then running to two rooms on the first floor and three rooms on the second floor.

Receptacles. Radios, toasters, floor lamps, and similar devices must be portable; receptacles are used to plug in these devices as required. The basic idea is shown in Fig. 4-16: a pair of metal

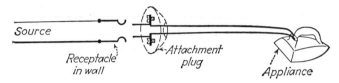

FIG. 4-16. The principle of a receptacle outlet.

clips or contacts, one attached to each of the two wires from SOURCE; a plug which has two corresponding clips or contacts which can be brought into connection with the first pair, and a pair of wires leading from them to the lamp or appliance. Figure 4-17 shows the finished product ordinarily known as a "duplex receptacle" (because it has *two* pairs of openings which will accommodate two plugs at the same time). The old-fashioned "single receptacle" of Fig. 4-18 is seldom used in new installations today.

FIG. 4-17. A duplex receptacle permits two different devices to be used at the same time. (*Arrow-Hart & Hegeman Electric Co.*)

FIG. 4-18. The single receptacle is rarely used. (*Arrow-Hart & Hegeman Electric Co.*)

In any wiring diagram, a receptacle can always be substituted for a socket; if, however, the socket is controlled by a wall switch, then whatever is plugged into the receptacle substituted for the socket will also be turned on and off by the switch. In any diagram or circuit, connect the receptacle in such a way that, if it were a lamp, it would always be on.   If in doubt, go back to the one-way-street idea, and see if the messengers can go from SOURCE to the receptacle and back again to SOURCE even if all switches are in the open or off position.

Double-pole Switches.   While opening one of the two wires to a lamp turns it on and off, still both wires can be opened if desired, as is done in Fig. 4-19.   The porcelain-base switch there

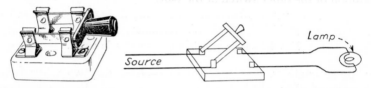

FIG. 4-19. Both wires are disconnected when a lamp is turned off with a double-pole single-throw switch.

shown is known as the "double-pole single-throw" type, and the corresponding flush toggle switch of the type shown in Fig. 4-7 is usually referred to simply as a "double-pole" switch.   It is identified by the fact that it has *four* terminals for wires *and* the words ON and OFF on the handle.

Double-pole switches are required by the Code when one of the two conductors is not grounded.   Grounding will be discussed later in this book.   In practice, this means that you must use double-pole switches when lamps operate at 230 rather than 115 volts.

Three-way Switches.   Often it is convenient to be able to turn a light on and off from two different places, for example, a hall light from upstairs and downstairs or a garage light from either the house or the ga-

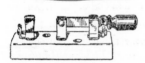

FIG. 4-20. A single-pole double-throw switch. It is commonly known as a "3-way" switch.

rage.   Fortunately this is easily done by the use of switches of the type known as "single-pole double-throw," pictured in the porcelain-base type in Fig. 4-20.   Figure 4-21 shows the diagram; call the two switches *A* and *B*.   Tracing the circuit will show that, when the handles of *A* and *B* are both *up*, the lamp will light; when they are both *down*, the lamp will also light. If either one is up and the other down, the lamp cannot light. Careful study will show also that if the light is on (regardless of whether the handles of the two switches are both up or both down), it can be turned off by throwing the handle of either *A* or *B* to the opposite position; likewise, if the light is off, it can be turned on by throwing the handle of either *A* or *B* to the opposite position. The light can be controlled by either switch *A* or switch *B*, regardless of the position of the other switch of the pair.

In actual wiring, a switch that looks like the switch in Fig. 4-7 is used, except that it has *three* terminals instead of two and the words ON and OFF do *not* appear on the handle. Switches

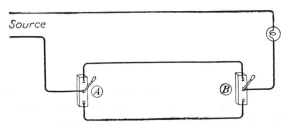

FIG. 4-21. The basic diagram for 3-way switches, which are used to control a light from two different points.

of this kind are known as 3-way switches, a name which is misleading because it seems to imply that by the use of such switches a light can be controlled from three points instead of only two. The name is no doubt derived from the three terminals on the switch. The terminal that corresponds to the center terminal of the porcelain-base switches *A* and *B* of Fig. 4-21 is usually marked by being of a different color, usually a dark or oxidized finish. Analyzing Fig. 4-21 carefully shows that the wiring of these switches is really very simple. On one of a pair of such switches, run the wire from SOURCE to the marked or "common" terminal; on the other switch, run a wire from the lamp to the marked terminal. Then run two wires from the two remaining terminals on one switch to the two remaining terminals on the other.

The mechanical construction of 3-way switches varies among manufacturers, so that the marked terminal is sometimes alone

on one end of the switch, sometimes alone on one side.   Therefore the pictorial diagram will be either that of Fig. 4-22 or that
of Fig. 4-23, depending on the brand of switch.   Fortunately
no harm is done if the wrong terminals are selected, except that
the circuit will not work, and if there is any doubt as to which

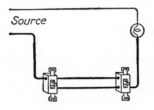

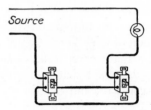

Fɪɢ. 4-22. If the "common" terminal
on 3-way switches is alone on one
side, use this diagram.

Fɪɢ. 4-23. If the "common" terminal
on 3-way switches is alone on one
end, use this diagram.

are the correct terminals, proceed by trial and error until a
combination is found that works properly.   For the purposes of
this book, whenever a pictorial diagram involves 3-way switches,
the terminal that is alone on one *side,* as in Fig. 4-22, is the common or marked terminal.

   Four-way Switches.   The preceding paragraphs showed how
to control a light from two different points.   What about three
different points?   It is a bit more complicated, although still relatively simple.   At the point nearest the sᴏᴜʀᴄᴇ, and also at the

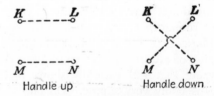

Fɪɢ. 4-24. This shows what happens inside a 4-way switch when the handle
is thrown from one position to the other.

point nearest the light, use the 3-way switches just described.
At the in-between point use what is known as a 4-way switch,
the construction of which is such that it performs the operations
shown in Fig. 4-24.   In one position of the handle the terminal
K is connected to the terminal *L;* also the terminal *M* is connected

to the terminal N. When the handle is thrown, K is connected
to N, and M is connected to L, as the diagram shows.

With this operation clearly in mind, now note Fig. 4-25, which
shows a light with three switches: a 3-way at A, another at B, and

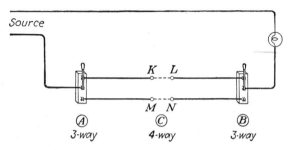

Fig 4-25. The basic diagram for a 4-way switch, used with a pair of 3-way
switches to control a light from three different points.

a 4-way at C in the center. As long as the 4-way switch C is in
the position shown, the current flows through the switch from
K to L and from M to N. The wires from A to B might just as
well be continuous wires without the switch C. In this picture
the handles of switches A and B are both in the up position, and

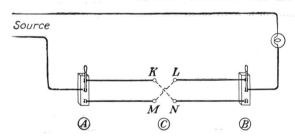

Fig 4-26. The same as Fig. 4-25, but with the handle of the 4-way switch
thrown to the opposite position.

of course, the light is then on. If, then, the wires from A to B
are considered as continuous wires (forgetting for the moment
that switch C is there), Fig. 4-25 becomes identical with Fig. 4-21,
merely a light controlled from two points by two 3-way switches.

Now see Fig. 4-26, which is exactly the same as Fig. 4-25 except
that the handle of the 4-way switch C has been thrown to the

opposite position.   Trace the circuit.   Chase the messengers any
way at all; they cannot get through and the light is off.   Draw
a few diagrams similar to Fig. 4-26, but with the handles of
switches *A*, *B*, and *C* in different positions; the diagrams will

Handle up   Handle down

FIG. 4-27. On some brands of 4-way switches, the connections inside change
as shown above, when the handle is thrown.

show that the light can be controlled from any one of the three
switches.   To control a light from three positions, use two 3-way
switches and one 4-way switch.   The flush switch of Fig. 4-7 in
the 4-way type is identified by its *four* terminals and the fact that
it does *not* have the words ON and OFF on the handle (double-
pole switches also have four terminals but *do* have the words ON
and OFF on the handle).

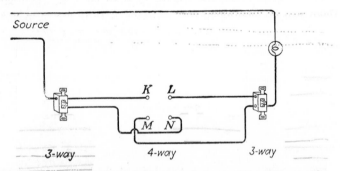

FIG. 4-28. With 4-way switches of the type shown in Fig. 4-27, use this
diagram instead of the one in Fig. 4-25.

Some manufacturers make their 4-way switches so that the internal connections, when the handle is thrown, change as shown
in Fig. 4-27.   In that case the diagram of Fig. 4-26 becomes that
of Fig. 4-28—simply cross two of the wires as shown.   As in the
case of 3-way switches, no harm can be done by wrong connections, except that the circuit will not work, and if there is doubt

as to the internal wiring of the switch, simply proceed by trial and error, as far as the four terminals of the 4-way switch are concerned, until a combination that works is found.

To control a light from four, five, or any number of points, use a 3-way switch at the point nearest the light, another at the point where the wires come from SOURCE, and 4-way switches at each of the other points; connect as shown in Fig. 4-29.

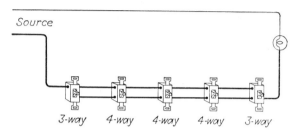

FIG. 4-29. When a light must be controlled from more than three points, use this diagram.

Miscellaneous Switches. Switches are available in many types besides the conventional toggle type so far discussed; some of them will be mentioned here. The lock type shown in Fig. 4-30 can be operated only by those having keys to fit. The momentary-contact type of switch looks like the ordinary toggle type,

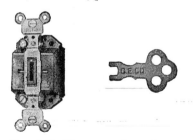

FIG. 4-30. This type of switch requires a key to operate. (*General Electric Co.*)

FIG. 4-31. A surface type of switch. (*General Electric Co.*)

but the handle is held in one position by a spring, returning to its original position when the operator releases the handle. The surface type of Fig. 4-31 is used chiefly in exposed wiring, as in garages and farm buildings.

Ratings of Switches. Most switches are approved for use up to 10 amp at not over 125 volts or 5 amp at not over 250 volts. This rating is stamped into the metal strap of the switch: "10 A 125 V—5 A 250 V." This rating is sufficient for most ordinary uses. If larger loads must be handled, switches with higher amperage and voltage ratings are available.

T-rated Switches. Ordinary lamps when first turned on consume an amperage from eight to fourteen times as great as when burning normally. For example, a lamp that consumes 2½ amp when burning at full brilliancy may consume 25 amp for a fraction of a second when first turned on. In other words, a 300-watt lamp momentarily uses about 3,000 watts for a moment when first turned on. This "cold inrush," as it is called, is a rather severe test for the switch that controls the lamp, and many switches rated at 10 amp and giving satisfactory service under average conditions will fail when used to control lamps normally consuming 10 amp.

However, special switches have been developed that will withstand the high inrush of lamps, and such switches have what the Underwriters and the Code call a "T rating" (the T stands for tungsten, the metal from which the filaments of lamps are made). If the switch is T-rated, the letter T follows the rating stamped on the metal strap of the switch, thus: "10 A 125 V—5 A 250 V T."

It is wise to use the T-rated switches (or "general-use AC-only" switches described in the next paragraph) in all cases. But the cheaper ordinary switches, not T-rated, *may* be used in ordinary residential work or in hotel rooms (but not in public rooms), but only if the switch controls only lighting fixtures installed in a single room. If the switch is used to control an inductive load (a transformer, for example), it must have an amperage rating at least twice the amperage of the load. See Code Sec. 380-14.

General-use AC-only Switches. The switches described can now be called "old-style" switches. They are approved for use on either AC or DC. A switch that will perform satisfactorily on DC is much more costly to make than one that will perform satisfactorily only on AC; there are very few areas where DC is still used. Why then make switches that are suitable for DC as well as AC?

Newer switches are of the type that the Underwriters and·the Code call "general-use AC-only switches." When used on AC, they can be used up to their full amperage rating even when controlling lamps. They look like other switches but can be identified by the letters "AC" that appear at the end of the rating stamped into the metal strap, thus: "10 A 125 V—5 A 250 V AC."

These general-use AC-only switches have one additional advantage: They are quiet in operating, do not have the annoying click found on older type of switches.

Type of Switch to Use. In ordinary residential work, any approved switch is suitable. The quietness of the newer type commends them for general use. Some Rural Electrification Administration projects specify T-rated switches. For nonresidential use, if the switches are for controlling lamps, use the new general-use AC-only switches or T-rated switches of the older type (see also Chap. 29).

Wall Plates. Switches and receptacles cannot be mounted in walls leaving untidy openings around them, nor can the terminals be left exposed, for that would not be safe. Therefore they are covered with "wall plates" or "face plates" after installation. Figure 4-32 shows several plates. The smaller ones are used for

FIG. 4-32. Wall plates are used to cover switches, receptacles, and similar devices. Such plates are available in many types and combinations of openings. (*General Electric Co.*)

single devices. Sometimes it is necessary to mount two or three or more devices side by side, requiring wider plates known as "2-gang," "3-gang," or "4-gang" plates, depending on how many devices the plate covers. They are available also in combinations so that switches, receptacles, and other devices can be mounted side by side, as the same figure shows.

Wall plates are made of a great variety of materials, such as bakelite in brown or ivory, brass and other metals in natural finish or plated in chromium, oxidized, and other styles to suit the user. The nonmetal plates are generally favored.

Sockets. In the Code any device into which a lamp is inserted is called a "lampholder." Practically everybody calls these

FIG. 4-33. A typical brass-shell socket. Besides the pull-chain type shown, there are several other types. (*General Electric Co.*)

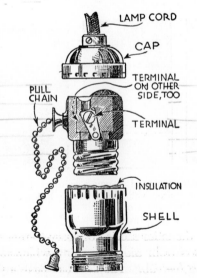

FIG. 4-34.   Cross section of the socket shown in Fig. 4-33.

devices "sockets"; sometimes the term "receptacle" is used for certain types of sockets, although this is not correct according to the Code, for a receptacle is a device where connection is made by plugging in an attachment plug.

Sockets are available in a very great variety of types. The

FIG. 4-35. The socket above fits directly on top of an outlet box. (*General Electric Co.*)

FIG. 4-36. The weatherproof socket shown is intended for outdoor use. (*General Electric Co.*)

type that was shown in Fig. 4-2, commonly called a "cleat receptacle," is not actually used in house wiring. The most commonly known socket is the brass-shell type; it may be either keyless or with a switching mechanism to turn the bulb on or off. There are three common types of switching mechanism: the key, the push-through, and the pull-chain type, all serving the same

FIG. 4-37. Sign receptacles are used mostly in the manufacture of lighting fixtures and similar devices. (*General Electric Co.*)

purpose. One of the pull-chain type is shown in Fig. 4-33. The socket consists of the brass shell with an insulating paper liner to insulate metal parts from the shell, the mechanism proper with two terminals, and the cap. The cap may have a threaded hub, used when the socket is used on a floor lamp, fixture, or similar device, or it may have an insulating bushing when the socket is used on the end of a piece of cord. A cross-sectional view is shown in Fig. 4-34. Instead of brass for the outer shell, bakelite or porcelain can be used. Other sockets are of the type shown in Fig. 4-35, used on top of outlet boxes; the weatherproof type shown in Fig. 4-36, for outdoor use; and "sign receptacles" shown in Fig. 4-37, used chiefly in the manufacture of lighting fixtures.

Other Devices. There are dozens of other devices, and these will be described in later chapters of this book as their use is discussed.

New Work; Old Work. When a building is wired while it is under construction, the electrical work is known as "new work." If the building is completely finished before the wiring is started, it is known as "old work."

Chapter 5

OVERCURRENT DEVICES

It is impossible for an electric current to flow through a wire without heating the wire. As the number of amperes increases, the temperature of the wire also increases. For any particular size of wire, the heat produced is proportional to the square of the amperage: Doubling the amperage increases the heat four times, tripling it increases it nine times, and so on.

Need for Protective Devices. As the temperature of a wire increases, the insulation may become damaged by the heat, leading to ultimate breakdown. With sufficient amperage the conductor itself may get hot enough to start a fire. It is therefore most necessary to limit carefully the amperage to a maximum value, one that is safe for any given size and type of wire; fortunately this is easily done. Any device that limits the current in a wire to a predetermined number of amperes is called an "overcurrent device" in the Code. There are many different types of overcurrent devices, and all of them may be considered the safety valves of electrical circuits. The two types that will be discussed here are fuses and circuit breakers.

Besides being used to protect *wires* against too great amperage, overcurrent devices are frequently used also to protect electrical *devices*. For example, an electric motor may require 15 amp to deliver the horsepower stamped on its name-plate. Yet a good motor can safely deliver considerably in excess of that horsepower for short periods, but it will then draw a correspondingly greater amperage. If the higher amperage is allowed to flow during a long period of overload, the motor probably will burn out. Therefore an overcurrent device is provided to protect the motor.

Fuses. The most common overcurrent device is a fuse. A fuse is merely a short length of metal ribbon or wire, made of an alloy with a low melting point and of a size that will carry any given amperage indefinitely, but which will melt when a larger amperage flows. When this wire inside the fuse melts, the fuse is said to "blow."

Plug Fuses. The common plug-type fuse is shown in Fig. 5-1. The fusible link is enclosed in a sturdy housing which prevents the molten metal from spattering when the fuse blows; there is a window through which you can see whether the fuse has blown; there are contacts for quick replacement when required. The largest fuse approved in the plug type is the 30 amp; smaller standard sizes are 10, 15, 20, and 25 amp. The Code requires that plug fuses rated at 15 amp or less be of hexagonal shape, or have a window or other prominent part of hexagonal form; those rated at more than 15 amp are round. This detail enables you to see at a glance whether a circuit in a home (where generally speaking a 15-amp fuse is the largest used) is overfused or not.

Fig. 5-1. Plug fuses are made only in ratings up to 30 amp. (*Bussmann Mfg. Co.*)

The Code limits the use of plug-type fuses to installations not exceeding 125 volts, except that they may be used on a 230-volt circuit with grounded neutral, for although the voltage is 230 between conductors, it is only 115 "to ground" (see Chap. 9). They may be used on a 230-volt water heater or other device even if the grounded neutral does not run to the device, provided that the two ungrounded wires are part of a system with a grounded neutral. This is the case in homes and farm installations.

Time-delay Fuses. Consider a circuit in a home, wired with the No. 14 wire generally used, having a maximum carrying capacity of 15 amp and protected by 15-amp fuses. Most of the time the wire will be carrying considerably under 15 amp; the temperature of the wire and its insulation will be well within safe limits. If the amperage is increased to 30 amp, the fuse will blow in a very few seconds. On the other hand, 30 amp flowing for only a few seconds or even for half a minute would not heat the wire or its insulation to the danger point, especially if the amperage was very small before it was increased to 30.

In practice, there are often conditions just as described; perhaps 3 amp are flowing in the wire, representing about 300 watts of lights. Then a motor is turned on, for example, a washing machine. The motor requires in the neighborhood of 30 amp for a few seconds while it is starting; after that it drops to a normal of around 6 amp. Very frequently the fuse blows during this starting interval, although the wire and its insulation are in no danger whatever.

Accordingly time-delay or time-lag fuses have been developed which carry their rated amperage indefinitely and blow within a few minutes like ordinary fuses on an overload of, say, 50%, but which carry overloads of 100% for about 30 sec and a 200% overload for about 5 sec. In other words, they *do not blow* like ordinary fuses on large but *temporary* overloads, but they do blow like ordinary fuses on *continuous* small overloads or on short circuits. A plug fuse of this type is shown in Fig. 5-2. The use of this type of fuse is very desirable, especially when motors are used. Power companies, especially, find the use of time-delay or time-lag fuses by their customers most desirable, for it is well known that a large percentage of service

Fig. 5-2. A typical time-delay fuse, known as a "Fusetron." Time-delay fuses carry *temporary* overloads safely without blowing. (*Bussmann Mfg. Co.*)

calls are caused by nothing more serious than blown fuses—and usually such blown fuses could be avoided by using the time-delay type, which carries short nondangerous overloads safely without blowing.

The Code in Sec. 240-4 requires that plug fuses in new construction in homes, if 20 amp or smaller, must be of the time-delay type.

"Type S" Nontamperable Fuses. Since each size of wire has a very definite maximum safe carrying capacity in amperes, the Code requires that the overcurrent device selected to protect the wire be of a rating no greater than that amperage. For example, the No. 14 wire used for ordinary residential wiring has a

carrying capacity of 15 amp and accordingly should be protected
by fuses no larger than 15 amp, yet all plug fuses up to 30 amp
are interchangeable. Nothing prevents the homeowner from
substituting a 30-amp for the 15-amp size, defeating the purpose
of the fuse. This led to the development of fuses of the nontamperable type, shown in Fig. 5-3; Fig. 5-4 shows a cross section
of its construction. The device consists of an adapter and the
fuse proper. The adapters have amperage ratings just like the
fuses, and a 15-amp adapter will permit only 15-amp or smaller
fuses to be inserted into it; a 25-amp adapter will permit only
25-amp or smaller fuses to be used; and so on.

The adapters fit into ordinary fuseholders but are so designed
that once installed, they cannot be removed. Obviously then if
a contractor when wiring a home with the usual No. 14 wire
(which has a carrying capacity of 15 amp) installs 15-amp adapters, he makes it impossible to use fuses larger than 15-amp size,

Fig. 5-3. This Fustat is designed to
resist tampering on the part of the
user. (*Bussmann Mfg. Co.*)

Fig. 5-4. Cross section of the fuse
shown in Fig. 5-3. (*Bussmann
Mfg. Co.*)

thus making overfusing impossible on the part of those who know
no better, or are inclined to take chances. This eliminates one
of the greatest causes of electrical fires and is obviously a sensible
move.

The most common of these nontamperable fuses is known as a
"Fustat" and, besides being of the nontamperable type, is also
of the time-delay type, the advantages of which have already been
discussed. Nontamperable fuses are called "Type S" in the

Code. The Code in Sec. 240-21 requires that in all *new* construction, plug fuses must be Type S.

Cartridge Fuses. Although the plug type is the common fuse for homes, the cartridge type is by far more common for non-residential purposes, and is the only kind that can be used anywhere if the rating must be more than 30 amp. There are two basic types of cartridge fuses: the ferrule-contact type shown in Fig. 5-5, and the knife-blade contact type shown in Fig. 5-6.

FIG. 5-5. The ferrule-contact type of cartridge fuse is made only in sizes up to and including 60 amp. (*Bussmann Mfg. Co.*)

FIG. 5-6. The knife-blade-contact type of cartridge fuse is made only in sizes larger than 60 amp. (*Bussmann Mfg. Co.*)

The ferrule construction is used only on fuses rated 60 amp or less, the knife-blade construction is used on fuses rated over 60 amp. Cartridge fuses are available in three types, depending on the maximum voltage rating of the circuit in which they are used: 250 volts, 300 volts, and 600 volts. Note the differing dimensions in the following table:

Fuse ratings, amperes	Dimensions in inches		
	250-volt type	300-volt Class G	600-volt type
10, 15	$\frac{9}{16} \times 2$	$\frac{13}{32} \times 1\frac{5}{16}$	$\frac{13}{16} \times 5$
20	$\frac{9}{16} \times 2$	$\frac{13}{32} \times 1\frac{13}{32}$	$\frac{13}{16} \times 5$
25, 30	$\frac{9}{16} \times 2$	$\frac{13}{32} \times 1\frac{5}{8}$	$\frac{13}{16} \times 5$
35 to 60	$\frac{13}{16} \times 3$	$\frac{13}{32} \times 2\frac{1}{4}$	$1\frac{1}{16} \times 5\frac{1}{2}$
70 to 100	$1 \times 5\frac{7}{8}$	Not made	$1\frac{1}{4} \times 7\frac{7}{8}$
110 to 200	$1\frac{1}{2} \times 7\frac{5}{8}$	Not made	$1\frac{3}{4} \times 9\frac{5}{8}$
225 to 400	$2 \times 8\frac{5}{8}$	Not made	$2\frac{1}{2} \times 11\frac{5}{8}$
450 to 600	$2\frac{1}{2} \times 10\frac{3}{8}$	Not made	$3 \times 13\frac{3}{8}$

The 250-volt and the 600-volt types have been in use for many years; the 300-volt type is a new kind called "Class G," introduced in 1963. But do note that the dimensions of the three types differ sufficiently so that it is impossible to use a type other than that originally installed.

From this table you can see that it is next to impossible to use a fuse of an amperage or voltage rating that differs widely from the amperage and voltage intended when the installation was first planned. This is an important safety feature.

Class G Fuses. This type was designed primarily for commercial and industrial buildings with lighting circuits operating at 277 volts (which will be discussed in Chap. 28). In such installations the overall size of the panelboards is very greatly reduced by

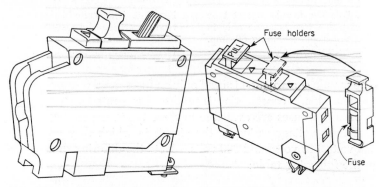

FIG. 5-7. A "switchfuse" unit for one circuit. Only Type G fuses can be used with it. (*Square D Co.*)

FIG. 5-8. This unit is similar to that of Fig. 5-7. It has fuses for two circuits, but no switches. (*Square D Co.*)

using this type in place of the large 600-volt type that was formerly required. Of course the Class G may also be used for residential and farm installations. Do note it can be used only in panelboards or fuse cabinets designed for it. The Class G is of the time-delay type.

Panelboards and fuse cabinets for the Class G are furnished empty except for an assembly of terminals and bus-bars. When installing, individual plug-in units of appropriate type and size are plugged in to complete the assembly. The plug-in units come in two types.

In the type shown in Fig. 5-7 each plug-in unit contains a switch for turning the circuit on and off; a fuse-holding block that can be removed for replacement of fuses only when the circuit has been turned off; and a signal light that glows only when the fuse is blown. It fits only panelboards designed for it.

In the less expensive type shown in Fig. 5-8, the switch is omitted. Each plug-in unit contains two removable fuse-holding blocks for two 115-volt circuits (or in slightly different types, two fuses for one 230-volt circuit). Removing the fuse-holding block opens the circuit; inserting the block upside-down turns off the circuit. The signal light glows only when a fuse is blown. This type fits only fuse cabinets designed for it.

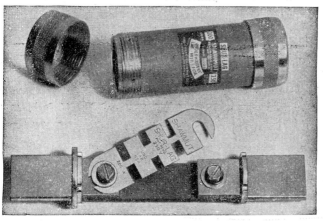

Fɪɢ. 5-9. The renewable type of fuse is easily disassembled for replacement of the fusible link. (*Chase-Shawmut Co.*)

In both types the plug-in units carry ampere ratings, so that it is impossible to use fuses of a higher amperage rating than was originally installed. For example, if the original unit was for a 20-amp fuse, it will accept only 15- or 20-amp fuses, but not larger. The fuses can be replaced only after removing the fuse-holding block from the plug-in unit.

Renewable Fuses. Cartridge fuses are divided into non-renewable and renewable types. The nonrenewable, once blown, have no further value. Since only the fusible link is destroyed when the fuse blows, renewable fuses are available that permit the fusible link to be replaced after blowing. Figure 5-9 shows a clear view of the construction; it is a very simple matter to replace the fusible link. In external appearance there is no basic difference between nonrenewable and renewable except that the latter are so constructed that they can be taken apart. Class G fuses are not available in renewable type.

Cartridge fuses are available in ordinary type, as well as in the time-delay type shown in Fig. 5-10.

Fig. 5-10. Time-delay fuses are also made in cartridge type. They are especially useful in protecting motors that usually require several times as many amperes while starting as while running. (*Bussmann Mfg. Co.*)

Circuit Breakers. The Code defines a circuit breaker as "a device designed to open under abnormal circumstances a current-carrying circuit without injury to itself. The term as used in this Code applies only to the automatic type designed to trip on a predetermined overload of current." Since all switches break circuits, they can in a sense be termed circuit breakers, and the definition merely states that as far as the Code is concerned, when it mentions circuit breakers, it refers only to the type that opens a circuit when an amperage greater than that for which it was designed flows through it.

A circuit breaker of the type used in homes looks like a somewhat overgrown toggle switch of the ordinary type used to turn lights on and off. One is shown in Fig. 5-11. Essentially it consists of a carefully calibrated bimetallic strip similar to that used in a thermostat. As the current flows through this strip, heat is created and the strip bends. If enough current flows through the strip, it bends enough to

Fig. 5-11. A typical single-pole circuit breaker. (*General Electric Co.*)

release a trip that opens the contacts, interrupting the circuit just as it is interrupted when a fuse blows or when a switch is opened. In addition to the bimetallic strip that operates on heat, most breakers have a magnetic arrangement that opens the breaker instantly in case of a short circuit. A circuit breaker, in fact, is a switch that opens itself in case of overload.

Circuit breakers are rated in amperes, just as fuses are rated. Breakers will carry their rated load indefinitely, will carry a 50% overload for perhaps a minute, a 100% overload for about 20 sec, and even a 200% overload for about 5 sec—long enough to carry the heavy current required to start a motor.

The trend is rapidly away from fuses to circuit breakers, for they have many advantages. When a fuse blows, spare fuses may or may not be on hand. When a circuit breaker trips, reset it like turning on a switch. The circuit breaker provides good protection and does not trip on large, but temporary, overloads. Modern homes are usually equipped with circuit breakers.

Determining Proper Rating of Overcurrent Device. The fuse must blow or the circuit breaker open when the amperage flowing through it exceeds the number of amperes that is safe for the wire in the circuit. The larger the wire, the greater the number of amperes it can safely carry.

The Code defines the number of amperes that may be carried by each size of wire. The 1965 Code adopted the word "ampacity" to designate "amperes carrying capacity." The ampacity of any size and kind of wire can be found in Code Tables 310-12 and 310-13 (see Appendix). There are some important exceptions, particularly in connection with motors, and these will be discussed in connection with related subjects in other chapters of this book.

It will be well to memorize carefully the ampacity of the smaller sizes of wire; these are also the maximum rating of the overcurrent device protecting that size of wire. These ampacities are as follows:

No. 14	15 amp	No. 6	55 amp
No. 12	20 amp	No. 4	70 amp
No. 10	30 amp	No. 2	95 amp
No. 8	40 amp	No. 1/0	125 amp

Note carefully that these are the ampacities of the kinds of wire usually used in ordinary residential wiring. Other types not generally used in residential work have higher ampacities, and are described in Chap. 27.

Joining Different Sizes of Wire. If two different sizes of wire are joined as in Fig. 5-12, then the fuse (or other overcurrent protection) may be no greater than that permitted with the smaller

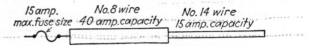

Fig. 5-12. When two different sizes of wire are connected in series, the largest fuse that may be used is the one that protects the *smaller* wire.

wire. Since in this case the smaller wire has an ampacity of only 15 amp, this is the maximum-size fuse permitted. In practice, a condition of this kind is sometimes met, especially in farm wiring, where a No. 8 wire is used for an overhead span to secure mechanical strength and to avoid voltage drop. Although the wire has an ampacity of 40 amp, the circumstances may be such that more than 15 amp is never required, and the maximum fuse permitted, 15 amp, will not in any way prove inconvenient.

On the other hand, there may be a condition, as shown in Fig. 5-13, where under similar circumstances No. 8 is again used but where more than 15 amp is to be carried altogether; in this case a second fuse is used at the point where the wire size is reduced. A 40-amp fuse may be used to protect the No. 8 wire, and a 15-amp fuse to protect the No. 14 wire. Usually when these conditions are present, additional wires protected by individual fuses are used, as shown in the dotted lines.

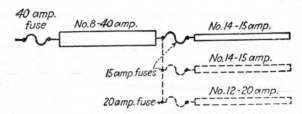

Fig. 5-13. If fuses are used where the wire size is reduced, select an amperage that protects the smaller wire.

There are a number of exceptions to these general requirements, the most important being the one permitted by Sec. 240-15 of the Code. No overcurrent protection is required at the point where the wire size is reduced if the smaller wire meets *all four* of the following conditions:

1. It must be not over 25 ft long.
2. It must be protected against mechanical injury.
3. It must have an ampacity at least one-third that of the larger wire.
4. It must end in a *single* overcurrent device of an amperage rating not greater than the ampacity of the *smaller* wire.

This condition is shown in Fig. 5-14, which portrays a combination of No. 8 with No. 14. Beyond the final fuse or other overcurrent device at the end of the smaller wire, additional

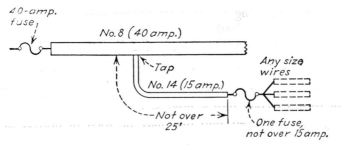

FIG. 5-14. Under certain conditions no fuse is required at the point where the wire size is reduced.

wires of any length or size (but not smaller than No. 14) may be run; they are protected by the 15-amp protective device ahead of them.

Considering the ampacity of various sizes of wire and the requirements of the preceding paragraph, it will be evident that, if all those requirements are met and if ordinary Type T or Type R wire is used,

No. 14 may be tapped to No. 8 or lighter
No. 12 may be tapped to No. 6 or lighter
No. 10 may be tapped to No. 3 or lighter
No. 8 may be tapped to No. 1 or lighter

Another exception is permitted by Sec. 240-15 of the Code. In the case of switchboards, panelboards, and similar devices, it is not unusual to have wires of considerable size run through such devices, with taps taken off to feed a smaller load. In such cases no overcurrent protection is required where the smaller wire is tapped to the larger, provided it is not over 10 ft long, provided it has an ampacity equivalent to the total of the carrying capacities of all the circuits it feeds, and provided it does not extend beyond panelboards or other devices in question.

An additional common-sense exception is contained in Code Sec. 210-19(c), which permits taps not over 18 in. long to be made from circuit wires of any size, to serve an individual socket, fixture, or outlet, provided only that the short wire is heavy enough to serve its specific load and never smaller than No. 14 (on 50-amp circuits, No. 12). Section 210-19(c) also permits wiring inside fixtures, also portable cords, to be smaller than the circuit wires serving them, provided they are heavy enough to carry their specific loads. Section 240-5, in turn, authorizes the omission of overcurrent protection at such points where wire sizes are reduced.

Chapter 6

TYPES AND SIZES OF WIRES

Wires are used to conduct electric power from the point where it is generated to the point where it is used. Copper is the material used in practically all cases. The Code makes very little reference to "wire" but speaks frequently of the "conductor," which it defines as "wire or cable or other form of metal suitable for carrying current." All wires therefore are conductors, but not all conductors are wires. Copper bus bars, for example, are conductors but are not referred to as wires.

Previous chapters showed that all wire has resistance that prevents an unlimited flow of current and causes voltage drop. For any given load, you must select a size of wire that causes only a reasonable voltage drop.

Current flowing through a wire causes heat; the heat varies as the *square* of the amperage. There is a limit to the degree of heat that various types of insulation will safely withstand, and even a bare wire must not be allowed to reach a temperature that might cause fire. The Code carefully and in great detail specifies the maximum amperage that is considered safe for wires of different sizes with different insulations and under different conditions. These maximum amperages will be given later.

Circular Mils. In order to discuss intelligently the different sizes of wire, you must understand something about the scheme used in numbering these sizes. The units used are "mils" and "circular mils." A mil is one one-thousandth (0.001) inch. A circular mil (abbreviated c.m.) is the area of a circle one mil in diameter. Thus a wire that is 0.001 in. or 1 mil in diameter is said to have a cross-sectional area of 1 circular mil. Since the areas of two circles are always proportional to the squares of their diameters, it follows that the cross-sectional area of a wire 0.003 in., or 3 mils, in diameter is 9 circular mils; that of one 0.010 in., or 10 mils, in diameter is 100 circular mils; that of one 0.100 in., or 100 mils, in diameter is 10,000 circular mils, etc. The cross-sectional area of any round wire in circular mils is equivalent to the diameter of the copper only, in mils or thousandths of an inch, squared or multiplied by itself.

Wire Sizes. Instead of referring to common sizes of wire by their areas, sizes or numbers have been assigned to them. The gauge commonly used is the American Wire Gauge, abbreviated AWG; it is the same as the Brown and Sharpe, or B&S gauge. This gauge is not the same as that used for steel wires used for nonelectrical purposes, for example fence wires.

FIG. 6-1. Actual diameters of typical sizes of copper wire, without insulation.

Number 14 wire, which is a size most commonly used for ordinary house wiring, has a copper conductor 0.064 in., or 64 mils, in diameter. Wires smaller than this are Nos. 16, 18, 20, and so on. Number 40 has a diameter of approximately 0.003 in., as small as a hair; many still finer sizes are made. Sizes larger than No. 14 are Nos. 12, 10, 8, etc. Note that the bigger the number, the smaller the diameter of the wire.

In this way, sizes proceed until No. 0 is reached; the next sizes are No. 00, No. 000, and finally No. 0000, which is almost ½ in. in diameter. Numbers 0, 00, 000, and 0000 are usually designated as 1/0, 2/0, 3/0, and 4/0 (one-naught, two-naught, etc.). As still heavier sizes are reached, they no longer are designated by a numerical size, but simply by their cross-sectional areas in circular mils.

Figure 6-1 shows the approximate actual sizes of typical sizes of wire, without the insulation. The sizes from Nos. 40 to 20 are used mostly in manufacturing electrical devices of all kinds. Numbers 18 and 16 are used chiefly for flexible cords, for signal systems, and for similar purposes where relatively small amperages are involved. Numbers 14 to 4/0 are used in ordinary residential and farm wiring and, of course, in industrial work, where the still heavier sizes are also used. Number 14 is the lightest size permitted for ordinary wiring. The even sizes of wire, such as Nos. 18, 16, 14, 12, 10, 8, etc., are commonly used;

FIG. 6-2. Typical wire gauge. Measure the wire by the slot into which it fits. This picture is actual size. (*Brown & Sharpe Mfg. Co.*)

the odd sizes, as Nos. 15, 13, 11, 9, are seldom used in wiring. The odd sizes, however, are commonly used in the form of magnet wire for manufacturing motors, transformers, and so on, for which purposes even fractional sizes such as No. 15½ are not at all uncommon.

In Fig. 6-2 is shown the usual gauge used in measuring wire sizes. The wire is measured by the slot into which it will fit, not by the hole behind the slot.

Table 8 of the Code shows the commonly used sizes of wire,

their areas in circular mils, their resistances in ohms per thousand feet, their dimensions in fractions of an inch, and their areas in fractions of a square inch. For convenience this table is reproduced in the Appendix of this book.

You will find it useful to remember that any wire which is three sizes heavier than another will have a cross-sectional area exactly twice that of the other. For example, No. 11 has an area exactly twice that of No. 14; No. 3 wire has an area exactly twice that of No. 6. Any wire that is six sizes heavier than another has exactly twice the diameter, four times the area, of the other. For example, No. 6 wire has exactly twice the diameter, and four times the area, of No. 12.

Stranded Wires. When common sizes of wire are used for ordinary wiring purposes, there is usually no reason why the copper conductor should not be one single solid conductor. Where considerable flexibility is needed, as in flexible cord, the conductor instead of being one solid wire consists of a great many strands of fine wire twisted together. The number assigned to such a conductor is determined by the total cross-sectional area of all these individual strands added together. For example, per Table 8 of the Code, the cross-sectional area of No. 16 wire is 2,583 circular mils. The total cross-sectional area of 65 strands of No. 34 wire is 2,585 circular mils; the total cross-sectional area of 26 strands of No. 30 wire is a trifle above this figure. Therefore wire made up of either of these two combinations, or any other combination totaling substantially 2,583 circular mils, is known simply as No. 16 wire. If it is necessary to describe such wire in more detail, the first-mentioned combination is described simply as No. 16, 65/34, and the second as No. 16, 26/30.

Building wires in No. 6 and heavier are stranded; solid wires are too stiff to be practical. The stranding of each size has been entirely standardized, so it is not necessary to specify the size of the individual strands. However, the number of strands and the size of each can be found for each size of wire in Table 8 of the Code (see Appendix).

Colors of Wire. Building wires come in various colors, and there is, of course, a purpose in this. Only white wire may be used for the grounded neutral wire in wiring; this will be explained in more detail later. Other wires may be any color except white. If there are two wires in a circuit, one is white, one black. If there are more than two wires, one is white, the others may be another color. Using varying colors makes it easy to trace circuits.

In cables and cords, the same scheme is used; the colors are as follows:

2-conductor	.....	White, black
3-conductor	.....	White, black, red
4-conductor	.....	White, black, red, blue
5-conductor	.....	White, black, red, blue, yellow

Plastic-insulated Wire. Building wire with thermoplastic insulation is called "Type T" by the Code. This type of wire is

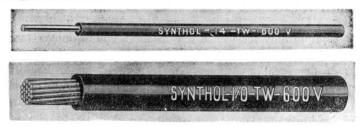

FIG. 6-3. Type T wire is used for general wiring. No. 6 and larger sizes are standard. (*Crescent Insulated Wire & Cable Co.*)

shown in Fig. 6-3 and is the most common kind in use today. It consists of the copper conductor, tinned for easy soldering and covered with a layer of plastic insulating compound, the thickness of which depends on the size of the wire. The wire is clean and easy to handle and strips easily.

Ordinary Type T wire may be used only in dry locations. A subtype known as Type TW may be used in either dry or wet.

Rubber-covered Wire. Before Type T wire became so popular, the wire commonly used was what is commonly known as "rubber-covered" wire. According to the Code, Sec. 310-3(a), "rubber insulations include those made from natural and synthetic rubber, neoprene and other *vulcanizable* materials." Its construction is shown in Fig. 6-4.

It consists of the copper conductor, tinned to make it easier to remove the rubber insulation and for easy soldering. Over the copper is a layer of rubber, the thickness of which depends on the size of the wire.   Then follows an outer fabric braid which is saturated in moisture-resistant and fire-retardant compounds; if it is set on fire with a blowtorch, the flame dies out when the torch is removed.   If the final color is to be something other than black, the color is painted on.   Over all is a wax finish to make the wire cleaner and easier to handle.

FIG. 6-4. Type R wire has rubber insulation, and a protective braid over the insulation.   (*Crescent Insulated Wire & Cable Co.*)

There are several subtypes, which will be discussed in more detail in Chap. 27.   Briefly however the basic Type R (which was suitable only for use in dry locations) is no longer made. The most ordinary now is Type RW which may be used in wet or dry locations.   Type RH is used in hotter-than-usual locations. Type RHW combines the properties of Types RH and RW.   However, throughout this book, to avoid awkward references to many types, the references will be to the now nonexistent "Type R"; it must be understood that the other types may be used even when Type R is mentioned.

Cable.   Usually a stranded wire heavier than No. 4/0 is called a "cable."   Thus you would refer to a wire with a cross-sectional area of 1,000,000 circular mils as a "1,000,000-circular-mil cable." The word "cable" is also used equally often as outlined in the next paragraph.

Cables.   For many purposes, especially in residential and farm wiring, it is desirable to have two or more wires grouped together in the form of a cable.   This makes a compact assembly which is easy to install, especially when used to wire a building that was completed before the wiring is installed, for the cable lends itself well to being fished through wall spaces.

A cable that contains two No. 14 wires is known as "14-2" (fourteen-two); if it contains three No. 12 wires, it is known as "12-3"; if it contains only one No. 8, it is known as "8-1"; etc.

Nonmetallic-sheathed Cable.   This cable consists of two or three Type T or Type R wires bundled together.   It costs less than other types of cable, is light in weight and very simple to install; no special tools are needed. All that makes it very popular. The Code recommends it for use where an especially good ground is *not* found, which makes it the ideal cable for farms. There are two types which the Code calls Type NM and Type NMC.

Type NM is the ordinary kind that has been available for many years and may be used only in permanently dry locations. It is known by such names as Romex, Cresflex, Loomwire, etc. It is shown in Fig. 6-5. In construction each wire is wrapped

Fɪɢ. 6-5. Nonmetallic-sheathed cable is popular for ordinary wiring. This is Code Type NM and may be used only in dry locations. (*Crescent Insulated Wire & Cable Co.*)

with a spiral layer of paper for additional protection. Over the wires is a fabric braid saturated in moisture-resistant and fire-retardant compounds; it will not support a flame. Over the braid there is a layer of wax for cleanliness. The empty spaces inside are filled with jute cords.

This material is entirely suitable in permanently dry locations and once was also used in locations having high humidity, such as barns on farms. It was found that the fibrous materials used in its construction (the paper, the jute cords, the fabric outer braid) acted like wicks, pulling moisture into the inside of the cable. The result was rotting, of both the insulation and the other parts of the cable, which quickly led to dangerous conditions, with respect both to shock and to fire. For that reason it may now be used only in permanently dry locations, and a different kind of cable has been developed for wet locations.

Code Type NMC is shown in Fig. 6-6, and you will note that the individually insulated wires are embedded in solid plastic, no fibrous, wicklike materials are used. Therefore it may be used in any location, dry or wet, and under certain circumstances may even be buried in the ground. This will be discussed in more detail in Chap. 11.

Armored Cable. Another common type is armored cable, commonly called BX. The Code calls it Type AC. It is shown in Fig. 6-7 and is available under a great variety of trade names such as BX, Flexsteel, etc. In construction it consists of two or three Type T or Type R wires, wrapped with a spiral layer of tough kraft paper, enclosed in a continuous galvanized spiral steel armor. The paper affords protection against abrasion by

FIG. 6-6. Type NMC nonmetallic-sheathed cable may be used in dry or wet locations. (*Crescent Insulated Wire & Cable Co.*)

the steel and serves another very useful purpose which will be discussed later.

Service-entrance and Underground Cables. There are several kinds of special cables in use for bringing wires into a building in the service entrance, either overhead or underground. These will be described in Chap. 13.

Weatherproof Wire. When wires are run between buildings, there is no great likelihood that anyone will ever touch them.

FIG. 6-7. Armored cable has a layer of steel armor for its final protection. (*Crescent Insulated Wire & Cable Co.*)

They are usually suspended a considerable distance above the ground and not close to each other. Therefore there is not the need for the same kind of insulation found on wires for interior use, where the wires usually lie next to each other inside conduit or cable. On the other hand, wire used out of doors must stand exposure to the weather, a factor that need not be considered for interior use. A special wire known as "weatherproof wire" is used for outdoor work; it may never be used indoors. The Code in no way prohibits the use of Type T or Type R wire out of doors, but it is common practice to use weatherproof wire for that purpose; as a matter of fact, it will last longer, and especially in the large sizes, it costs less.

As shown in Fig. 6-8, there is a copper conductor, usually with three separate cotton braids; the entire assembly is satu-

FIG. 6.8. Triple-braid weatherproof wire. It may never be used indoors. (*Anaconda Wire & Cable Co.*)

rated with weatherproofing moisture-resistant compounds, usually of an asphaltic nature, and is finished off with an application of flake mica for cleanliness. Most of the wire of this type made today is manufactured to the specifications of the Utilities' Research Commission and is known as Type URC. In recent years, weatherproof wire with neoprene (or sometimes thermoplastic) insulation in place of cotton has appeared on the market.

Weatherproof wire was formerly recognized in the Code as Type WP, but it was dropped in the 1959 Code. The Code concerns itself primarily with interior wiring, and basically with *safety;* weatherproof wire is used only outdoors, and in such fashion that safety is practically automatic. As a matter of fact, the Code does not even consider weatherproof wire an *insulated* wire; it considers it a *covered* wire, which in Art. 100 is defined as "having one or more layers of nonconducting materials that are not recognized as insulation under the Code."

Since weatherproof wire is installed only outdoors, any heat that develops is radiated into the air. For this reason it is customary to assign higher ampacities to this type of wire than to ordinary Type T or Type R. In practice the size of the wire used will depend on the necessary mechanical strength required for a span of any given length and on the voltage drop that can be tolerated. In general, however, you would be wise to use the ampacities assigned by the Code to "Bare and covered conductors" (Table 310-13, see Appendix) which are the same as assigned to weatherproof wires by Codes prior to 1959, as follows:

No. 14	30 amp	No. 6	100 amp
No. 12	40 amp	No. 4	130 amp
No. 10	55 amp	No. 2	175 amp
No. 8	70 amp	No. 1/0	235 amp

Aluminum Conductors. When there is a shortage of copper, there is a trend toward using aluminum in its place for electrical work. When the shortage of copper passes, the trend is away from aluminum. This is due to the fact that the introduction of aluminum presents many new problems.

First of all, aluminum does not conduct electricity as well as copper; the resistance of aluminum is higher than that of copper. For that reason, for any given load, it is necessary to use an aluminum conductor larger than is required when using copper. When using aluminum, instead of using the ampacities shown in Tables 310-12 and 310-13 of the Code, you must use the capacities shown in Tables 310-14 and 310-15. (Tables 310-12 and 310-13 are shown in the Appendix of this book; for Tables 310-14 and 310-15, refer to your copy of the Code.) For ordinary wiring, this usually means in practice that you must use aluminum wire two sizes larger than would be necessary if using copper. In other words, use No. 12 aluminum wire in place of No. 14 copper wire, No. 4 aluminum in place of No. 6 copper, and so on.

Aluminum is next to impossible to solder by methods available to the contractor; therefore solderless connectors must be used. But ordinary connectors designed for copper are not acceptable for use with aluminum, for the two dissimilar metals lead to electrolytic action which in turn leads to high-resistance joints. Special connectors must be used. Ordinary connectors that have been cadmium-plated are usually considered acceptable for aluminum wires, copper wires, or combinations of aluminum to copper.

In practice this has led to using aluminum mostly in heavy sizes and where long runs (few joints) are the rule. The most common usage is in weatherproof wire and in bare wires in transmission lines.

Flexible Cords. When wires are installed permanently, they need be only sufficiently flexible to permit reasonably easy installation. If the wires must be moved about, as on a floor lamp, a vacuum cleaner, or a portable motor, they must be very flexible. This is necessary first of all for convenience and second to prevent the conductors from breaking, which would be likely if they were solid copper of considerable diameter. Flexible wires of this type are called "flexible cords" in the Code. There are a great many different kinds, the more common of which will be described here.

FIG. 6-9. Type SP lampcord is commonly used on floor lamps, clocks, and similar devices. (*General Electric Co.*)

Types SP and SPT. This is the cord commonly used on lamps, clocks, radios, and similar appliances. As shown in Fig. 6-9 the wires are embedded directly in a solid mass of insulation. If the insulation is rubber, the Code calls the cord Type SP; if the insulation is plastic, it becomes Type SPT.[1] The insulation is of a high quality, so that the cord requires no further protection such as an overbraid. Often the cord is made with a depression between the two conductors for ease in separating the conductors to make connections.

The Code further labels such cords with suffixes -1, -2, and

FIG. 6-10. Type C lampcord is a good all-around knockabout cord.

-3. Types SP-1 and SPT-1 are available only in No. 18, and the insulation is $\frac{2}{64}$ in. thick. They are the types most commonly used. Types SP-2 and SPT-2 are available in Nos. 18 and 16 and have insulation $\frac{3}{64}$ in. thick. Type SPT-3 is available in Nos. 18 to 12 and has insulation $\frac{4}{64}$ in. thick.

Type C. This kind of cord was once common but is little used today. It is shown in Fig. 6-10, which shows its basic construc-

[1] The 1953 and earlier Codes called these kinds of cord Types POSJ and POT, instead of SP and SPT.

tion. It consists of two individual conductors, insulated, then covered with individual fabric braids, then twisted. The fabric braids are usually green and yellow in color, from which the cord gets its common name of "green and yellow." It is available in Nos. 18 to 10.

Types S, SJ, SV. The cords described in the preceding paragraphs are designed for ordinary household devices, which generally speaking are moved very little once they are plugged into a receptacle. They will not stand a great amount of mechanical wear and tear. Neither are they particularly moisture-resistant. A cord that has a sturdier construction is needed for vacuum cleaners, motors on washing machines, portable tools such as electric drills, and so on.

Such a cord is shown in Fig. 6-11. It consists of two or more

FIG. 6-11. Type S cord is very tough and durable. (*Crescent Insulated Wire & Cable Co.*)

stranded conductors with a serving of cotton between the copper and the insulation to prevent the fine strands from sticking to the insulation. Jute or similar "fillers" are twisted together with the conductors to make a round assembly, which is held together by a fabric overbraid. Over all comes a jacket of high-quality rubber to complete the cord.

Cord as described is made with the outer rubber jacket in varying thicknesses, which determine the Code type. Type S has the heaviest jacket, is available in Nos. 18 to 10, and is used for the hardest service, such as in industrial applications. Type SJ has a lighter jacket, is available only in Nos. 18 and 16, and is used for household purposes and light industrial applications. Type SV has a still lighter jacket, is available only in No. 18, and is used *only* on household vacuum cleaners.

Both Types S and SJ are available in two styles: stationary and constant service. The stationary type has a conductor which is not so finely stranded as the constant-service type. For example, in No. 18, the stationary type has a conductor consisting of 16 strands of No. 30, whereas the constant-service type has a conductor consisting of 41 strands of No. 34. The constant-service type will last longer on tools and similar devices where the cord is flexed continuously in use.

Types ST, SJT, SVT. If the outer jacket is made of plastic material instead of rubber, Types S, SJ, and SV become Types ST, SJT, and SVT.

Types SO and SJO. When rubber is exposed to oil, the oil attacks the rubber, which swells and falls apart. For that reason ordinary cords cannot be used where exposed to oil, as, for example, in garages. When the outer jacket of Types S and SJ cords is made of a special oil-resistant material such as neoprene, they become Types SO and SJO.

Heater Cord. Cords that are used on flatirons, toasters, portable heaters, and similar appliances that develop a lot of heat fall

FIG. 6-12. Heater cords have a layer of asbestos over the rubber insulation. They are used on toasters, flatirons, and similar appliances. (*Crescent Insulated Wire & Cable Co.*)

into the classification known as "heater cords." The basic standard conductor has the usual serving of cotton to prevent the rubber insulation from sticking to the copper, but over the rubber there is a layer of asbestos to withstand the heat developed should there be accidental contact with the hot surface of the appliance. Moreover, in this particular type of construction the Code permits an ampacity of 10 amp for No. 18 and 15 amp for No. 16, as compared with 5 and 7 amp respectively, for the same sizes of ordinary flexible cords. This higher amperage causes more heat, and the asbestos layer is a safety measure. The asbestos is applied in various ways but in any event must cover each conductor completely before twisting. Over all comes a layer of rayon or cotton which makes a compact assembly and gives a neat appearance. The type described is HPD and is shown in Fig. 6-12; if the outer layer is rubber instead of cotton or rayon, it is Type HSJ; if each conductor is given an outer layer of cotton over the asbestos, before the two conductors are twisted together, it becomes Type HC.

Cycles. The smaller the size of the individual strands in a cord, the greater the flexibility of the cord. Depending on the stranding, heater cords are known as "3,000 cycle" or "10,000 cycle," the latter being the more flexible.

Fixture Wire. For the internal wiring of lighting fixtures, special wire known as "fixture" wire is used. There are many types of fixture wire, and the particular type used depends to a great extent on the temperature that exists in the wire in use. Those with rubber insulation may be used only if the tempera-

FIG. 6-13. Fixture wire is used only in the internal wiring of lighting fixtures. Above is shown one of several approved constructions. (*Crescent Insulated Wire & Cable Co.*)

ture of the wire while carrying current does not exceed 140°F (60°C), but the most common is the Type CF pictured in Fig. 6-13, which employs no rubber in the insulation. It may be used at temperatures not exceeding 194°F (90°C). At higher temperatures, Type AF using asbestos for insulation must be used.

Other Types. There are many other types of wires, cables, and cords. Some are rarely used in the type of wiring discussed in this book and will not be mentioned. Other types are used for specific purposes such as underground wiring and will be discussed in the chapters pertaining to that kind of wiring.

FIG. 6-14. Annunciator ("bell") wire has very little insulation and is used only for low-voltage work.

Low-voltage Wire. Certain types of wire are intended only for low-voltage work, usually under 30 volts, such as wires for doorbells, telephones, etc. Usually the source of current for operating such devices is very limited in capacity, so that ordinarily it is safe to assume that, even under short circuit, no danger of fire exists. Therefore the Underwriters do not concern themselves with wire for such purposes.

Bell Wire. This wire is pictured in Fig. 6-14. It consists of a copper conductor over which are two layers of cotton, the two wrapped in opposite directions, then paraffined to give it some semblance of being moisture resistant. It is commonly known as bell wire or annunciator wire. Frequently two or more such wires are bundled together into one cable, which

FIG. 6-15. Thermostat cable consists of two or more separate annunciator wires bundled into one cable. (*Crescent Insulated Wire & Cable Co.*)

then receives a final outer braid of cotton, again paraffined. An assembly of this kind appears in Fig. 6-15; it is commonly known as "thermostat cable" because it is most frequently used in connection with furnaces and thermostats. Instead of fabric insulation, plastic material is becoming far more common.

Chapter 7

SELECTION OF PROPER WIRE SIZES

For any given combination of volts and amperes you must use a size of wire that is big enough to prevent the development of dangerous temperatures, and also big enough to avoid wasted power in the form of excessive voltage drop. Regardless of the size of wire selected, it is impossible to prevent all voltage drop; nevertheless, the drop must be held to nominal, practical proportions.

Advantage of Low Voltage Drop. Voltage drop is simply wasted electricity. If the drop is 5%, it means that 5% of the power is wasted as unwanted heat in the wires. Moreover, all electrical devices operate most efficiently on the voltage for which they are designed. If an electric motor is operated on a voltage 5% below its rated voltage, its power output drops almost 10%; if operated on a voltage 10% below normal, its power output drops 19%.

If a lamp is operated on a voltage 5% below its rated voltage, the amount of light it delivers drops about 16%; if the voltage is 10% below normal, its light output drops over 30%. So it is with most other electrical devices—the output drops off much faster than the reduction in voltage. It should then be readily apparent that voltage drop must be limited to as small a figure as is practical.

Practical Voltage Drops. The Code in Sec. 210-6(c) recommends that wire sizes be chosen so that the voltage drop will not exceed 3% in any branch circuit, measured at the most distant outlet. It further recommends not over 5% drop for feeders and branch circuits combined.

In ordinary residential wiring there are no feeders; the

branch circuits begin at the fuse or circuit breaker cabinet. In farm wiring however, the wires between the meter on the pole, and the point where they enter a building, are feeders. The drop in the feeders then should not exceed 2%, with an additional 3% in the branch circuits. Do note that these are recommendations as to the *maximum* drop that should be permitted; good practice suggests that a lower figure be the goal. A commonly accepted standard is 2% drop over all the wires from the point where they enter a building, to the farthest outlet. On farms a compromise must be reached because of the feeders from pole to building.

This means that on a 115-volt circuit the voltage drop from entrance to most distant outlet should not exceed 2.3 volts; on a 230-volt circuit it should not exceed 4.6 volts.

In residential wiring, if No. 14 wire is used for the ordinary branch circuits, the voltage drop will usually not greatly exceed the 2% figure. On the other hand, the lamps commonly used in floor lamps are getting bigger and bigger, appliances consuming 1,000 to 1,500 watts are becoming more and more common, and, all told, people are using more electric power every day, so that circuits are being loaded closer and closer to the limit of their carrying capacity. Therefore there is good reason for the trend toward considering No. 12 the smallest size wire to be commonly used for residential wiring. Some future Code may require No. 12 as the minimum size permitted for ordinary wiring, just as today No. 14 is the minimum. Some local Codes already require No. 12 as the minimum.

Determining Minimum Wire Size. First determine the maximum amperage that the wire will be called upon to carry. Then refer to Table 310-12 [1] of the Code (see Appendix) and determine the smallest wire that may be used. For example, if 18 amp is to be carried, reference to this table will show that if Type T or Type R wire is to be used, No. 14 is too small, No. 12 is suitable. If, however, weatherproof wire is to be used, No. 14 is big

---

[1] Use Table 310-12 for all types of wiring except the knob-and-tube system, for which Table 310-13 is used. In either case, for purposes of illustration, it is assumed that only ordinary Type T or Type R wire is to be used. Chapter 27 will discuss other types.

enough. This table merely shows what the minimum size may be from a safety standpoint. The minimum size may be entirely too small when voltage drop is considered.

Calculating Voltage Drops by Ohm's Law. The actual voltage drop in any problem can be determined by the use of Ohm's law, which was discussed in Chap. 2:

$$E = IR \quad \text{or} \quad \text{voltage drop} = \text{amperes} \times \text{ohms}$$

For example, assume that a 500-watt floodlight is to be operated at a point 500 ft from the meter; this requires 1,000 ft of wire. At 115 volts, 500 watts is equivalent to about 4.4 amp. Taking No. 14 wire as a random size, Table 8 in the Appendix shows that it has a resistance of 2.575 ohms per 1,000 ft. The voltage drop then is 4.4 × 2,575, or 11.33 volts, considerably over the limit of 2%, or 2.3 volts.

Trying other sizes, No. 6 with 0.410 ohms per 1,000 ft involves a drop of 1.804 volts; No. 8 with 0.641 ohms per 1,000 ft, 2.82 volts. Therefore, if the floodlight is to be used a great deal, use No. 6 wire; if it is to be used relatively little, No. 8 is acceptable; and if it is to be used only in emergencies, No. 10 with 4.479 volts drop (or even No. 12) will be entirely suitable, in that the amount of power wasted per year would not begin to pay for the extra cost of the heavier wire.

If in this example the distance had been 400 ft instead of 500 ft, the length of the wire would have been 800 ft instead of 1,000 ft. The voltage drop would then have been 800/1,000, or 80% of what it is for 1,000 ft.

Now assume that the same floodlight is to be operated at the same distance of 500 ft but at 230 volts instead of 115 volts. The amperage now becomes 2.2 instead of 4.4. Making the same calculations, No. 14 wire gives a drop of only 5.66 volts, still above the 4.6 volts (2% of 230 volts) considered permissible on a 230-volt circuit. Number 12 with a resistance of 1.619 ohms per 1,000 ft gives a drop of 2.2 × 1.619, or 3.563 volts, well under the 4.6-volt limit that has been set. This emphasizes the desirability of using higher voltages where a considerable distance is involved as well as where considerable power is involved.

Desirability of Higher Voltages. For any given *wattage* and any given *distance*, the voltage drop *measured in volts* on any given size of wire is exactly twice as great on 115 volts as it is on 230 volts. Doubling the voltage (regardless of what the actual voltages are) reduces the voltage drop *in volts* exactly 50% if the wattage, the distance, and the wire size remain the same. It is the *wattage* and not the *amperage* that must remain unchanged for this statement to be correct.

When the voltage drop *in percentage* is considered, remember that in the case of the 230-volt circuit the initial voltage is twice as large but the actual voltage drop only half as large as in the case of the 115-volt circuit. From this you can see that the voltage drop *in percentage* will be only one-fourth as great using 230 volts as it is using 115 volts—the wattage, the wire size, and the distance, of course, remaining unchanged during the discussion. For example, in the first instance, 500 watts, 500 ft distance (1,000 ft of wire), No. 14 wire on the 115-volt circuit involved a drop of 11.33 volts, which is 9.8% of 115 volts; on the 230-volt circuit the drop was 5.5 volts, which is 2.45% of 230 volts; 2.45% is one-fourth of 9.8%.

All the foregoing can be simply restated: Any size of wire will carry any given wattage on 230 volts four times as far as on 115 volts with the same *percentage* of voltage drop. This statement should not be confused with the statement made above, that any size wire will carry any given wattage twice as far with the same *number of volts* drop.

Another Method of Calculating Voltage Drop. Another formula that is frequently used is

$$\text{Circular mils} = \frac{\text{distance in feet} \times \text{amperage} \times 22}{\text{volts drop}}$$

Applying this to the floodlight example, which involves a distance of 500 ft, 4.4 amp, and a voltage drop that is to be limited to 2.3 volts, the formula becomes

$$\text{Circular mils} = \frac{500 \times 4.4 \times 22}{2.3} = \frac{48,400}{2.3} = 21,043$$

In other words, to limit the voltage drop to exactly 2.3 volts, wire having a cross-sectional area of 21,043 circular mils must be used. Reference to Table 8 of the Code (see Appendix) shows that there is no wire having exactly this cross-sectional

area, which falls about halfway between No. 6 and No. 8.   Therefore compromise on No. 6 with a little under 2.3 volts drop or on
No. 8 with a little over 2.3 volts drop.

If, instead of determining the size of wire that will produce
a given voltage drop, the actual voltage drop with a given size
wire is to be determined, merely transpose the formula to read

$$\text{Volts drop} = \frac{\text{distance} \times \text{amperes} \times 22}{\text{circular mils}}$$

To determine the number of feet any given size of wire will
carry any given amperage, transpose the formula once more to
read

$$\text{Distance} = \frac{\text{volts drop} \times \text{circular mils}}{\text{amperes} \times 22}$$

Three-phase Voltage Drop.   The formulas given above are
correct for direct current as well as for single-phase alternating
current.   In the case of 3-phase current a correction factor must
be applied.   Calculate the drop, using the formula above; then
multiply the answer by 0.865.[2]   A simple short cut is to deduct
$\frac{1}{7}$ from the answer, whether it is in volts or circular mils.   If
preferred, the single-phase formula above can be used by substituting 19 for 22.

Voltage-drop Tables.   For most purposes there is no need
of going through tedious calculations to arrive at the right size
wire to use.   Suitable tables follow immediately, one for 115
volts, the other for 230 volts, each based on 2% drop.   Under
each wire size is shown the *one-way* distance which that size
wire will carry the amperage shown in the left-hand column.   To
clarify, not the number of feet of wire in any problem, but the
distance from the starting point to the load in question is given.
When the distance appears in **boldface** type, it indicates that
Type T or Type R wires in open wiring, but not in conduit or
cables, may be used.   When the distance appears in *italics*, it
indicates that only weatherproof wire will carry the corresponding
amperage in the left-hand column; distances shown in ordinary
type are applicable to all approved wires.

[2] 0.865 is $\frac{1}{2}\sqrt{3}$.

Wire Table—115 Volts—2 Per Cent Voltage Drop

Amperes	Volt-amperes* at 115 volts	No. 14	No. 12	No. 10	No. 8	No. 6	No. 4	No. 2	No. 1/0	No. 2/0	No. 3/0
1	115	450	700	1,100	1,800	2,800	4,500	7,000			
2	230	225	350	550	900	1,400	2,200	3,500			
3	345	150	240	350	600	900	1,500	2,300	3,750		
4	460	110	175	275	450	700	1,100	1,750	2,750	3,500	
5	575	90	140	220	360	560	880	1,400	2,250	2,800	
7½	860	60	95	150	240	375	600	950	1,500	1,900	2,400
10	1,150	45	70	110	180	280	450	700	1,100	1,400	1,800
15	1,725	30	45	70	120	180	300	475	750	950	1,200
20	2,300	22	35	55	90	140	225	350	550	700	900
25	2,875	18	28	45	70	110	180	280	450	560	720
30	3,450	15	25	35	60	90	150	235	340	470	600
35	4,025	...	20	30	50	80	125	200	320	400	500
40	4,600	...	17	27	45	70	110	175	280	350	440
45	5,175	...	...	25	40	60	100	155	250	310	400
50	5,750	...	...	22	35	55	90	140	225	280	360
60	6,900	...	...	...	30	45	75	120	185	240	300
70	8,050	...	...	...	25	40	65	100	160	200	260
80	9,200	...	...	...	...	35	55	85	140	180	220
90	10,350	...	...	...	...	30	50	75	125	160	200
100	11,500	...	...	...	...	28	45	70	115	140	180

* The figure in this column is also the wattage of the circuit if the power is direct current or if it is single-phase alternating current and the load has a power factor of 100 per cent, as is the case with lamp bulbs and most appliances.

In this table, the figures below each size wire represent the maximum distance which that size wire will carry the amperage in the left-hand column, with 2 per cent voltage drop. All distances are one-way; in a circuit 100 ft long, of course 200 ft of wire is used, but look for the figure 100 above.

If a distance appears in **boldface** type, it indicates that the amperage in the left-hand column is too great for Type T or R wire in conduit but not too great for Type T or R wire in open air.

If a distance appears in *italics*, it indicates that the amperage in the left-hand column is too great for Type T or R wire under any circumstances but not too great for weatherproof wire.

Theory and Basic Principles

Wire Table—230 Volts—2 Per Cent Voltage Drop

Amperes	Volt-amperes* at 230 volts	No. 14	No. 12	No. 10	No. 8	No. 6	No. 4	No. 2	No. 1/0	No. 2/0	No. 3/0
1	230	900	1,400	2,200	3,600	5,600	9,000				
2	460	450	700	1,100	1,800	2,800	4,500	7,000			
3	690	300	480	700	1,200	1,800	3,000	4,600	7,500		
4	920	220	350	550	900	1,400	2,200	3,500	5,500	7,000	
5	1,150	180	280	440	720	1,020	1,750	2,800	4,500	5,600	
7½	1,720	120	190	300	480	750	1,200	1,900	3,000	3,800	4,800
10	2,300	90	140	220	360	560	900	1,400	2,200	2,800	3,600
15	3,450	60	90	140	240	360	600	950	1,500	1,900	2,400
20	4,600	45	70	110	180	280	450	700	1,100	1,400	1,800
25	5,750	35	55	90	140	220	360	560	900	1,100	1,440
30	6,900	30	50	70	120	180	300	470	680	940	1,200
35	8,050	...	40	60	110	160	250	400	640	800	1,000
40	9,200	...	35	55	90	140	220	350	560	700	880
45	10,350	...	...	50	80	120	200	310	500	620	800
50	11,500	...	...	45	70	110	180	280	450	560	720
60	13,800	...	...	...	60	90	150	240	370	480	600
70	16,100	...	...	...	50	80	130	200	320	400	520
80	18,400	...	...	...	...	70	110	170	280	360	440
90	20,700	...	...	...	...	60	100	150	250	320	400
100	23,000	...	...	...	...	55	90	140	230	280	360
125	28,750	...	...	...	...	...	75	110	180	220	290
150	34,500	...	...	...	...	...	...	95	150	190	240
175	40,250	...	...	...	...	...	...	80	130	165	210
200	46,000	...	...	...	...	...	...	...	115	140	180

* The footnotes on page 107 apply to this table also.

In the event that these tables are used for 3-phase runs, *do not* use the "volt-amperes" column; use only the "amperes" column. Then, increase all distances by $\frac{1}{6}$. In the formulas above, $\frac{1}{7}$ was deducted, which is the same as multiplying by $\frac{6}{7}$; for the tables, add $\frac{1}{6}$, which is the same as multiplying by $\frac{7}{6}$.

Note that these tables are based on an assumed voltage drop of 2%. If, under certain circumstances, other voltage drops are to be permitted, the tables are easily converted, as follows:

> For a voltage drop of 1% decrease all distances by 50%
> For a voltage drop of $2\frac{1}{2}$% increase all distances by 25%
> For a voltage drop of 3% increase all distances by 50%
> For a voltage drop of 4% increase all distances by 100%
> For a voltage drop of 5% increase all distances by 150%

Cost of Voltage Drop. As already discussed, voltage drop represents wasted electricity, power used to heat the wires in carrying the current to the point where it is to be used. The smaller the wire and the greater the distance, the greater the loss will be. Voltage drop cannot be eliminated, but it can be kept to reasonable figures.

It is not difficult, although a bit tedious, to calculate the money wasted in heating by unwanted voltage drop. On page 110 is reproduced a tabulation[3] showing what price is paid per year for the wasted power when different amperages are carried by various sizes of wire over several different distances. The table is based on the assumption that power flows exactly 500 hr per year (less than $1\frac{1}{2}$ hr per day) and that power costs 2 cents per kilowatthour.

To use the table, follow the amperage column downward until it intersects with the size-and-distance line involved. The figure at the intersection represents the cost per year of the wasted power in that circuit. For example, assume a 115-volt 2-hp motor consuming about 20 amp, operating at a distance of 200 ft from the service switch. If No. 12 wire is used, the cost of the power wasted in the wires is $2.56 per year. The following tabulation shows the cost with other sizes of wire. It also shows the cost of the wasted power in operating the same motor over the same size wires, but operating at 230 volts, and then consuming only 10 amp.

[3] By J. B. Stere, *Electricity on the Farm*, April, 1946.

Theory and Basic Principles

Cost of Power Wasted by Voltage Drop

Wire size	Distance, feet	Load, amperes										
		10	15	20	25	30	40	50	60	70	80	90
No. 14	50	0.25	0.60									
	100	0.50	1.20									
	200	1.00	2.40									
	300	1.50	3.60									
No. 12	50	0.16	0.36	0.64								
	100	0.32	0.72	1.28								
	200	0.64	1.44	2.56								
	300	0.96	2.16	3.84								
No. 10	50	0.10	0.23	0.40	0.62	0.90						
	100	0.20	0.45	0.85	1.24	1.80						
	200	0.40	0.90	1.60	2.48	3.60						
	300	0.60	1.35	2.40	3.72	5.40						
No. 8	50	0.06	0.15	0.25	0.40	0.60	1.00					
	100	0.12	0.30	0.50	0.80	1.20	2.00					
	200	0.24	0.60	1.00	1.60	2.40	4.00					
	300	0.36	0.90	1.50	2.40	3.60	6.00					
No. 6	50	0.04	0.09	0.16	0.25	0.36	0.64	1.00				
	100	0.08	0.18	0.32	0.50	0.72	1.28	2.00				
	200	0.16	0.36	0.64	1.00	1.44	2.56	4.00				
	300	0.24	0.54	0.96	1.50	2.16	3.84	6.00				
No. 4	50	0.03	0.06	0.10	0.15	0.22	0.40	0.62	0.90	1.22		
	100	0.05	0.12	0.20	0.30	0.44	0.80	1.24	1.80	2.44		
	200	0.10	0.24	0.40	0.60	0.88	1.60	2.48	3.60	4.88		
	300	0.15	0.36	0.80	0.90	1.32	2.40	3.72	5.40	7.32		
No. 2	50	0.02	0.04	0.06	0.10	0.13	0.25	0.40	0.60	0.77	1.00	1.26
	100	0.03	0.07	0.12	0.20	0.25	0.50	0.80	1.20	1.54	2.00	2.52
	200	0.06	0.15	0.24	0.40	0.50	1.00	1.60	2.40	3.08	4.00	5.04
	300	0.09	0.22	0.36	0.60	0.75	1.50	2.40	3.60	4.62	6.00	7.56

This table shows the cost of electrical power wasted as heat in wires, in the form of voltage drop. Start with the size of wire involved, select the proper line representing the one-way length of the circuit, follow that line to the right until it intersects the column showing the amperage under consideration. The figure shown there is the cost of the wasted power over a period of 500 hr, with power costing 2 cents per kilowatthour.

Wire size	115 volt 20 amp	230 volt 10 amp
No. 12	$2.56	$0.64
No. 10	1.60	0.40
No. 8	1.00	0.24
No. 6	0.64	0.16
No. 4	0.40	0.10
No. 2	0.24	0.06

This study shows the advantage of using 230-volt devices where possible, instead of using the corresponding 115-volt type, resulting in less wasted power, more efficient operation, and much smaller initial investment in wire. It also shows, regardless of voltage, the advantage of using the heavier sizes of wire.

As Stere[4] in his article points out, the most economical electrical installation is that in which the cost of the wire is equal to the cost of the wasted electric power during the useful life of the wire. Considering obsolescence, this should not be considered to be more than five to eight years. This condition is approximated when the equipment is used 500 hr per year and power costs 2 cents per kilowatthour if the voltage drop is limited to 2%. If the equipment is operated 1,000 hr per year, it will probably prove economical to limit the drop to 1%.

Outdoor Wiring. In outdoor wiring there is one additional factor to be considered: mechanical strength. The wires must be heavy enough to support not only their own weight but also the strain imposed by winds, ice loads, etc. In many areas it is not unusual to see a layer of ice an inch thick around outdoor wires after a severe sleet storm. For this reason it is best to use nothing lighter than No. 12 wire for spans up to 25 ft, No. 10 up to 50 ft, No. 8 up to 100 ft, and No. 6 over 100 ft. If distances over 150 ft are involved, use heavier wires or install extra poles for supports.

In installing outdoor overhead wires, take into consideration the expansion and contraction that take place with changes in the temperature. A 100-ft span of copper wire will be almost 2 in.

[4] J. B. Stere, *Electricity on the Farm,* April, 1946.

shorter when it is 30° below zero than on a hot summer day when the thermometer stands at 100°.   Therefore if the wires are installed on a cold winter day, they may be pulled as tight as practical.   If installed on a hot day, allow considerable sag in the span so that when the wires contract in the winter, no damage will be done.

Chapter 8

WIRE CONNECTIONS AND JOINTS

Wires must be connected to switches, receptacles, and other devices. This is very simply done, yet many times such connections are poorly made. Study carefully the following points.

Removing Insulation. Cut through the insulation down to the copper conductor, holding the knife not at a right angle but at about 60 deg. This precaution reduces the danger of nicking the conductor, which weakens it and sometimes leads to breaks. After the insulation has been cut all around, pull it off, leaving the conductor sticking out far enough to suit the purpose (see Fig. 8-1). For a good electrical connection you must clean off all traces of rubber or other insulation very carefully.

RIGHT   WRONG

Fig. 8-1. In removing insulation from wire which is to be attached to a terminal, hold knife at an angle of about 60 deg.

Fig. 8-2. Terminals for attaching wires.

Terminals. Wire is fastened to devices by means of terminals designed for the purpose. If the device is intended for wire No. 8 or lighter, it is usually provided with ordinary screw terminals of the type shown in Fig. 8-2. The end of the terminal is bent upward to prevent the wire from slipping from under the terminal screw. This screw is often "upset" so that it cannot be removed entirely and lost.

Screw closes loop   Screw opens loop·

RIGHT   WRONG

Fig. 8-3. Insert the loop under screw of terminal, so that tightening screw tends to *close* the loop.

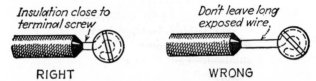

Insulation close to   Don't leave long
terminal screw   exposed wire.

RIGHT   WRONG

Fig. 8-4. Do not leave exposed conductor next to terminals.

Bend the end of the wire into a loop to fit and insert it under the terminal screw in such a way that tightening the screw tends to close rather than to open the loop. Figure 8-3 should

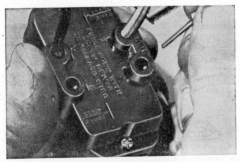

Fig. 8-5. Many modern devices have no terminal screws. Push the bare wire into the device for a good permanent connection. (*General Electric Co.*)

make this clear. It is best to close the loop completely with long-nosed pliers after it is inserted under the screw. Cut off any excess length of wire so that the insulation comes up close to the terminal (see Fig. 8-4).

Many switches and receptacles are now made so that the straight, stripped end of the wire is merely pushed into holes in the device; automatically a good connection is made. Strip the insulation off the wire as far as indicated by the marker on the device. If it is necessary to remove a wire, push a small screwdriver into a slot on the device to release the wire. Some of

Fig. 8-6. A typical solderless connector. (*Ilsco Copper Tube & Products, Inc.*)

such devices have no terminal screws; others do have the screws, so that the user can use either method for connections (see Fig. 8-5).

For No. 6 or heavier wire, solderless terminals of the type shown in Fig. 8-6 are commonly used. Simply insert the stripped and cleaned end of the conductor into the terminal or connector, drive home the nut or screw, and the connection is completed.

At other times soldering lugs of the type shown in Fig. 8-7 are used. In such cases it is necessary to solder the wire into the lug; the way to do this will be explained later in this chapter.

Fig. 8-7. A typical solder-ing lug.

Joints. In many cases joints between two different pieces of wire are prohibited by the Code; these will be mentioned as the related work is discussed in this book. At other times joints are necessary; consequently it is most important that they be made properly. The requirements for joints are simple. Mechanically the joint must be as strong as a continuous length of the wire,

Electrically it must be as good a conductor as a continuous piece of the same wire. After the joint is completed, insulation equivalent to the original insulation on a continuous piece of the wire must be placed over it.

To accomplish these three things, it is necessary to remove the insulation where the wires are to be joined, make the mechanical joint, using solder or solderless connectors, and replace the insulation by means of tapes made for the purpose.

Removing Insulation.   In removing insulation for a joint, hold the knife at an angle as in sharpening a pencil, rather than at a 60-deg angle as in preparing wire for a terminal.   When stripping

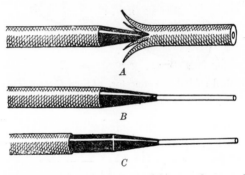

Fɪɢ. 8-8. Preparing end of wire which is to be joined to another and later soldered.

stranded wires, be careful not to damage any of the individual strands.   After the insulation has been cut all the way around the wire, it can often be removed to the end of the wire with one pull.   In the case of rubber-covered wire it is necessary to remove also the outer braid only, for some distance back, depending on the size of the wire.   Be careful to cut only through the outer braid, not into the insulation proper.   All this is shown in steps in Fig. 8-8.

Making the Splice.   The simplest and most common method of joining two solid wires is shown in successive steps in Fig. 8-9 and hardly needs additional explanation.

Small stranded wires can be spliced in the same way.   If the stranded wire is of considerable size, it will be better to make the type of splice shown in successive steps in Fig. 8-10.

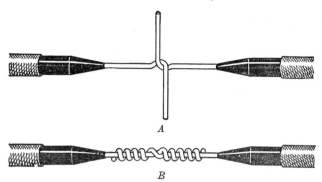

A

B

FIG. 8-9. A simple splice; it is strong mechanically.

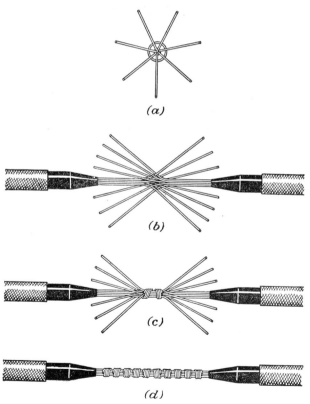

(a)

(b)

(c)

(d)

FIG. 8-10. Splicing stranded wires.

This may appear a bit difficult but with practice becomes relatively easy. Spread the individual strands evenly, as in A. Place the two wires end to end with the several strands inter-

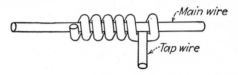

FIG. 8-11. A simple tap.

secting, as in B. Then wrap one of the strands around the assembly and repeat with one of the strands of the opposite piece, wrapping it in the opposite direction; this is shown in C. Follow through with alternate strands of each piece and con-

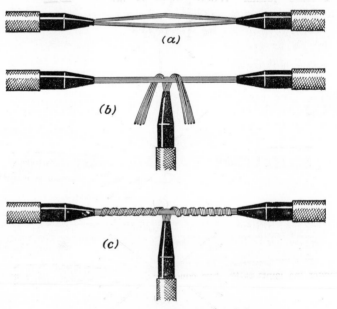

FIG. 8-12. Making a tap with stranded wires.

tinue in this fashion until each strand has been wrapped, giving the final appearance of D in Fig. 8-10. Naturally considerable practice is required to learn just how long to leave the strands for different wire sizes.

Taps. The simplest and most commonly used form of tap is shown in Fig. 8-11. It is so simple that the picture should be self-explanatory.

With stranded wire the same kind of tap can be used, but, especially in heavier sizes, it is better to proceed as shown in successive steps in Fig. 8-12. First separate the strands in the main wire into two groups, as in *A*, so that the tap wire can be inserted into the opening. Divide the strands of the tap wire into approximately equal groups, as in *B*. Next wrap each group around the main wire, one in the clock-wise and the other in the counterclock-wise direction, working toward opposite ends, until the tap is completed as in *C* of Fig. 8-12.

Fixture Joints. Where there is no mechanical strain whatever on the wire, usually the two ends are merely twisted together, as shown in Fig. 8-13, then soldered and taped.

Fig. 8-13. When there is no strain on the wires, they may be spliced by simply twisting.

Splices in Lamp Cords. In splicing cords, splice each conductor separately, but stagger the two joints so that, when the splice is completed, they will not lie next to each other in the finished job (see Fig. 8-14). This makes a much less bulky joint in the finished job. A much better practice is never to make such a splice at all— follow the Code requirement and use only continuous lengths of cord.

Fig. 8-14. It is best not to splice lamp cord. If a splice must be made, stagger the joints in the two conductors. This makes a smaller and safer splice.

Soldering. The joint having been made mechanically, the next step is to solder it. It is best to practice first on solid wires rather than stranded. Good soldering is an art; to become proficient in it requires considerable practice. The requirements for good soldering are:

1. Absolutely clean conductors.
2. Careful use of flux.
3. Clean soldering copper.
4. Correct temperature of soldering copper.
5. Proper solder.

Clean the Conductor.   The insulation having been removed, the next step is to clean the conductor carefully.   If this is not done, it will be utterly impossible to do a good soldering job.   The cleaning is usually done by scraping with a knife and is no great task.   Most building wires have tinned conductors which make it easier to strip the insulation.   If you use care in scraping off the remaining traces of insulation, the tinned surface remains intact, making soldering much easier.

The cleaning of small stranded conductors does call for considerable patience, for it is definitely necessary to clean each strand separately.   Do not skimp on this detail.

Flux.   In soldering, a flux of some type is necessary to permit solder to form a solid bond with the copper.   For some kinds of nonelectrical soldering, acid is used as a flux, but under no circumstances may it be used for electrical soldering.   The acid reacts with the copper to form a new compound, usually of an insulating nature, and, especially on fine stranded wires, often eats through the copper, destroying the conductor.   Use any kind of noncorrosive paste, of which several brands are on the market.   Use it sparingly.   Rosin makes a good flux, and rosin-core solder is entirely practical.

Keep Soldering Copper Clean and at Right Temperature.   If a soldering copper is used, whether it is electrically heated or heated by a blowtorch, keep it clean.   Applying the hot copper to a cake of sal ammoniac will clean it.   The right temperature can best be learned by experience, too hot a copper being just as impractical as one that is not hot enough.

Apply the soldering copper directly to the conductor, as shown in Fig. 8-15.   You must heat the conductor to a temperature high enough so that when the solder is touched to the conductor (not the soldering copper), it will melt completely and flow into every little space.   If the soldering copper is not hot enough, it will *slowly* increase the temperature of the conductor, but much of the heat will follow the conductor away from the spot where the heat is being applied, and flow along the conductor so that it will be heated not only where you want it hot, but also for some distance inside the insulation, probably damaging the insulation. Have the soldering copper hot enough so that it will heat the conductor *quickly* at the joint, but not inside the insulation.

While the actual solder that will remain in the finished joint is applied to the hot conductor, you will find that a drop of solder on the soldering copper itself, at the point where you apply it to the conductor, will help in transferring heat from the soldering copper to the conductor; the unsoldered joint will heat

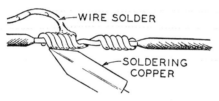

Fig. 8-15. In soldering, do not drop hot solder on cold wire. Heat the wire until it is hot enough to melt solder.

faster. If you have done no work of this kind, experiment on scrap pieces of wire to gain experience.

In the case of very fine wires, the drop of solder on the soldering copper will probably be enough to solder the joint. This then becomes an exception to the rule of applying the solder to the conductor and letting the heat in the conductor melt the solder.

If you use a blowtorch for soldering, remember that the tip of the flame is the hottest spot; there is no heat in the inner cone of the flame. When using a torch it is easy to heat the conductor too much, damaging the insulation. Practice on scrap till you get the knack of it.

Figure 8-16 shows the difference between dropping hot solder on a cold conductor and heating the conductor sufficiently to melt the solder, which then flows into the smallest crevice.

Reinsulating the Joint. After a joint has been soldered, you must replace the insulation originally on the wire. The insula-

tion on the finished joint must be electrically and mechanically
as good as that on a continuous piece of wire. Formerly this
required two kinds of tape, but today a single variety of tape is
used. Both methods will be described.

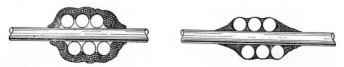

FIG. 8-16. When hot solder is applied to cold wires, as at the left above,
a poor joint results. When the hot wires melt the solder, it flows into every
crevice and makes a good joint, as shown at right above.

Plastic Tape. The new plastic electrical tape will probably in
due course of time replace the two kinds of tape formerly used.
It is tough mechanically, and has very high insulating value (per
mil or thousandth of an inch of thickness) so that a comparatively thin layer of it is sufficient, thus doing away with clumsy,

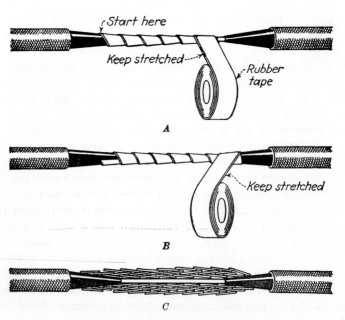

FIG. 8-17. Applying tape to a splice.

bulky joints. This leads to a less crowded condition inside boxes, especially when there must be many joints within the same box.

In applying this tape on a joint, start at one end, laying the end of the tape over the tapered end of the original insulation, then winding it diagonally toward the opposite end, letting the successive turns slightly overlap (see A of Fig. 8-17). Keep the tape stretched so that, wherever the turns overlap, they will fuse to each other. From the opposite end, work back toward the starting point in exactly the same manner. The individual turns of tape in successive layers will be almost at right angles to each other (see B of the same picture). Work back and forth in this fashion until the thickness of the tape you have applied is as thick as the original insulation on the wire. The job is finished.

Do note that Fig. 8-17 at C shows in exaggerated fashion a cross section of the finished joint; the small openings between turns and layers will in actual practice be nonexistent, for the pressure created by keeping the tape tight during application will result in one solid mass of insulation.

Splicing Compound and Friction Tape. In the older method, two kinds of tape are used: splicing compound (commonly called rubber tape), which replaces the original insulation, and friction tape to protect the splicing compound mechanically.

Splicing compound is a very high grade of rubber put up in rolls. The rubber is unvulcanized and under slight pressure vulcanizes with another layer of the same material. A layer of cloth between layers of rubber in the roll prevents the layers from sticking to each other; the cloth is thrown away as the tape is used. Wrap several layers of this tape around a pencil, one layer on top of the other, stretching the tape tightly as it is applied. Cut through the mass of rubber with a knife and you will find a solid mass of rubber instead of the several layers you have applied; the layers have vulcanized into a solid mass.

Apply this tape to a joint as already described for plastic tape and as shown in Fig. 8-17. Then follow with several layers of friction tape, and the joint is finished.

Weatherproof Wire. If the joint is in weatherproof wire (which has a relatively poor insulation), use either plastic tape alone or friction tape alone. Rubber tape is not required.

Soldering Lugs. A typical soldering lug was shown in Fig. 8-7. The conductor is soldered into this lug, which then is connected to the device with bolts provided for the purpose. This sounds simple, yet it is safe to say that a goodly percentage of such soldering jobs are very poorly done, resulting in high-resistance joints which lead to arcing, overheating, and sometimes damage from the resulting heat. Figure 8-18 shows a cross section of a poorly soldered lug. Note how most of the individual strands of wire have no trace of solder. Careful study of this picture should indicate the points to watch in soldering a wire into a lug.

To solder a wire into a lug is undoubtedly more difficult than soldering, for example, a simple splice. The copper conductor

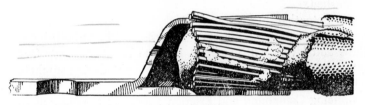

FIG. 8-18. Cross section of poorly soldered lug. Not enough solder was used, probably not enough flux, and certainly not enough heat.

first must be properly cleaned. If the wire is stranded, the individual strands must not be spread out, which would prevent a good mechanical fit in the lug. Tin the exposed end of the conductor; apply a reasonable quantity of flux; dip the end into a ladle of melted solder, making sure that it is hot enough so that it will flow freely into every crevice, every space, between individual strands. When it cools, there will be a single solid mass of metal: copper and solder. If a blowtorch is used instead of a ladle, heat the end of the conductor sufficiently so that, when solder in wire form is applied, it will melt and flow down into the space between the strands. Do not overheat the wire lest the insulation be damaged.

Tin the inside of the soldering lug in the same way; then melt sufficient solder into it so that, when the conductor is inserted, the lug, the conductor, and the solder will form a single mass of metal. Of course, heat must be applied to the lug, by means of either a soldering copper or a blowtorch, to melt the solder previously inserted in order to permit complete fusion of the three elements.

Because it is recognized that a large percentage of soldered joints involving tubular lugs and heavy sizes of wire are poorly made in the field, the Code in Sec. 230-72 prohibits their use in connection with service equipment and in Sec. 250-113 prohibits their use in connection with grounding conductors and clamps. Connections must be made by means of "pressure connectors," as heavy-duty solderless lugs are termed in the Code.

Solderless Connectors. When there is no strain on the joint, as, for example, in an outlet box, solderless connectors of the type shown in Fig. 8-19 may be used.

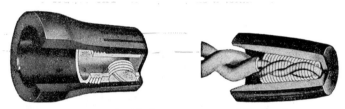

Fig. 8-19. Two types of solderless connectors. (*Ideal Industries, Inc.*)

One type has a brass insert with a set screw. The wires are clamped into this insert; then the insulating shell is screwed on over the insert. The one-piece type is screwed directly onto the stripped wires. If one of the wires is lighter than the others,

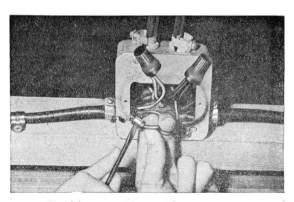

Fig. 8-20. This shows the use of solderless connectors. (*Ideal Industries, Inc.*)

let it project a bit beyond the heavier wires before installing the connector. Connectors of this type are made in several sizes; use a size suitable for the number and size of wires being connected. Figure 8-20 shows several connectors in use.

Regardless of which of these two types you use, strip the wires just far enough so that no bare conductor will be exposed beyond the end of the insulating shell. No tape is required.

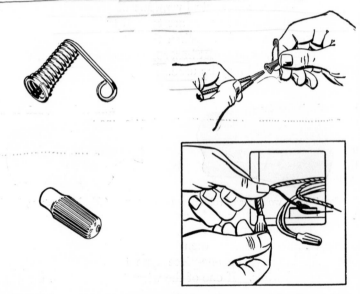

Fig. 8-21. These spring-type connectors are very practical. Screw them over the wires to be joined. If the pre-insulated type is used, no taping of the joint is necessary. (*Minnesota Mining & Mfg. Co.*)

The spring-type connectors shown in Fig. 8-21 are also popular. They are available in two types—uninsulated and pre-insulated—and in several sizes. Lay the wires to be joined so that the stripped ends are parallel. Using the uninsulated type, screw the connector over the wires with the projecting end of the connector serving as a handle. The twisting action tends to uncoil the spring during the screwing-on process, but it promptly contracts and puts very heavy pressure on the wires when the work is completed. Then twist the "handle" at right angles, and it will break off, leaving the completed splice. Tape, of course, must be applied over it.

When the preinsulated type is used, there is no handle, but the insulation makes the connector larger in diameter and provides a good grip, making the handle unnecessary. No tape is

Fig. 8-22. A connector of this type permits one wire to be tapped to another *continuous* wire. (*Burndy Engineering Co., Inc.*)

necessary if you have been careful in stripping the insulation off the wires so that no bare wire is exposed.

A still different type of connector which is very popular, especially in farm wiring, is shown in Fig. 8-22. The body has a U cross section, and the nut slips over the threaded legs of the U,

Fig. 8-23. Where no strain is involved in the joint, simple connectors of the type shown here may be used. (*Burndy Engineering Co., Inc.*)

making it very handy for tapping one wire to another continuous wire. When there is no strain on the finished joint and heavy sizes of wire are involved, the simple type of connector shown in Fig. 8-23 is commonly used. Being made of metal, the connectors must be taped after the joint is made.

Chapter 9

THEORY OF GROUNDING

The term "ground" is used with great regularity in all electrical work. Grounding simply means connecting a wire or piece of equipment to the earth, usually by connecting it to a water pipe or, in the absence of such a pipe, to an "artificial ground" as the Code used to call it, or a "made electrode" as the present Code calls it.

When a wire is properly grounded, there is no more danger in touching that wire at any exposed point than there is in touching the kitchen faucet or water pipe. The wire is already connected to the earth and therefore to all these pipes. To all intents and purposes, you touch that wire every time you touch a faucet or a pipe.

Neutral Wire. In ordinary residential wiring, there are brought into the home either three wires delivering 115 and 230 volts (as was shown in Fig. 2-8), or two wires corresponding to the middle wire and one of the two outside wires of the same drawing, and delivering 115 volts only. The middle wire is grounded.[1] It then becomes known as the "neutral" wire. In wiring diagrams, a connection to ground is indicated by the symbol of Fig. 9-1.

Purposes of Grounding. Grounds are made to promote safety both from shocks and from fire hazards. Consider the circuit of Fig. 9-2, which represents a device X connected to two ungrounded wires, one of which is, however, *accidentally* grounded at Y. The two wires are protected by fuses A and B. If fuse B

---

[1] This chapter will discuss single-phase installations. In industrial and commercial work where the installation is of the 3-phase type, grounding is different and will be discussed in another chapter.

128

blows, it prevents device *X* from operating. The average owner in looking for his trouble will probably inspect device *X*. Assume that he touches one of the wires at an exposed terminal while standing on the damp floor of his basement. What happens? He completes the circuit through his own body, through the ground along the route shown in the dotted line, back through the accidental ground to the main line. He may be injured; at the least he will receive a severe shock.

Fig. 9-1. This symbol indicates a connection to ground.

Compare this with Fig. 9-3, showing the same device *X* connected to the same two wires, one of which has now been *deliberately* grounded *and which may then never be fused*. The device is then protected by a single fuse *A*. If this fuse blows and the owner touches any exposed wire on device *X*, there is no danger, even if he is standing on wet ground, because the one wire connected to *X* is already grounded, and the other wire from

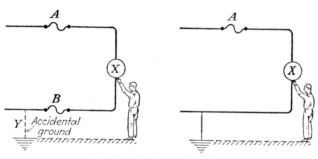

Fig. 9-2. Ungrounded systems are dangerous.   Fig. 9-3. Grounded systems are safe.

X up to fuse *A* is dead because that fuse is blown; it is the same as if the wire were cut at point *A*. A serious danger has therefore been removed by grounding.

Consider now Fig. 9-4, which represents the same device *X* connected to the same two ungrounded wires and protected by fuses *A* and *B*. In this case the wires run through conduit. Assume that wire *A* accidentally comes in contact with the conduit and that wire *B* becomes accidentally grounded as at *Y*.

Anyone touching the conduit will immediately complete the circuit through the ground and will be subject to injury or at least shock. If, however, the wire is deliberately grounded, as in Fig. 9-5, and the conduit itself is grounded, as it is in actual practice,

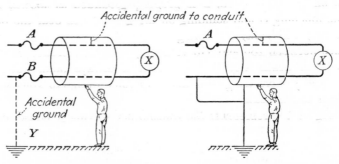

FIG. 9-4. Ungrounded conduit or other metal raceway is dangerous.

FIG. 9-5. Grounding the conduit or other metal raceway reduces danger.

then when wire A comes into accidental contact with the conduit, there is a short circuit and fuse A will immediately blow; thereafter all the wires except the short piece up to A are completely dead.

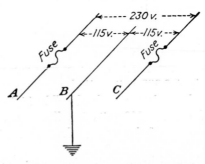

FIG. 9-6. A 3-wire 115/230-volt system with grounded neutral greatly reduces danger of shocks.

Figure 9-6 represents the three wires of a 3-wire 115/230-volt system. Wire B is grounded as shown and, of course, is not fused; A and C are fused. If either A or C becomes accidentally grounded, for example, to the grounded conduit covering all three wires, immediately a fuse blows.

If wire *B* is *not* grounded and if *A* becomes accidentally grounded, then any person standing on the ground and touching wire *C* will complete the connection from *A* to *C*, in other words will receive the full shock of 230 volts between *A* and *C*. If, on the other hand, *B* is properly grounded as shown, anyone touching *C* and standing on the ground will bear the brunt of only 115 volts, the voltage between *B* and *C*. The difference between 230 and 115 volts may be the difference between life and death—not that 230 volts is always fatal, but it is decidedly more dangerous than 115 volts; even 115 volts sometimes causes death.

Figure 9-7 represents the transformer serving a house and a

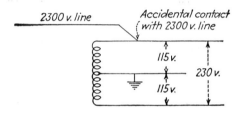

FIG. 9-7. In an ungrounded system, if a 2,300-volt line falls across the low-voltage wires, it raises their voltage to 2,300; in a grounded system their voltage is raised only a little above the usual 115/230 volts.

high-voltage line of, say, 2,300 volts which has accidentally fallen and made contact with the wires running into the house. If the wires are ungrounded, touching any of the wires in the house will involve a shock of 2,300 volts. If the neutral wire is grounded as shown, the voltage that is involved will be higher than 115 volts, but it will be far from 2,300 volts; it will increase above 115 volts only by the amount of the voltage drop across the path to the ground.

Voltage to Ground. This term is frequently used in the Code. If one of the wires in a circuit is grounded, the voltage to ground is the maximum voltage that exists between the grounded wire and any ungrounded wire. If no wire is grounded, then voltage to ground is the maximum voltage that exists between any two wires (Code, Art. 100).

In an installation consisting of a 3-wire 115/230-volt service, if the two ungrounded wires run to a 230-volt motor but the grounded wire does not run to the motor, the voltage *to ground* as far as the two wires to the motor are concerned is still only 115 volts. If an installation consists of a 2-wire service at 230 volts and no neutral or grounded wire runs into the installation at all, the voltage to ground is still only 115 volts provided there is a ground at the transformer mid-point, that is, at the point from which a grounded wire of a 3-wire circuit would be run if it were used. If there is no such ground, the voltage to ground is 230 volts.

Equipment Grounds. Figure 9-8 represents a motor operating on 230 volts, which means that neither wire is grounded. If a person accidentally touches one of the two wires while standing on the ground, he will be subject to shocks of 115 volts, for this is exactly the case outlined in Fig. 9-6. Assume that,

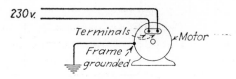

FIG. 9-8. It is always well to ground the frames of motors and other equipment.

while the motor is in operation, somewhere inside the motor one of the wires of the windings becomes grounded to the frame of the motor. If the motor frame is not grounded, touching the motor will impart a shock up to 115 volts. If the frame is grounded as shown, there will be no shock whatever. This illustrates the grounding of equipment as compared with the grounding of conductors.

Continuous Grounds. When a grounded neutral wiring system is used (and that is just about 100% of the time), and if *a metallic* raceway or armor is used, you must ground not only the neutral wire but also this metallic raceway or armor, as well as many pieces of equipment. As will be shown in the next chapter, at every point where connections are made, an "outlet box" of metal is used. The raceway is securely fastened to every outlet box so that there is a continuously grounded enclosure, raceway, or armor for the wires throughout the entire building. When lighting fixtures are supported on outlet boxes, they usually become automatically grounded. The raceway or armor is fastened to motors and other permanently connected devices so that they in turn are grounded. In this way a completely grounded system is secured with assurance of minimum hazard.

White Wire. As already mentioned, the white wire is known as the "neutral" wire. The Code in Sec. 200-6 requires that the neutral wire must always be a white or a neutral gray color. Likewise the Code with one exception (which will be explained later) requires that white wire may never be used for a purpose other than the grounded neutral. However, No. 4 and heavier wires are never stocked except in the black color. For this reason the Code permits black wire in these heavier sizes to be used throughout an installation, provided that in each case where a white wire should be used the ends of the black wire are painted white. Painting the ends makes a white wire out of a black one.

For outdoor use it is not necessary to use white wire for the grounded neutral. Weatherproof wire, which is the type ordinarily used for the purpose, is available only in a black color.

The grounded neutral wire is never interrupted by a fuse, a switch, or other device unless the device used is so designed that in opening the grounded wire it simultaneously opens also all the ungrounded wires, but such devices are not used in *residential* work. The white wire, with the exception noted, always runs directly from the point where it enters the building up to the device where the current is finally consumed. This simple fundamental requirement of wiring must at all times be kept firmly in mind.

Since the neutral wire is actually grounded and there is no possible danger in touching it, why put insulation on that wire? Many engineers argue in favor of using uninsulated neutral wires, but this scheme is not permitted by Code; the few exceptions permitted today will be covered separately in other chapters. Unless otherwise stated, it is necessary to use the same kind of insulation, the same care to avoid accidental grounds, and the same careful splices for the neutral wire as for the hot wires.

Green Wire. The Code distinguishes between a *grounded* and a *grounding* wire. A wire which carries current during the normal operation of the circuit and is grounded is called just that: a grounded wire. If a wire is in the circuit only as a safety measure and does *not* carry current during normal operation of the circuit, but only in an abnormal situation as when a motor winding accidentally grounds to the frame of the motor, the Code calls it a grounding wire.

A *grounded* wire must always be white. A *grounding* wire may be bare, uninsulated under certain conditions which will be discussed later. If it is insulated and if it is run with the regular circuit conductors, the wire must be green, or green with a yellow stripe (the combination used in many European countries). But if it is run alone, as for example, the grounding wire in a service entrance, it may be any color.

Polarizing. The process of maintaining a grounded wire throughout a wiring system, always identified by its white color, is known as polarizing. The hot wires may be any color other than white or green. In conduit wiring, in order to help in identifying conductors when a number of them are in a single conduit, different colors are used, as shown below. In cables of all types, also in flexible cords, each wire is a different color.

2-wire	White, black
3-wire	White, black, red
4-wire	White, black, red, blue
5-wire	White, black, red, blue, yellow

If, however, the cable or cord contains an insulated *grounding* wire in addition to the white *grounded* wire, that grounding wire must be green (or green with a yellow stripe).

Colors of Terminals. The color of the terminals on switches, receptacles, and so on, identifies the kind of wire that may be connected to each one. Natural-brass-color terminals are for hot wires. Terminals of a whitish color such as nickel, tin, or zinc plated are for a *grounded* wire. Terminals of a green color are for a *grounding* wire.

Methods of Grounding. The exact method of grounding a wiring *system* will be discussed in Chap. 17.

Chapter 10

OUTLET AND SWITCH BOXES

In the very early days of electrical wiring, it was the general practice to run wires on the surface of walls or inside them, without further protection, up to the devices to be connected. Fixtures were mounted directly on the ceiling, switches on the plaster walls, without any further ado. All this has been changed in the interests of safety from both fire and shock, and today, with few exceptions, outlet boxes are used at every point where connections are made to electrical devices.

Purposes of Boxes. Outlet boxes house the ends or splices in wires at all points where the original insulation has been removed. There is little danger in a continuous piece of wire, but a poorly made joint may lead to short circuits, grounds, or overheating at that point. Inside walls there are naturally loose dust, cobwebs, and other easily ignitible materials. Therefore there is some danger of fire at joints, but when the joint is enclosed in a metal outlet box, this danger is practically eliminated. Moreover, outlet boxes provide a continuity of ground, as explained in the previous chapter. The Code requires that boxes be supported in walls and ceilings according to definite standards which provide mechanical strength for supporting fixtures, switches, and other devices, eliminating the danger of mechanical breakdown.

Common Types of Outlet Boxes. Figure 10-1 shows a 4-in. octagon box, one of the most common boxes in use. Around the sides and in the bottom are found "knockouts"—sections of metal that can be easily knocked out to form openings for wire to enter. The metal is completely severed around these sections except at one small point which serves to anchor the metal until it is to be removed. It is a simple matter to remove these knockouts—usually a stiff blow with a pair of pliers on the end of a heavy screwdriver held against the knockout will start it, and with a pair of pliers the metal disk is then easily removed. If the knockout is near the edge of a box, a pair of pliers is the only tool needed.

On some brands of boxes the pry-out type of knockout is furnished. The pry-out is simply a small slot near or in the knockout, into which it is necessary only to insert screwdriver to pry out the metal disk, which prepares the knockout for use.

The outlet boxes are usually provided with ears and screws to make it easy to mount covers, switches, or other devices used on the boxes.

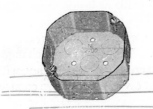
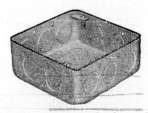

FIG. 10-1. Typical octagon outlet box. (*National Electric Products Corp.*)

FIG. 10-2. Square outlet box. This box is 4 in. square and much roomier than an octagon box. (*National Electric Products Corp.*)

There is also in common use a box similar to the one shown in Fig. 10-1 but only 3¼ in. in size. The two are more or less interchangeable; the larger size is by far the more common because it is easier to do a good job using it, especially if a large number of wires enter the box.

Another common box is the 4-in. square box shown in Fig. 10-2, more or less interchangeable with the octagon but decidedly roomier and handier to use. Especially when conduit rather than cable is used, this box is used almost exclusively for reasons that will be explained later. There is another box identical in appearance but larger, 4¹¹⁄₁₆ in. square, used mostly for commercial work as distinguished from residential.

Depth of Outlet Boxes. The Code in Sec. 370-14 requires that boxes of all descriptions be at least 1½ in. deep, except when the use of a box of this depth "will result in injury to the building structure or is impracticable," in which case a box not less than ½ in. deep may be used.

Switch Boxes. For mounting switches, receptacles, and similar devices flush in the wall, switch boxes of the type shown in Fig. 10-3 are used. The sides are removable; this makes it easy to make a double-size, or "2-gang," box out of two single ones by simply throwing away one side on each box and joining together the two boxes. No extra parts are needed. This is shown in Fig. 10-4. In similar fashion it is possible to make boxes of any required size, to mount three or more devices side by side.

Depth of Switch Boxes. Switch boxes range in depth from 1½ in. to a maximum of 3 in. The 2½-in. depth is the most popular, for it provides generous room for connectors, wire, etc., between

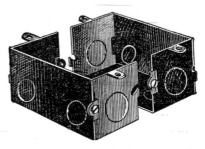

Fig. 10-3. A typical switch box. The sides of such boxes are removable. (*National Electric Products Corp.*)

Fig. 10-4. Two single boxes may be ganged to form one larger box of double size. Any number of boxes may be ganged to form a box of any necessary size.

the switch or other device and the bottom of the box. Use the 1½-in. depth only when two boxes in two different rooms happen to come back to back in the wall separating the two rooms; usually the wall is not thick enough to permit two deeper boxes to be used.

Material and Finish of Boxes. Boxes are usually made of steel, with a choice of galvanized or black-enamel finish. The galvanized is by far the more durable of the two, and the black enamel is little used today. In fact it is sometimes difficult to locate boxes with black-enamel finish, and many local ordinances prohibit them. For certain purposes boxes made of an insulating material such as bakelite or porcelain are used; these will be discussed in Chap. 24, which covers farm wiring.

Number of Wires Entering Box. The Code in Sec. 370-6 limits the number of wires that may *enter* each size of box, as shown in the table at the end of this paragraph. When wires are counted, one that enters a box and is spliced to one running from a fixture mounted on the box is counted as one wire—in other words the wire running *from* the fixture is disregarded. If a wire runs into a box and out again without splice or joint, as is often the case in conduit wiring, count it as only one wire. If the box contains a fixture stud and/or a cable clamp, deduct one from the number of wires shown in the table. If the box will contain a switch, receptacle, or similar device, deduct one from the number shown in the table for each device or combination of devices mounted on a single strap.

Table 370-6(a-1). Deep Boxes

Box dimensions, inches, trade size	Maximum number of conductors				
	No. 14	No. 12	No. 10	No. 8	No. 6
1½ x 3¼ octagonal........	5	5	4	0	0
1½ x 4 octagonal..........	8	7	6	5	0
1½ x 4 square.............	11	9	7	5	0
1½ x 4 11/16 square.......	16	12	10	8	0
2⅛ x 4 11/16 square.......	20	16	12	10	6
2 x 1¾ x 2¾.............	5	4	4		
2½ x 1¾ x 2¾.............	6	6	5		
3 x 1¾ x 2¾.............	7	7	6		

Where there is not sufficient space for a deeper box, four No. 14 AWG conductors may enter a box provided with cable clamps and containing one or more devices on a single mounting strap.

Table 370-6(a-2). Shallow Boxes
of Less than 1½ In. Depth

Box dimensions, inches, trade size	Maximum number of conductors		
	No. 14	No. 12	No. 10
3¼	4	4	3
4	6	6	4
1¼ x 4 square	9	7	6
4 11/16	8	6	6

Securing Conduit and Cable to Boxes. To provide a good, safe continuous ground throughout an installation, it is absolutely necessary to fasten the boxes rigidly and solidly to each piece of conduit, cable, etc., entering the box.

In the case of conduit this is very simply done by means of a locknut and bushing, both of which are shown in Fig. 10-5.

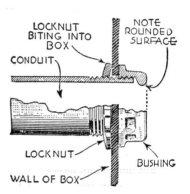

Fig. 10-5. Locknuts and bushings are used at the ends of each run of conduit. They anchor the conduit to the box and also provide a continuous grounded raceway.

Fig. 10-6. Cross section showing how locknut and bushing are used at outlet boxes or other boxes.

Note that the locknut is not a flat piece of metal but that it is dished or bent, so that the lugs around the circumference become teeth on one side. The inside diameter of the bushing is slightly less than the inside diameter of the conduit. This causes the wire where it emerges from the conduit to rest on the rounded surface of the bushing. Slip a locknut on the threaded end of the conduit with the teeth facing the box. Slip the conduit into the knockout. Then install the bushing on the conduit inside the box, screwing it on as far as it will go. Only then tighten up the locknut on the outside, driving it home solidly so that the teeth will bite into the metal of the box, thus making a good sound ground. This construction is shown in Fig. 10-6. Detailed instructions for cutting and using the conduit will be found in the next chapter.

In the case of cable, connectors of the type shown in Fig. 10-7 are used. After the connector is fastened to the cable, slip the connector into a knockout, install the locknut on the inside of the box, and run the locknut home tightly, as in the case of conduit.

Clamps. The use of boxes having built-in clamps which eliminate the need for special connectors for cable is common. A typical box of this type is shown in Fig. 10-8, and the picture should be self-explanatory.

Round Boxes. Instead of being octagonal or square, boxes may be round, in which case locknuts and bushings may not be used on the rounded wall of the boxes but only on the bottom. Round boxes usually have clamps for cable. They are used mostly in "old work," in wiring a building after it is completed.

FIG. 10-7. Cables are anchored to boxes with connectors of this type.

Supporting Outlet Boxes. The usual method of supporting an outlet box in a new building of frame construction is by means of a hanger. In the type shown at *A* of Fig. 10-9, the

FIG. 10-8. Often boxes are provided with clamps which serve the same purposes as separate connectors. (*National Electric Products Corp.*)

hanger is fastened to the box by means of stove bolts, whereas in the type shown at *B* and *C*, the middle knockout in the bottom of the box is removed, the box slipped over the "fixture stud" which is part of the hanger, and the locknut driven home on the fixture stud inside the box. The fixture stud later may be used also to support a fixture mounted on the box. There are

also available factory-assembled combinations of the type shown
in Fig. 10-10.

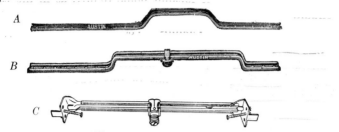

FIG. 10-9. Outlet boxes are usually supported in buildings with the aid of
offset hangers of this type.

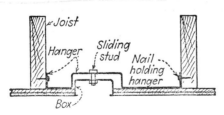

FIG. 10-10. Factory-assembled combinations of box and hanger are convenient and save time.

In any case the assembly is mounted between joists, as
shown in Fig. 10-11. The hanger described is of the "shallow"
type, and its depth is such that with boxes 1½ in. deep the front
of the box will be flush with the plaster. The plaster must come
right up to the box; there may be no open space around the box.

FIG. 10-11. The mounting of boxes with hangers is very simple.

This shallow-type hanger is used with all wiring systems with
the exception of conduit. When conduit is to be used, "deep"
hangers are used instead of "shallow." The only difference is
that the offset is about ½ in. deeper, which brings the front edge
of the outlet box about ½ in. below the surface of the plaster

but leaves sufficient room behind the plaster for the conduit, the locknut, etc. Since the Code in Sec. 370-10 requires that the front edge of the box must be not more than ¼ in. below the finished surface of the wall or ceiling (if the surface is combustible, it must be flush), some expedient must be adopted to overcome the fact that the front edge is over ¼ in. below the surface. Accordingly, it is customary to use covers, the front edges of which are flush with plaster. Figure 10-12 shows an assortment

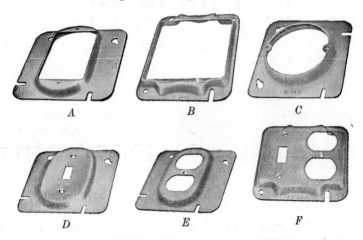

Fig. 10-12. Typical raised covers for 4-in. square boxes. (*National Electric Products Corp.*)

of covers fitting the 4-in. square box which is usually used with conduit. Each cover serves a specific purpose, that at A accommodating one switch or receptacle, that at B two such devices. At C is shown a "plaster ring" which has an opening of the same size as a 3¼-in. box. When this is mounted on top of the 4-in. square box, it permits devices designed for the 3¼-in. box to be used. At D, E, and F are shown covers that are used only when the boxes are mounted on the surface, as in basements, factory walls, etc. They accommodate, respectively, one toggle switch, one receptacle, and a switch and receptacle. Many other types are available. Of all these covers the types at A, B, and C are the most common. Figure 10-13 shows a completed installation.

Instead of requiring hangers to support boxes, the Code generally permits any other type of support which is sturdy and which becomes part of the building structure. Wooden strips may be used provided they are at least ⅞ in. thick. This method is shown in Fig. 10-14 but is little used.

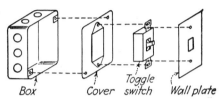

FIG. 10-13. All parts of an electrical outlet are standardized in size so as to fit each other properly and easily.

If the box is attached to a run of conduit which in turn is securely anchored, no further support is required for the box. Good judgment must be used, especially if the box is later to support a fixture. Remember that the local inspector is the final judge as to whether the spirit and intent of the Code are met by any given type of installation.

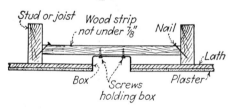

FIG. 10-14. Mounting an outlet box on wooden strip, instead of using the usual steel hanger.

In old work (buildings wired after completion) as compared with new work (buildings wired while under construction), different methods of support are used, and these will be discussed in the chapter on old work.

Supporting Switch Boxes. Instead of switch boxes, 4-in. square boxes with covers are frequently used, as previously described. Usually, however, switch boxes are used, and since they are available in depths up to 3 in., there is no problem in connection with the use of conduit as there is with 1½-in.-deep outlet boxes.

Perhaps the most common switch box for new work is the bracket type of box, of which several are shown in Fig. 10-15. The bracket is merely nailed to the studding of the building, as shown also in the same illustration. Some boxes have a

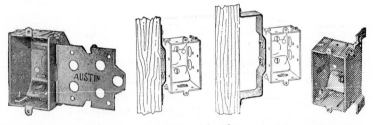

FIG. 10-15. Switch boxes with mounting brackets save time in mounting.

trough which holds up the ends of the lath that end at the box and that would otherwise be left unsupported. The brackets themselves have a number of projections that form a good support and anchor for the plaster when it is applied.

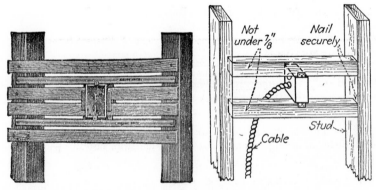

FIG. 10-16. Switch boxes may be mounted between studding by means of special steel mounting strips.

FIG. 10-17. Using wooden strips to support switch boxes.

Also available and generally used are mounting strips which permit any number of switch boxes to be mounted at any point between two studs. These are shown in Fig. 10-16, and the picture will be self-explanatory.

Switch boxes may be mounted on wooden strips like outlet

boxes, and a finished installation is shown in Fig. 10-17. The strips must be at least $\frac{7}{8}$ in. thick and so mounted that the front edge of the boxes will be flush with the plaster.

Outlet Box Covers. An outlet box may never be left uncovered. When a fixture is mounted on top of the box, no further cover is necessary. An outlet box cover must be used in every other case. Figure 10-18 shows an assortment for the conventional $3\frac{1}{4}$- or 4-in. boxes; there are corresponding ones for other styles of boxes. At A is shown a blank cover used to cover the box when it serves merely to house joints in wire. The box then is known as a "pull" box or "junction" box. Such boxes may be

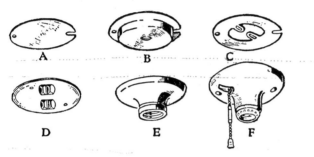

FIG. 10-18. Outlet box covers are made in dozens of different types; the six shown here are typical.

located only where accessible without damaging the structure of the building. At B is shown a drop-cord cover used with drop cords; the hole is bushed to do away with sharp edges which might otherwise injure the insulation of the cord. At C is shown a "spider cover" on which surface style switches are mounted. At D is shown a cover with a duplex receptacle, used mostly in basements, workshops, and similar locations. E shows an outlet cover and F a similar cover provided with pull-chain control. These covers are widely used in closets, attics, basements, farm buildings, and similar locations.

The covers illustrated are the ones most commonly used; most jobs can be completed using only the ones shown. There are, however, dozens of other types, each serving a specialized purpose. For example, there are blank covers similar to that shown in A of Fig. 10-18, but with a knockout in the center, permitting

an armored cable connector to be used when running the flexible
cable to a stationary device like a motor. There are covers
with openings to accommodate sign receptacles of the type that
were shown in Fig. 4-37. For square boxes there are covers
with many other combinations of openings in addition to the ones
shown in Fig. 10-12.

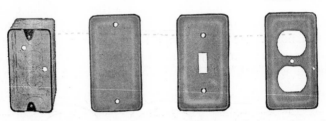

FIG. 10-19. The box and covers shown here are used for surface wiring.
(*National Electric Products Corp.*)

Surface Boxes. When the wiring is on the surface of a wall
so that it will be permanently exposed, ordinary boxes are impractical because of the sharp corners, both on the boxes and on
the covers for switches or similar devices. For that reason a
special kind of box known as a utility box or handy box was developed, together with various kinds of covers, both shown in
Fig. 10-19.

Chapter 11

DIFFERENT WIRING METHODS

Although similar basic materials are used in all of them, there are six different common methods or systems used in ordinary residential wiring. These systems are:

1. Rigid conduit.
2. Thin-wall conduit.
3. Nonmetallic-sheathed cable.
4. Armored cable.
5. Flexible conduit.
6. Knob and tube.

The knob-and-tube system is so little used today that it no longer warrants space in this book. Detailed information concerning each of the other systems will be given in a later chapter, and only the basic principles will be discussed here.

Rigid Conduit. In this type of wiring, all wires are enclosed in steel pipe known as "conduit." Conduit differs from ordinary water pipe in that it is especially annealed to permit easy bending. The inside surface is carefully prepared so that the wires can be pulled into it with a minimum of effort and without damage to the insulation or outer braid. It has a corrosion-resisting finish, so that the installation may be permanent.

It comes in 10-ft lengths in a choice of galvanized or black-enamel finish. The galvanized is considered the better of the two, and the black-enameled type may be used only indoors. As a matter of fact, the black-enamel type of conduit is seldom stocked today. Rigid conduit with a galvanized finish is shown in Fig. 11-1; each length bears an Underwriters' label.

The ½-in. size is the smallest used in ordinary wiring. All sizes are identical in dimensions with the corresponding sizes

Fig. 11-1. Rigid conduit looks like water pipe but differs in many ways. (*General Electric Co.*)

of water pipe, and therefore, as in the case of water pipe, the nominal size in no way denotes the actual physical dimensions, as the following table shows.

Trade size, inches	Internal diameter, inches	Internal area, square inches	External diameter, inches
½	0.622	0.30	0.840
¾	0.824	0.53	1.050
1	1.049	0.86	1.315
1¼	1.380	1.50	1.660
1½	1.610	2.04	1.900
2	2.067	3.36	2.375
2½	2.469	4.79	2.875
3	3.068	7.38	3.500
3½	3.548	9.90	4.000
4	4.026	12.72	4.500

To thread conduit, use tools as used in threading water pipe, except with dies that cut a thread with a taper of ¾ in. to the foot.

Cutting Conduit. Conduit can be cut with an ordinary pipe

Fig. 11-2. A typical pipe cutter. (*The Ridge Tool Co.*)

cutter, as used for water pipe, of the type shown in Fig. 11-2. This unfortunately leaves a sharp edge at the cut, as shown in

Fig. 11-3. This sharp edge might seriously damage the insulation of the wire as it is pulled into the conduit; therefore common sense suggests, and the Code requires, that each cut be reamed smooth. A reamer of the type shown in Fig. 11-4 serves the

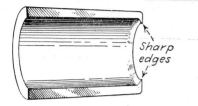

FIG. 11-3. When pipe is cut, a sharp edge is left which must be removed before conduit is used.

FIG. 11-4. A reamer of this type is used to remove sharp burrs from the cut end of pipe.

purpose. Some prefer to use a hack saw with 18 teeth to the inch, claiming that this leaves less burr to be reamed than when a pipe cutter is used.

Bending Conduit. Because the wires are pulled into conduit after it is installed, it is important that all bending be carefully done so that the internal diameter is not substantially decreased in the process. Make the bends uniform and gradual. The Code in Sec. 346-10 specifies the minimum radius of the bend, which varies from six to eight times the nominal inside diameter

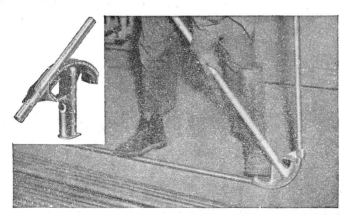

FIG. 11-5. A typical conduit bender, and method of use. (*Republic Steel Co.*)

of the conduit (unless lead-sheathed cable is to be installed in the conduit, in which case it varies from ten to twelve times the inside diameter). The table is as follows:

Size of conduit, inches	Minimum radius of bend, inches	
	Conductors without lead sheath	Conductors with lead sheath
½	4	6
¾	5	8
1	6	11
1¼	8	14
1½	10	16
2	12	21
2½	15	25
3	18	31
3½	21	36
4	24	40
5	30	50
6	36	61

A popular type of bending tool is shown in Fig. 11-5. The smaller sizes of conduit bend easily, but it is not easy to bend the heavier sizes. Factory-bent elbows of the type shown in Fig. 11-6 are available in all sizes and are used generally on the larger sizes.

Fig. 11-6. For large sizes, factory-bent elbows are commonly used. (*General Electric Co.*)

Conduit is secured to boxes by means of locknuts and bushings, as already outlined in connection with outlet boxes in Chap. 10.

Number of Wires in Conduit.   The number permitted depends on the size of the conduit and of the wires. For new work, see table below.   If you are replacing wires in an existing conduit, a greater "fill" is permitted; see page 439.

Size of wire	Number of wires in one conduit					
	1	2	3	4	5	6 .
14	½	½	½	½	¾	¾
12	½	½	½	¾	¾	1
10	½	¾	¾	¾	1	1
8	½	¾	¾	1	1¼	1¼
6	½	1	1	1¼	1½	1½
4	½	1¼	1¼*	1½	1½	2
3	¾	1¼	1¼	1½	2	2
2	¾	1¼	1¼	2	2	2
1	¾	1½	1½	2	2½	2½
1/0	1	1½	2	2	2½	2½
2/0	1	2	2	2½	2½	3
3/0	1	2	2	2½	3	3
4/0	1¼	2	2½	3	3	3

* Where an existing service run does not exceed 50 ft in length and does not contain the equivalent of more than two quarter bends from end to end, two No. 4 insulated and one No. 4 bare wires may be installed in 1 in.

If your installation involves wire sizes larger than shown in the table or more than six wires, refer to Table 1 of the Code (see Appendix).

If your installation involves lead-sheathed cable inside conduit, the following applies for one cable per conduit.

Use ¾-in. conduit for 14-2, 12-2, 10-2, 14-3 cable.
Use 1-in. conduit for 8-2, 12-3, 10-3, 8-3 cable.
Use 1¼-in. conduit for 6-2, 4-2, 2-2, 6-3 cable.
Use 1½-in. conduit for 1-2, 4-3, 2-3 cable.

For larger sizes of cable or more than one cable per conduit, see Table 2 in your copy of the Code.

For combinations of conductors (plain or lead-sheathed) not

covered by Tables 1 and 2, see Tables 3 to 7 in your copy of the Code.

Number of Bends. The Code in Sec. 346-11 prohibits more than four quarter bends or their equivalent in one "run" of conduit or the distance between outlet boxes or other openings. The fewer the bends, the easier it is to pull the wire into the conduit.

Splices in Wires. Wires must be continuous, without splice, throughout all conduit. Splices are permitted only at outlet boxes (Sec. 300-13).

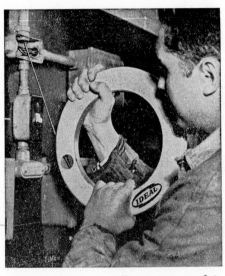

Fig. 11-7. Fish tape is necessary to pull wires into conduit. This material is made of springy steel. (*Ideal Industries, Inc.*)

Pulling Wires into Conduit. If the run is short and the wires occupy a relatively small portion of the area of the conduit, they can frequently be pushed in at one outlet and through the conduit up to the next outlet. If the run is of considerable length, especially if it contains bends, then "fish tape" is used. For occasional work, a length of ordinary galvanized steel wire will serve the purpose, but a special fish tape made of stiff but flexible steel is more frequently used. In size it is usually about ⅛ by 0.060 in. Often it is put up in special reels (see Fig. 11-7). Bend a small loop or hook on the end of the tape; this will permit it to go easily around bends as it is pushed into conduit. Since this tape is highly tempered, it will break if bent sharply unless the temper is taken out; this can be done by heating it to a red heat with a blowtorch, then letting it cool.

Push the tape into the conduit through which the wires are to be pulled; when the end emerges, attach all the wires which are to be pulled into the conduit to the fish tape, taking care to leave no sharp ends which might catch at the joints in the conduit. Then pull the wires into position; this usually requires one man pulling at one end and another feeding the wires into the opening at the other end, to make sure there will be no snarls and in general to ease the wire on its way. Powdered soapstone may be used as a lubricant to make it easier to pull the wires. The Code in Sec. 300-14 requires a minimum of at least 6 in. of wire projecting at each outlet box where a connection is to be made; it is easy to cut off a few inches later if there is too much, but it is hard to do good work if the ends are too short to be convenient.

Supporting Conduit. Conduit must be supported within 3 ft of every box, fitting, or cabinet. Use straps shown in Fig. 11-8. Half-inch and ¾ in. must be further supported every 10 ft; 1 in. every 12 ft; 1¼ and 1½ in. every 14 ft; 2 and 2½ in. every 16 ft; 3 in. every 20 ft.

Electrical Metallic Tubing. The material which the Code has labeled with this rather unwieldy name is commonly known by its abbreviation "EMT" or by its descriptive common name of "thin-wall conduit." It is shown in Fig. 11-9,

FIG. 11-8. Either cast or stamped straps may be used for supporting conduit.

and, as in rigid conduit, each length bears the Underwriters' label. It is available only in sizes up to and including 4 in. For residential purposes it may be used interchangeably with rigid conduit.

The internal diameter, size for size, is the same as rigid conduit, but as the name implies, the walls are thinner. For this reason the material is never threaded, but all joints and connections are made with special threadless fittings which hold the material through pressure. Figure 11-10 shows both a coupling and a connector.   Each consists of a body plus a split ring through which tremendous pressure is exerted on the conduit when the nut

FIG. 11-9. Thin-wall conduit is never threaded.   It is lighter and easier to use than rigid conduit.   (*General Electric Co.*)

is forced home tightly.   Another type of fitting is the "telescope" type, which requires a special tool to apply, the tool indenting both fitting and tubing for good mechanical and electrical joints. The fittings and the tool are both shown in Fig. 11-11.

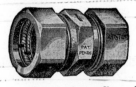

FIG. 11-10. A connector and a coupling used with thin-wall conduit.

Thin-wall conduit may be cut either with a hack saw (use a blade with 32 teeth to the inch) or with a special tool, one type of which is shown in Fig. 11-12.   After the cut, the end must be reamed to remove burrs or sharp edges.   Bends are made in the same way and under the same conditions as for rigid conduit.

FIG. 11-11. With this style of fittings, the fitting and the conduit are indented with the special tool shown.   (*Briegel Method Tool Co.*)

Occasionally it will be necessary to join a length of thin-wall conduit to a length of rigid conduit or to a fitting with threaded hubs for rigid conduit.   The simplest method is to use a connector of the type shown in Fig. 11-10. The threaded portion of the thin-wall connector will always fit the internal thread of any fitting designed for the corresponding size of rigid conduit. The adapter shown in Fig. 11-13 can also be used.

Nonmetallic-sheathed Cable. The Code in Sec. 300-1(c) recommends this cable for locations where *poor grounds are the rule rather than the exception:* farms and other locations where a continuous underground water system is not available for grounding.

Fig. 11-12. A handy tool for cutting thin-wall conduit. (*Briegel Method Tool Co.*)

As you have already learned in Chap. 6, there are two kinds of nonmetallic-sheathed cable. Code Type NM has wires enclosed in a fibrous-fabric outer braid, and Type NMC has the wires embedded in a solid plastic mass. The two types are

Fig. 11-13. This adapter makes it possible to use thin-wall conduit in fittings designed for rigid conduit.

shown in Figs. 11-14 and 11-15. Statements made in this chapter will apply to either type unless otherwise mentioned.

Type NM may be used only indoors and only in permanently dry locations. It may not be embedded in plaster. It may not be used in farm buildings where the humidity is high, specifically barns and similar buildings. The Type NMC on the other hand may be used wherever Type NM is acceptable and may also be used in wet locations. It may be embedded in plaster but must then be protected by a strip of

Fig. 11-14. Type NM nonmetallic-sheathed cable may be used only in dry locations. (*Crescent Insulated Wire & Cable Co.*)

steel $\frac{1}{16}$ in. thick and $\frac{3}{4}$ in. wide to guard it against nails. The Type NMC is the successor to the so-called "barn cable" that was in use some years ago.

The facts that nonmetallic-sheathed cable is very easy to install, is light and comparatively inexpensive all are partly responsible for the growing popularity of this cable. If in doubt as to whether its use is permissible locally, consult local codes or your electrical inspector.

FIG. 11-15. Type NMC nonmetallic-sheathed cable may be used in either dry or wet locations. (*Crescent Insulated Wire & Cable Co.*)

Removing the Outer Cover.   The outer cover must be removed at the ends for a distance of about 8 in.   On the Type NM this can be done by slitting the braid with a knife; usually the slit is merely started, then by pulling on the jute or fiber filler with a pair of pliers, you can rip the opening as far as you wish.   Cut off the dangling cover with a jackknife. Be very careful not to damage the individual conductors.   The use of a cable ripper, shown in Fig. 11-16, will save time and avoid damage to the insulation.

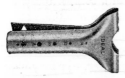

FIG. 11-16. This cable stripper saves much time. (*Ideal Industries, Inc.*)

For the Type NMC a knife is the only tool needed.   Again be especially careful not to damage the insulation.

Anchoring Cable to Boxes.   The cable is anchored to switch and outlet boxes by the use of connectors,

FIG. 11-17. An assortment of connectors used in attaching cable to outlet and switch boxes, and similar devices.

several types of which are shown in Fig. 11-17.   The connector is first solidly fastened to the cable; the locknut then removed, the connector slipped into the knockout of the box, and the locknut of the connector then driven solidly home on the inside of the box. As mentioned in Chap. 10, many boxes have built-in clamps that serve the purpose of connectors.

Joints. Joints and splices are never permitted in nonmetallic-sheathed cable except in outlet boxes, where they are made as in any other type of wiring.

Mechanical Installation. If installed while a building is under construction, nonmetallic-sheathed cable is installed inside the walls. The Code requires that it be anchored at least every 4½ ft and in any case within 12 in. of every outlet box. Straps of the types shown in Fig. 11-18 are used for the purpose. In old work where the cable is fished through the walls, this requirement is waived. All bends in cable must be gradual so

Fig. 11-18. A typical strap for supporting nonmetallic cable.

as not to injure the cable; the Code requirement of Sec. 336-10 is that, if a bend were continued so as to form a complete circle, the diameter of the circle would be at least ten times the diameter of the cable.

Where the cable is run exposed, as in basements, attics, barns, etc., it must be given reasonable protection against mechanical injury. This protection can be provided in a variety of ways (see Fig. 11-19). If the cable is run along the side of a joist, rafter, or stud as at A or along the bottom edge of a timber as at B, no further protection is required. If it is run at an angle to the timbers, the cable may be run through bored holes as at C. No additional protection is required; neither are porcelain tubes, loom, or any similar materials needed where the cable goes through the bored holes. The holes should be bored in the approximate center of the timbers. If the cable is not run through bored holes but instead is secured to the bottoms of the joists, then it must be run on substantial running boards, as shown at D; this requirement is waived if the cable is size 6-2, 8-3, or heavier. A final method is to let the cable follow the structure of the building as shown at E, when again no further protection is required. This method, however, is very wasteful of material, leads to unnecessarily long lengths of cable with consequently large voltage drops, and is therefore to be discouraged. Whichever method is used, the cable must be supported at least every 4½ ft and also within 12 in. of every outlet box.

In accessible attics, if the cable is run at angles across the

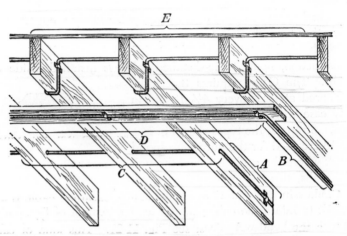

Fig. 11-19. This shows five different ways in which cable may be run on an open ceiling. Various methods of protecting the cable are used, depending on the method of installation.

top of floor joists, the cable must be protected by guard strips at least as high as the cable, as shown in Fig. 11-20. If run at

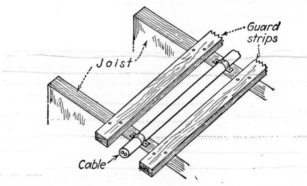

Fig. 11-20. When cable runs crosswise of floor studs in attics, guard strips must be used.

right angles to studs or rafters, it must be protected in the same way at all points where it is within 7 ft of the floor joists. No protection is required under other conditions. If the attic is not accessible by means of permanent stairs or ladder, this protection is required only for a distance of 6 ft around the opening to the attic.

In any event, the cable must always follow the approximate contour of the building—never any short cuts across open space.

FIG. 11-21. Nonmetallic-sheathed cable in both Types NM and NMC is available with an extra, bare wire for grounding purposes. (*Crescent Insulated Wire & Cable Co.*)

Cable with Ground Wire. Nonmetallic sheathed cable is also available with a bare, uninsulated wire in the assembly, in addition to the insulated wires; see Fig. 11-21. This kind of cable was made mandatory by the 1962 Code if metal boxes are used; with nonmetallic boxes it is required only to boxes containing plug-in receptacles. The grounding wire contributes to safety. It does complicate the wiring a bit, but it is not difficult to learn how to do it. How to connect this bare grounding wire will be explained in detail later in this chapter.

FIG. 11-22. Armored cable. A continuous steel armor wrapped around the wires protects them against injury and at the same time provides a continuous ground. (*Crescent Insulated Wire & Cable Co.*)

Armored Cable. Today's armored cable, as pictured in Fig. 11-22, is known as the "ABC type"—armored bushed cable. It consists of two or more Type T or Type R wires, wrapped with a spiral layer of kraft paper, and a spiral outer steel armor. Under the armor there is a narrow, uninsulated strip of copper, which reduces the resistance of the armor itself, thus providing better continuity of ground. This copper strip thus becomes a safety device in case of short circuits or accidental grounds.

Cutting Cable. A hack saw is generally used to cut armored

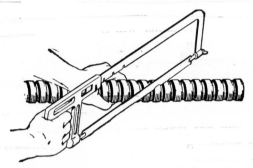

FIG. 11-23. In sawing armored cable, hold the hack saw as shown. (*National Electric Products Corp.*)

cable. Do not hold it at a right angle to the cable, but rather at a right angle to the strip of armor as it runs around the cable, as shown in Fig. 11-23. After the cut is made, grasp the two ends of armor, give a twist as shown in Fig. 11-24, and the two ends

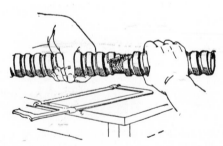

FIG. 11-24. After sawing, twist the cut ends of the armor to separate them. (*National Electric Products Corp.*)

will separate; it is then a simple matter to cut through the wires.

To use the cut end, first remove about 6 in. of the armor. Proceed as before, holding the hack saw in the same position, being extremely careful to saw through only the armor, not touching the insulation. The paper inside the armor provides some little spacing, making this possible. Nevertheless, considerable practice is necessary to get the knack of sawing through the armor without damaging the insulation. When the armor is severed, a twist will remove the short end.

Fiber Bushings. Careful examination of the cut end of the armor will show that the hack saw has left sharp teeth on the armor, some of them quite long. These teeth point inward toward the wires and might damage the insulation, causing a short or ground. Therefore a bushing of thin but tough fiber which has a high insulating value is inserted between the armor and the wires. Such

Fig. 11-25. A bushing of tough fiber is inserted between the armor and the wires to guard against danger of grounds from sharp points at cut end of armor. (*National Electric Products Corp.*)

a bushing is shown in Fig. 11-25. Since there is little room between the paper and the armor, space is provided by removing the paper. The steps shown in Figs. 11-26 and 11-27 demonstrate how to unwrap the paper beneath the armor, and then with a sudden yank to tear it off some distance inside the armor, thus leaving room for the bushing, which is inserted as shown in Fig. 11-28. Figure 11-29 shows the final assembly.

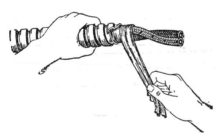

Fig. 11-26. Unwrap the paper found over the wires up to a point some distance *within* the armor. (*National Electric Products Corp.*)

Connectors. The connectors used with armored cable are practically identical with those shown in Fig. 11-17 for nonmetallic cable, except that the end of the connector which goes into the box has openings or peepholes through which the red color of the antishort bushing can be seen by the inspector. Because of these peepholes, the connectors are known as the "visible type."

To install the connector properly, first you must bend the bare copper grounding strap that runs under the armor back over the

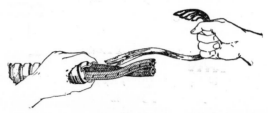

FIG. 11-27. Yank the paper wrapper, removing it for some distance *inside* the armor. This makes room for the fiber bushing. (*National Electric Products Corp.*)

FIG. 11-28. Inserting fiber bushing. (*National Electric Products Corp.*)

outside of the armor. Then insert the fiber bushing inside the armor, and slip the connector over the cable. Push the cable into the connector as far as it will go, so that the fiber bushing cannot

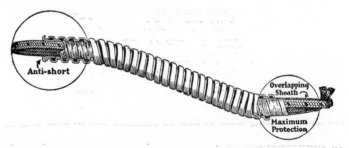

Anti-short

Overlapping Sheath

Maximum Protection

FIG. 11-29. Cross section of cable, showing paper removed beneath armor and fiber bushing in place. (*National Electric Products Corp.*)

slip out of place, and so that it can be seen through the peepholes on the connector. Then tighten the screw on the connector to anchor it solidly to the cable. Be sure that the bare grounding strip is placed in the connector so that it will be solidly squeezed by the connector, rather than lying loosely in the connector. Remove the locknut, slip the connector into the knockout of the box, and drive the locknut solidly home inside the box, as with other types of cable (see Figs. 11-30 and 11-31). If this is carefully

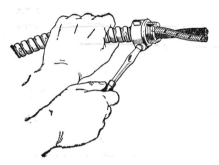

Fig. 11-30. Installing connector on cable. (*National Electric Products Corp.*)

done, all the outlets are then tied together through the armor of the cable, and the grounding strip under the armor, providing the continuity of ground discussed in Chap. 9.

Where Used. Like Type NM nonmetallic-sheathed cable, armored cable may be used only in permanently dry locations.

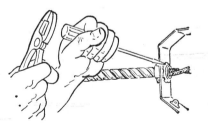

Fig. 11-31. Driving home locknut on connector and securing it to the box.

For residential wiring it is more or less interchangeable with nonmetallic-sheathed cable, but it must not be used on farms or other locations where poor grounds are the rule. Some local codes prohibit it for new work.

Supporting. Armored cable is supported and protected exactly as is nonmetallic-sheathed cable. Staples of the type shown in

Fig. 11-32 are perhaps a bit more convenient than the conventional straps. These staples are not used with nonmetallic-sheathed cable because there is danger that they might be driven in so solidly that they would actually damage the cable. This danger does not exist in the case of armored cable, which has steel armor for protection.

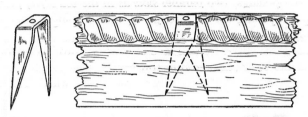

FIG. 11-32. Staples of this type are used to anchor armored cable to wooden surfaces.

Flexible Conduit. This material is generally called "green-field." It is shown in Fig. 11-33 and is substantially the empty armor of armored cable, without the wires, and, of course, in a larger diameter. Except in a few scattered areas, this material is relatively little used. Where it is popular, it is used like armored cable, except that the flexible conduit is first installed

FIG. 11-33. Flexible conduit. The wires are pulled into place after the conduit is installed. (*Crescent Insulated Wire & Cable Co.*)

and the wires are later pulled into place just as in the case of rigid conduit or EMT. Connectors are used as in armored cable, except that the peepholes are not required, since fiber bushings are not used.

Another application is in connection with installations where a certain amount of flexibility is required, for example when motors are installed with sliding bases to take up slack in belts. Obviously the wires to any motor so installed cannot be in rigid conduit because then the motor would be immovable. Similarly, a certain amount of flexible conduit is used where the use of rigid conduit would involve extremely difficult or awkward bends.

Problems in Installing Receptacles. Most people are accustomed only to old-style receptacles with two parallel openings for plugs. This type may now be used only for replacements. The new type, which the Code requires on all *new* installations, has three openings: two parallel slots as in the old style, plus one U-shaped opening for a third prong on the plug. Receptacle and plug are shown in Fig. 11-34.

In use, the appliance has a 3-conductor cord. Two of the wires in the cord (those terminating at the two parallel prongs) are connected to the appliance in the usual way. The third

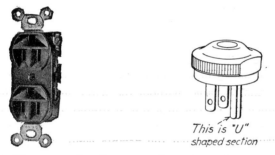

This is "U" shaped section

Fig. 11-34. This receptacle will accommodate either ordinary 2-prong plugs, or 3-prong plugs which ground the appliance involved. (*General Electric Co.*)

wire in the cord (the one terminating at the U-shaped prong) is connected to the frame of the appliance; in case of a washing machine or similar motor-operated appliance, it is connected to the frame of the motor.

When the receptacle is properly installed, the terminal which corresponds to the third U-shaped opening is grounded. Then when an appliance with the 3-conductor cord and the 3-prong plug is plugged into this special grounding receptacle, the frame of the motor or appliance is automatically grounded. Why all this procedure? The answer is *safety*. When ordinary receptacles are used, many accidents are caused by defective appliances. If an appliance is accidentally grounded internally and the operator is standing on a moist or wet basement floor, garage floor, or the ground, he is subject to a severe shock when he touches that appliance. But when the appliance is provided with the 3-conductor cord, with 3-prong plug, plugged into a properly installed 3-opening receptacle of the grounded type, the danger of shock is greatly reduced or eliminated.

Does this mean that if you install such grounding receptacles you must change over all your appliances from 2-wire cords to the 3-wire cords and rewire them to ground the frames on the third wire? That will not be necessary, for this receptacle is so designed that while it will accept the special 3-prong plug, it will also accept the ordinary 2-prong plug used heretofore. But in the future more and more appliances will be manufactured with the special 3-prong plug and 3-wire cord as standard equipment to fit the special receptacles. As a matter of fact, the Code in Sec. 250-45 requires many appliances to be equipped with 3-prong plugs. These include among others: clothes washers, clothes dryers, dishwashers, and most portable hand-held tools such as drills, hedge trimmers, and the like. In the future more and more appliances will be made with 3-prong plugs.

If an appliance comes equipped with a 3-prong plug but the receptacle in a home is the old type, accepting only 2-prong plugs, a special adapter must be used. A better solution would be to install a new receptacle of the grounding type, provided it is possible to properly ground its green terminal.

If you will take apart one of these grounding-type receptacles, you will find that its U-shaped opening is grounded to the mounting strap of the receptacle, and is also connected to a special grounding screw which is identified by its *green* color. In every case, the U-shaped opening must be *effectively* grounded to the wiring system.

Conduit or Armored Cable. Since the conduit or the armor of armored cable is already grounded, it is only necessary to ground the U-shaped opening to the box. It could be argued that since the strap of the receptacle is mounted to the box with steel screws, grounding will be automatic. That is theoretically a correct conclusion, were it not for the fact that the mounting strap is rarely in direct, solid contact with the box. In most cases the plaster ears of the strap of the receptacle hold the strap some distance away from the box, so that whatever ground there is depends on two small mounting screws; these more often than not make very poor contact with the mounting strap. In other words, whatever ground exists automatically is a very poor and undependable ground.

For this reason, the Code in Sec. 250-74 requires that a grounding wire (bare or insulated) must run from the green terminal of the receptacle to the box. Anchor it to the box using a special metal clip shown in Fig. 11-35, or install a small screw through an unused mounting hole of the box, as shown in the same installation. *This screw may not be used for any other purpose.*

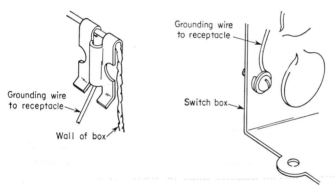

Fig. 11-35. The clips shown are most convenient in grounding the green terminal of a receptacle.

Exceptions: If the receptacle has a specially-designed mounting strap that will maintain good contact with the box even if plaster ears on the strap keep the receptacle spaced away from the box (or if you use specially-designed devices which provide a good contact through the mounting screws) then the grounding wire may be omitted. In the case of *surface-mounted* boxes, direct metal-to-metal contact between the mounting strap and the box is sufficient.

Type NM or NMC. If you are using *metallic* boxes, you must use cable with the extra bare grounding wire described earlier in this chapter. At the starting point, connect the grounding wire to the neutral in your fuse cabinet or circuit breaker cabinet. At each box, connect the ends of all the grounding wires entering the box together; a connector of the type that was shown in Fig.

8-19 will prove convenient. From the junction that you have just made, run a short piece of wire to the box itself as described in preceding paragraphs. If the box contains a receptacle, run another short piece from the junction to the green terminal of the receptacle.

If you are using *nonmetallic* boxes, the cable with the bare grounding wire needs to run only to those boxes that contain (a) receptacles or (b) switches with a metal cover within reach

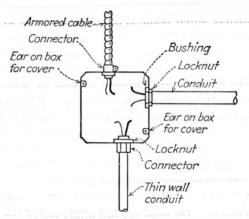

Fig. 11-36. How to change from one wiring method to another. Three different methods are shown.

of a grounded object such as a water pipe, faucet, and so on. (Switches with green grounding terminals are available.) Connect as outlined in the preceding paragraph, except that there is no need for a connection to the box itself.

Changing from Conduit to Cable. At times it will be necessary to change from conduit wiring to cable wiring, but this presents no problem. Make the change at an outlet box as shown in Fig. 11-36. Connect all black wires together, also all the white wires. The box must be permanently accessible. Cover with a blank cover.

Chapter 12

ADEQUATE WIRING

An adequately wired home is one that has been so wired that the occupant will get the maximum of convenience and utility from the use of electric power, with a minimum of inconvenience.

He must have light available where needed, in the amount needed, from permanently installed fixtures or portable lamps. He must be able to plug in lamps, radio, and TV where he pleases, without resorting to extension cords, even after the furniture is moved around. He must be able to turn lights on and off in any room without stumbling through darkness to find a switch, to move from basement to attic with plenty of light but without leaving an unneeded light turned on behind him.

He must be able to plug in needed appliances without first unplugging others. He must get full utility out of the appliances by having them heat quickly, and without lights dimming as the appliances are turned on. Circuit breakers must trip rarely.

Many people feel that if a house is wired "according to the Code," it will automatically be adequately wired. Far from it—despite the real estate advertisements that so imply. The introduction to the Code contains this statement: "This Code contains basic minimum provisions considered necessary *for safety.* Compliance therewith and proper maintenance will result in an installation essentially free from hazard; but not necessarily efficient, convenient, or *adequate for good service* or future expansion of electrical use."

A house will be adequately wired only if you carefully plan it that way. Many houses are being wired with entirely too little thought about adequacy, even though today electric power is expected to provide ten to fifty times as much light per room as in the early days of electricity and is expected to run radios and television, vacuum cleaner and toaster, washing machine and clothes dryer, air conditioners and fans, and dozens of appliances not even thought of then. There is no reason to think that we are now at a time when additional new uses for electric power will not come along in the next 10 or 20 years. These things must be planned for.

An inadequately wired home is like the automobile of 40 years ago, which furnished transportation but did not have such conveniences as spare tires, electric starters, an enclosed body, or a lighting system, not to speak of such refinements as heaters or radios. Today these things are considered essentials. Plan the house to include even those things that today you may not consider essential but within 10 or 15 years will be.

Factors in Adequate Wiring. In order that a home may be adequately wired, careful attention must be paid to the following details:

1. Service entrance of sufficient capacity.
2. Wires of sufficient capacity throughout the home.
3. Sufficient number of circuits.
4. Receptacle (plug-in) outlets in sufficient number.
5. Lighting outlets in sufficient number.
6. Lighting fixtures of scientific design.
7. Wall switches in sufficient number for complete flexibility.
8. Miscellaneous outlets and devices for signaling, radio, and so on, in proportion to the size and pretentiousness of the house.

Service Entrance. This general term includes all wires and equipment from the outside of the building up to and including the meter and the overcurrent protection (circuit breakers or fuses). It must be of sufficient size so that the maximum load in use at one time will neither overload the entrance wires, causing excessive voltage drop and wasted electricity, nor trip breakers or blow fuses. Provision must be made for future equipment that the owner will no doubt want to install.

Wire Sizes. Remember that the Code specifies only minimum sizes. While No. 14 wire may generally speaking be used throughout the average installation, the trend is toward No. 12 as a minimum.

Circuits. If all the lights in a house were protected by a single circuit breaker or fuse, the entire house would be in darkness when the breaker tripped or the fuse blew. To avoid this the outlets are subdivided into groups or circuits each protected by an individual breaker or fuse. The greater the number of circuits, the greater the flexibility, the less danger of tripping breakers or blowing fuses (because it reduces the likelihood of overloading any one circuit), and the less the voltage drop, thus making for brighter lights.

Receptacle Outlets. Sufficient receptacle or plug-in outlets do away with the need of extension cords, which are unsightly, inconvenient, and dangerous, both from the standpoint of possible injury caused by tripping over them and also from the standpoint of electrical and fire hazards caused by fraying and short circuits. The Code in Sec. 210-22(b) requires that

In every kitchen, dining room, breakfast room, living room, parlor, library, den, sunroom, recreation room, and bedroom, receptacle outlets shall be installed so that no point along the floor line in any wall space is more than 6 ft, measured horizontally, from an outlet in that space, including any wall space 2 ft wide or greater and the wall space occupied by sliding panels in exterior walls. The receptacle outlets shall, in so far as practicable, be spaced equal distances apart.

This is a Code minimum, but remembering that floor lamps, radios, and other electrical devices are seldom equipped with cords 6 ft long, you may want to reduce the 6 ft to 5 ft for a really adequate installation.

Lighting Outlets. Usually each room with the exception of the living room requires a ceiling outlet for general lighting. Additional lighting, of course, is provided by floor or table lamps.

Careful attention should be paid to lighting outlets in miscellaneous locations. It costs very little to install lights in clothes closets, hall, porches, and attics; this subject will be treated at greater length later in this chapter.

Lighting Fixtures. The selection of lighting fixtures is sufficiently important to warrant a separate chapter, and this will be the subject of Chap. 14.

Wall Switches.   Lights that are controlled by a pull chain, or a similar switch on the fixture itself, are inexcusable today, except perhaps in closets or other rooms so small that it is impossible to miss the cord or pull chain.   Outside this one exception, every light should be controlled by a wall switch.

If there is only a single door leading into a room, the logical location for the switch is near the door.   If, however, there are two entrances, it is equally logical that there should be a switch at each so that the light can be controlled from either point; in other words, use a pair of 3-way switches.   Should there be three entrances, a switch at each of the three entrances is a touch of luxury that the owner will appreciate.   In a house that has been really adequately wired, you can enter by any entrance and move from basement to attic without ever being in darkness, yet without ever having to retrace your steps to turn off lights.

Miscellaneous Outlets.   Every house will have a minimum of at least a doorbell system which will permit signaling from either front or back door.   Frequently other signaling devices are used, such as a buzzer signal in the kitchen operated by a button at the dining-room table.   Pilot lights will be used at switches which control lights that cannot be seen from the location of the switch, to indicate whether the lights are on or off; common uses are in connection with basement, attic, or garage lights.   Careful consideration of these details will make a home much more livable. Other suggestions will be found in Chap. 20.

Adequacy by Rooms.   Some rooms require much more light than others.   Likewise the need for receptacle outlets is greater in some rooms than others.   Consider what is good practice in each room.

Living Rooms.   Not too many years ago lamps larger than 100 watts were not often used in floor lamps.   Today 300-watt lamps are common.   This trend toward larger lamps was responsible for a tendency to eliminate lighting fixtures entirely from living rooms.   With white ceilings, high-wattage floor lamps do produce very excellent lighting, but since these lamps must necessarily be used mostly in corners or at least in locations along the wall, they frequently leave dark spaces in the middle or the farther end of the room.   They sometimes do not provide enough general illumination.   For this reason some people want a ceiling fixture in the living room. Provide one ceiling outlet; in a very large room provide two.

In the living room more than in any other room, be generous with receptacle outlets. The Code ruling that no point along the wall may be more than 6 ft from an outlet is a *minimum* requirement; for a living room 5 ft would be more nearly adequate. Place outlets in such a way that a floor lamp can be placed anywhere without using an extension cord. Also remember to locate them in such a way that after the furniture is located in the room, at least one outlet will always be accessible for the vacuum cleaner.

The ordinary duplex receptacle is so constructed that both halves are either on or off. There is also available a type so constructed that one of the two outlets in each device is permanently live for clock or radio but the other is controlled by a wall switch. Instead of each floor lamp having to be turned off separately, the entire group of lamps can be controlled by a single wall switch (see Chap. 20).

In planning the switches for the living room be sure to use 3- and 4-way switches so that lights can be turned on or off from all entrances (and preferably from upstairs as well).

Sunroom, Den. Provide a ceiling outlet for a lighting fixture, with a wall switch, and a generous number of receptacle outlets for floor lamps, radio, or similar devices.

Dining Room. Be sure to provide a ceiling outlet for a lighting fixture, controlled by 3-way switches located at both entrances to the room. Visualize the arrangement of the furniture, and locate the ceiling light so that it will be over the center of the dining table rather than in the center of the room. Wall brackets are little used; they are more decorative than useful. Receptacle outlets should be provided, not less than three, preferably four, taking into special consideration the probable location of the furniture. Too many dining-room outlets are located where it is impossible to get at them easily for vacuum cleaner, fan, and table appliances.

Kitchen. There are kitchens—and kitchens. One will be the modest kitchen in a small five-room house, with relatively few appliances; another will be the de luxe kitchen in a larger house, with several thousand dollars' worth of equipment. What is adequate in the one will be too little in the other.   But whatever the nature of a particular kitchen, more of the housewife's working hours are probably spent there than in any other room.   Therefore it is but logical that special attention should be paid to adequacy of wiring in that room.

For general lighting, there should be a ceiling outlet, controlled by switches at each entrance to the kitchen.   A light over the sink and another over the stove are essential, for without these the housewife will be standing in her own shadow when she works at these points.   These lights should preferably be controlled by wall switches.   If, however, they are to be controlled by a pull chain, be certain that there is an insulating link in each chain as a safety measure.

The kitchen more than any other room needs lots of receptacle outlets.   The minimum number of receptacles specified by the Code is, in general, reasonably acceptable in other rooms for floor lamps, clocks, radio, and so on, each consuming a small amount of power.   In the kitchen, however, many of the common appliances used consume 1,000 watts or more, and often several are in use at one time.   The Code recognizes this and requires *two* special circuits of No. 12 wire (protected by 20-amp overcurrent protection) for appliances only in kitchen, laundry, pantry, dining room, and breakfast room collectively.

If there is a built-in counter, locate these receptacles about 6 to 8 in. above the counter top, every 3 ft or so apart, so that appliances can be placed where convenient and still be within reach of a nearby receptacle.   Be certain to locate one so that the refrigerator can be plugged in with the cord completely concealed.   Place a clock outlet up on the wall so that your clock with a short, stubby cord will cover it, with no part of the cord exposed. One of these is shown in Fig. 12-1.

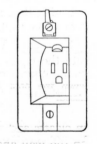

Fig.   12-1.   This outlet supports the clock, and conceals the cord on the clock from view.

Whether you intend to install an electric range immediately or not, it is wise to include a special range receptacle in your initial planning, for it is quite likely that sooner or later an electric range will be installed.

Should your kitchen be of the type that includes utilities that are more often placed in the basement (automatic washer, clothes dryer, water heater, and similar appliances), be sure to provide the extra individual outlets required for that purpose. To add such receptacles later as an afterthought usually is quite expensive, much more so than when included in the beginning.

Breakfast Room. A ceiling fixture controlled by a wall switch is necessary. At least one receptacle outlet at table height is an essential for operating a toaster or coffee maker.

Bedrooms. Every bedroom should be provided with a ceiling light controlled by a wall switch. In addition, provide a minimum of two receptacle outlets, preferably three. One at least should be located where readily accessible for the vacuum cleaner. The other two should be located on opposite sides of the room and will serve bed lamps, electric heating pad, radio, and so on. Again special attention should be paid to the location of these outlets with regard to the probable location of the furniture so that they may be readily accessible and yet not leave the cords to the lamps unduly prominent.

FIG. 12-2. A door switch of this type turns on closet lights when the door is opened, turns them off when the door is closed.

Closets. It is most exasperating to grope around trying to find something in a dark closet. Provide a ceiling light; usually closets are so small that it is fairly easy to find the pull chain or cord on the fixture. A de luxe installation will include an automatic door switch of the type shown in Fig. 12-2, which automatically turns on the light in a closet or other room as the door is opened and turns it off as the door is closed.

The Code in Sec. 410-8 prohibits drop cords in closets and requires that fixtures be installed on the ceiling or on the wall above the door. This is a wise provision, for lamps in drop cords too often come into contact with clothes, thus leading to fires.

Bathrooms. Provide a ceiling light for general illumination. However, such a ceiling light does not give enough light for shaving or make-up; for that reason provide additional light near the mirror, either one light above the mirror (which, however, casts too much shadow for easy shaving) or preferably two lights, one on each side of the mirror.   Provide an outlet near the mirror for using an electric razor.

In general the use of portable appliances in bathrooms is to be emphatically discouraged.   In bathrooms, the occupant of a tub or shower is in direct contact with ground, the ideal condition for shock.   In case of a defective appliance, the person already in contact with ground, touching such an appliance, can easily receive a fatal shock.   As a matter of fact there are on record dozens of fatal accidents each year caused by people in bathrooms, especially while in tubs, touching a defective appliance or letting some appliance such as a heater or radio (even if not defective) drop into the water.   The same fatal result can be brought about by touching defective cords, switches, or fixtures while at the same time touching a faucet or other grounded object.

There is real need in the bathroom for a quick-action electric heater, but it should be one built into the wall and controlled by a wall switch, not one controlled by being plugged into an outlet.

Porches.   If the porch is a simple stoop, a ceiling or wall light illuminating the floor and steps is sufficient.   Illuminated house numbers are a touch an owner and his friends will appreciate. If the porch is larger, so that it is used in summer as an outdoor living room, provide a number of receptacle outlets for radio or lamps.

Basements.   First of all there should be a light that illuminates *the stairs,* controlled by a switch at the head of the stairs.   If the switch is in the kitchen or some other point from which the light cannot be seen, install at the switch a pilot light which will always be on when the basement light is on.   Beyond this, the requirements vary, depending entirely on how elaborate the basement is.

If there is an all-purpose room, which might be anything from a children's playroom to a second living room, provide as good lighting as in the living room.   Since the ceilings will probably be relatively low, flush fixtures of the type shown in Fig. 12-3 may be considered.   Naturally they will not provide illumination over so wide an area as the more conventional fixtures but do give most excellent light directly below, especially convenient for cards, ping-pong, and other games. Provide receptacle outlets generously. Let the lights be controlled by wall switches.

Near the laundry tubs provide an outlet for washing machine, iron, or similar appliance, locating it at a convenient height.

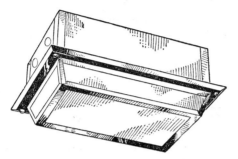

FIG. 12-3. Flush ceiling fixtures are convenient when ceiling is low.

Having it controlled by a wall switch will be an added attraction. Often ironing will be done in the laundry room, so a good ceiling light will be helpful.

At other points in the basement, install ceiling lights as required. The storage room, if there is one, needs a ceiling light; surely one is needed near the furnace. Nearly every basement has at least a corner that becomes a workshop, and a good ceiling light plus at least one receptacle is essential.

On all basement ceiling lights, especially if the ceiling is not plastered, it will be well to install a reflector of the general type shown in Fig. 12-4. Use of these reflectors will greatly increase the amount of useful light. Dark ceilings absorb light; reflectors throw the light downward where it is needed.

FIG. 12-4. A reflector behind a lamp greatly increases the amount of *useful* light obtained from the lamp. (*Steber Mfg. Co.*)

Halls. A ceiling light (or two in larger halls) controlled by wall switches will be necessary. Do not overlook a receptacle outlet in the hall for vacuum-cleaner use.

Attics. If the attic is used mostly for storage, a single light, so placed that *the stairway* is illuminated, will probably be sufficient.

It must be controlled by a switch at the bottom of the stairs.   If it is a large attic, provide additional lights as required; they can all be controlled by the same switch.   If the attic is really a second floor, unfinished but intended to be finished later into completed rooms, do not make the mistake of providing merely a single *outlet,* from which cable will later radiate in octopus fashion to a large number of additional outlets.   Bear in mind future construction, and provide at least one extra *circuit,* terminating it in some convenient location.

Stairs.   Thousands of people every year are involved in serious accidents due to falls on stairs.   They stumble because they cannot see some object that is lying on one of the steps, or fall be cause they think they have reached the bottom of the stairs when, in fact, there is one more step.   A fixture that lights up the general area of the stairs but does not light each individual step is an invitation to such an accident.   If necessary, provide two lights, one at the foot of the stairs and one at the head. Stairway lights should be controlled by 3-way switches so that they can be controlled from either level.

Chapter 13

SERVICE ENTRANCE AND BRANCH CIRCUITS

A single set of wires brings electric power from the power company's lines into the house. Inside the house wires are run to each outlet where power is to be used. Each group of outlets protected by a single circuit breaker or fuse is called a branch circuit. The Code defines a branch circuit as "that portion of a wiring system extending beyond the final overcurrent device protecting the circuit."

The wires *between* the *main* fuse of an installation and the final fuse *protecting the circuit* beyond that fuse are feeders. Note carefully the words "protecting the circuit." An overcurrent device installed just ahead of a motor, or built into the motor, is there to protect the motor and not the circuit. Therefore you must disregard it when determining where a circuit begins.

This chapter will discuss how to decide how many circuits to install, the sizes of wire in each circuit, size of the incoming wire, and similar details. Chapter 17 will discuss the actual selection and installation of the particular components involved.

In this chapter there will be many references to overcurrent devices, which, as you have already learned, may be either fuses or circuit breakers, which are rapidly replacing fuses in new installations. It would be tedious to use repeatedly the long phrases "circuit breakers or fuses" or "the circuit breaker trips or the fuse blows." Likewise it is not practical to duplicate the illustrations showing circuit breakers in one and fuses in its counterpart. Therefore the references will be to fuses, but it must be understood that the reference applies equally to circuit breakers and fuses.

Advantages of Numerous Branch Circuits. Having separate circuits for groups of outlets leads to the practical result that an entire building is never in complete darkness on account of a blown fuse except on the rare occasions when a main fuse blows. There is added safety in having a considerable number of separate branch circuits. Most of the time each fuse carries but a portion of its maximum carrying capacity. However, there are times during each day when a considerable number of lights are turned on. A washing machine may be running; perhaps a flatiron is being used; other devices may also be put into service at the same time. With a sufficient number of circuits in a properly designed installation, the load will be fairly well divided among the various fuses with the result that none is overloaded and none blows. Where there are only a few circuits, each fuse will carry a heavier load and fuses will blow far more frequently. Fuses that blow often tempt the owner to use an amperage larger than permitted with the usual No. 14 wire used in the average installation, or perhaps even to resort to substitutes which defeat the purposes of fuses entirely. Naturally, this introduces distinct danger of fire. Another practical consideration is that the greater the number of circuits, the less will be the voltage drop in each circuit, with less wasted power and higher efficiency of lamps and appliances.

Area Determines Number of Circuits. The Code in Secs. 220-2 and 220-3 has definite requirements concerning the *minimum* number of circuits that may be installed. The starting point is floor area. The Code requires that this shall be computed "from the outside dimensions of the building, apartment, or area involved, and the number of floors; not including open porches, garages in connection with dwelling occupancies, nor unfinished spaces and unused spaces in dwellings *unless adaptable for future use.*"

Those last five words "unless adaptable for future use" are important. Many houses are being built that have unfinished spaces not at first used for living purposes but intended to be completed later by the owner, when his need for added living space or his financial ability suggests that this be done. Too often this future space is disregarded in planning the original electrical installation. One outlet may possibly be installed in such a space, and when the space is later finished, many more outlets are added, branching off from the one and only outlet originally installed. That overloads the existing circuit. Run a separate circuit to the unfinished space.

The question of basements is not too clear in the Code. If the basement space is to be used for ordinary basement purposes as in older and less pretentious houses, it can be safely disregarded in your calculations. But if any part of the basement can be finished off into an amusement room or similar area, add its area to the total otherwise determined.

Houses and Apartments. The Code in Sec. 220-2 says you must allow a minimum of 3 watts for every square foot of floor area to determine the number of circuits for *lighting only*. Lighting circuits, of course, include not only outlets for permanently installed fixtures but also receptacles into which you plug floor and table lamps. These lighting circuits will also take care of minor devices such as clocks, radio, TV, and vacuum cleaner, all of which consume comparatively small amounts of power, but positively will not handle larger appliances such as kitchen appliances, room coolers, and so on.

A house that is 25 by 36 ft has an area of 900 sq ft per floor or 1,800 sq ft for two floors. Assume that it has space for a finished recreation room in the basement, 12½ by 16 ft, or an area of 200 sq ft. This makes a total area of 2,000 sq ft and will require for *lighting* a minimum of 3 × 2,000, or 6,000 watts.

The average circuit is wired with No. 14 wire, which has a carrying capacity of 15 amp and at 115 volts is equivalent to 15 × 115, or 1,725 watts. For 6,000 watts, 6,000/1,725 or 3.4 circuits will be required. Since there cannot be a fraction[1] of a circuit, three circuits must be installed to meet the Code minimum for lighting only.

You can reach the same answer another way. Since each circuit can carry 1,725 watts, and since 3 watts is required for

---

[1] If an answer involves a fraction smaller than one half, drop the fraction. If the fraction is half or more, use the next higher number.

each square foot, each circuit can serve 1,725/3, or 575 sq ft. For 2,000 sq ft there will then be required 2,000/575, or 3.4, which means three circuits.   The answer is the same whichever method is used.

Now bear in mind that the Code is concerned primarily with *safety*. As the Code itself points out, an installation made strictly in accordance with Code requirements will be safe, but it may not be practical, convenient, or adequate. Few people will be satisfied with a house wired using the minimum number of circuits required by the Code.

The Code in Sec. 220-3(a) recommends, but does not require, one circuit for every 500 sq ft of floor area for lighting. In the case of a 2,000-sq-ft house, following the recommendation will result in four lighting circuits instead of the minimum of three required by the Code.   Actually, providing one circuit for every 400 sq ft would be even more modern and practical and would result in five lighting circuits, affording more flexibility and more provision for future needs.

Special Appliance Circuits.   Once upon a time the kitchen appliances consisted of an electric iron and a toaster, each one consuming about 600 watts. These were plugged into ordinary circuits and worked fairly well; rarely were both used at one time.   A modern kitchen on the other hand is equipped with many appliances in addition to toaster and iron: coffee maker, deep-fat fryer, frying pan, roaster, mixer, garbage disposer, dishwasher, to mention some of the more common.   Individual appliances, such as toaster and iron, consume 1,000 watts, and an electric roaster even more. Often several appliances are used at the same time. The ordinary circuits can no longer handle such loads.

The Code in Sec. 220-3(b) now requires "For the small-appliance load in kitchen, laundry, pantry, family room, dining room, and breakfast room of dwelling occupancies, two[2] or more 20-amp branch circuits shall be provided for all receptacle outlets (other than outlets for clocks) in these rooms, and such circuits shall have no other outlets." No lighting outlets may be connected to these circuits.   They must be wired with No. 12 wire and pro-

[2] Only one such circuit was required by the 1956 and earlier Codes.

tected by 20-amp circuit breakers or fuses. Each then has a capacity of 20 × 115, or 2,300 watts, permitting two appliances, in most cases, to be used on each of the two circuits.

The kitchen must be served by both of these special circuits; each of the other rooms may be served by either of the circuits, or both if you prefer.

Instead of providing two 2-wire circuits, it is wise to consider, instead, one 3-wire circuit providing equal capacity and less voltage drop. The 3-wire circuit is described in Chap. 20.

Types of Branch Circuits. The Code recognizes two *types* of branch circuits. The first type is the circuit serving a single current-consuming device such as a range, a water heater, or similar load. The second type is the ordinary circuit serving two or more outlets. The load may consist of devices plugged into receptacles, or permanently connected lighting fixtures, or appliances, or a combination of them.

Branch Circuits Serving Single Outlets. It is customary to provide a separate circuit for each of the following appliances:

1. Range.
2. Water heater.
3. Clothes dryer.
4. Automatic laundry.
5. Each permanently connected appliance rated at 1,000 watts or more (for example, a bathroom heater).
6. Each permanently connected motor rated at ⅛ hp or more (oil burner, blower on furnace, water pump, garbage disposer, etc.).

According to the Code, an individual circuit is not necessarily required for some of the items listed, but as a practical matter it has become common usage to do so.

The circuits for appliances may be either 115- or 230-volt, depending on the rating of the appliance. The wire must be of sufficient size to carry the amperage of the device it is to serve. The amperage rating of the circuit breaker or fuse in the circuit depends on the specific appliance or motor served. It may not exceed 150% of the amperage rating of the appliance or motor and naturally may not exceed the ampacity of the wire in the circuit.

Circuits Serving Two or More Outlets. There are five such circuits: 15-, 20-, 30-, 40-, and 50-amp, based on the ampacities of Nos. 14, 12, 10, 8, and 6 wire.

Number of Outlets per Circuit. For wiring in houses and apartments, the Code places no limit on the number of outlets that may be connected to one lighting circuit. As a practical matter, if you have provided the recommended number of circuits, you will seldom have need for more than 10 outlets on one circuit.

Fifteen-ampere Branch Circuit. This is the ordinary circuit used in routine house wiring. It is wired with No. 14 wire and is protected by 15-amp overcurrent protection. The receptacles connected to it may not be rated more than 15 amp, which means that only the ordinary household variety of receptacle may be used. Any type of sockets for lighting may be connected to it. No *portable* appliance used on the circuit may exceed 12 amp (1,380 watts) in rating. If the circuit serves lighting outlets or portable appliances, as is usually the case, and also serves fixed or permanently connected appliances, the total of all the fixed appliances may not exceed 7½ amp (863 watts).

Twenty-ampere Branch Circuits. The special appliance circuits described earlier in this chapter are 20-amp circuits, but they are restricted as to their use, so they are *not* the "garden variety" of 20-amp circuits now under discussion.

Any circuit wired with No. 12 wire and protected by 20-amp overcurrent protection becomes a 20-amp circuit as defined by the Code. It may serve lighting outlets, receptacles, permanently wired appliances, or an assortment of them. Any kind of sockets for lighting purposes may be used on the circuit. The receptacles may be either the ordinary 15-amp type or special 20-amp type. No single portable appliance used on the circuit may exceed 16 amp (1,840 watts) in rating. If permanently connected appliances are also on the circuit, the total of all such fixed appliances may not exceed 10 amp (1,150 watts).

The wise homeowner will demand 20-amp circuits for general lighting purposes throughout the house.

Thirty-, Forty-, and Fifty-amp Branch Circuits. These circuits are never used in ordinary residential wiring; they will be discussed in Chap. 29 concerning nonresidential wiring.

Balancing Circuits. In a house served by a 3-wire 115/230-volt service (which includes, of course, a neutral wire), the neutral wire of each 115-volt branch circuit is connected to the incoming neutral   Care must be used in connecting the hot wires of the branch circuits so that they will be divided approximately equally between the two incoming hot wires. If this is not done, practically all the load may be thrown on only two of the three incoming wires, and a 2-wire service might as well have been used in the first place. Unbalanced conditions lead to frequent blowing of fuses.

Location of Branch-circuit Overcurrent Protection. The main switch with main fuses and branch-circuit fuses is usually a small, compact cabinet. If circuit breakers are used, the same

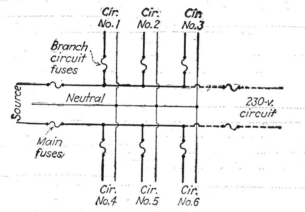

Fig. 13-1. The most common scheme: locating all fuses at one location.

applies. The Code requires that this equipment be located near the point where the wires enter the building.

In any house, most of the power is consumed in the basement and kitchen appliances, and relatively a small part of it is consumed in the remainder of the house. For minimum cost, plan your layout so that the wires enter the building at a point from which the large, heavy wires to the range, water heater, clothes dryer, and kitchen appliances can be short; let the smaller, less expensive wires to the remainder of the building be the long ones.

In most houses today this equipment is located in the basement. Sometimes it is located in the kitchen, where it is more accessible. Of course, if the house is really adequately wired, fuses will rarely blow, so this point becomes less important.

Branch-circuit Schemes. The most usual scheme of locating all branch-circuit fuses at one point is shown in Fig. 13-1. As far as fusing is concerned, the wires beyond the branch-circuit fuses may be as long as desired. Note that 230-volt circuits may be run at any point by simply tapping off the two black wires. For example, the black wire of circuit No. 1 and the black wire of circuit No. 4 together would make one 230-volt circuit, the white wires, of course, being disregarded. One such 230-volt circuit is shown in dotted lines.

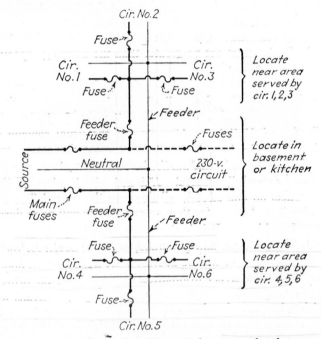

Fig. 13-2. In this scheme branch-circuit fuses are placed in groups at various locations throughout the house. In this case fuses are required at the point where the feeders to these groups of fuses begin.

In larger houses, some prefer to locate the branch-circuit fuses in various locations throughout the house, the fuses controlling the basement circuits, for example, being placed in the basement, those controlling the first floor being placed in the kitchen, those controlling the second floor being placed on that floor, and so on. The scheme of Fig. 13-2 is used. Assume that in an installation the service switch and the branch-circuit fuses are in the same cabinet. If the installation is made in accordance with Fig. 13-1, the fuses are branch-circuit fuses, and the wires beyond the fuses are branch-circuit wires. If the installation is made in accordance with Fig. 13-2, the same wires (but now running to another fuse box and of a heavier size) become feeders, and the fuses (but now of a higher amperage rating) become feeder fuses.

The wires from the fuse cabinet in Fig. 13-2 to each location where a group of branch-circuit fuses is installed are feeders, as already explained. The wires of any feeder must be of sufficient size to carry the total load of the branch circuits which that feeder serves. The ampere rating of the overcurrent protection for the feeder must not be greater than the carrying capacity of the feeder. In accordance with Sec. 215-2 of the Code, No. 10 is the smallest wire permitted when a 2-wire feeder serves *more than one* 2-wire circuit, when a 3-wire feeder serves *more than two* 2-wire circuits, or when it feeds *more than one* 3-wire circuit.

Distribution of Outlets on Circuits. If the usual scheme is used, placing all the branch-circuit overcurrent devices in one location, the question of what particular outlets to place on each circuit must be carefully studied. It is not wise to place all the first-floor outlets on one circuit, all those on the second floor on another circuit, and so on, for then an entire floor will be in darkness if one fuse blows. It is best to have on each circuit outlets of several different rooms and preferably different floors, for then when a fuse blows, there will be at least some light on each floor.

Service Entrance. Every installation includes wires for bringing the electric power into the building, with proper means as required by the Code for disconnecting the service, for grounding, for overcurrent protection, and so on. While by Code definition the overcurrent protection for the *branch* circuits is not considered part of the service entrance, yet it is a fact that such overcurrent protection is almost always integral mechanically with other parts of the service. Accordingly in this book, such overcurrent protection will be considered part of the service entrance.

The service entrance then consists of:

1. Service-drop wires (from the power company's lines to the building).

2. Service-entrance wires (from the outside of house to equipment on the inside).

3. Meter.

4. Disconnecting means (to disconnect the entire installation completely from the power company's lines).

5. Overcurrent protection.

6. Ground.

The details of these several components are dependent on many factors, such as the size of the building, the amount of power required, the number of circuits, and so on. In this chapter we shall discuss only the general design of the service entrance, and in Chap. 17 we shall discuss the actual installation of the service entrance.

Minimum Size of Service Entrance. This chapter will concern only houses, not commercial or industrial projects. The Code in Sec. 230-71 has specific requirements regarding the minimum size of service-entrance equipment. References here are to the size of the main switch or main circuit breaker.

If the installation has either one or two 15-amp 2-wire circuits, the minimum is a 30-amp service. Under all other conditions the minimum is 60-amp capacity when fused equipment is used, 50-amp capacity if circuit breakers are used. But this minimum usually will not apply because of a most important exception: If the load calculated in the manner which will be outlined is 10,000 watts or more, the minimum becomes 100 amp. Automatically, then, if the house is to have an electric range, the minimum is 100 amp.

The ratings of the service when fused equipment is used are 30, 60, 100, and 200 amp, corresponding to standardized ratings of service-entrance switches. When circuit breakers are used, the ratings become 30, 50, 70, 100, 140, 200, and 400 amp, corresponding to the standardized ratings of circuit breakers.

The actual minimum size of wire that may be used for a service of any given amperage will be discussed in the next paragraph. Do remember that the minimum specified by the Code is based on safety, not practicality or convenience. You will often want to use a service larger than the minimum. In some localities local codes already require 200-amp services as a minimum.

Size of Wire for Various Services. As you learned in Chap. 6, the capacity of a given size of wire depends not only on its size but also on the kind of insulation on the wire. Sometimes also the ampacity depends on whether the wire is installed in a wet or dry location; a properly installed service entrance in conduit is considered to be a dry location even if the conduit is outdoors. The ampacity of each size and kind of wire is found in Table 310-12 of the Code (see Appendix). The minimum size of wire required for a service of any given amperage is as follows:

Amperage of service	Minimum size of wire if Code Type	
	R, RW, T, TW	RH, RH-RW, RHW, THW
30	No. 8	No. 8
50	No. 6	No. 6
60	No. 4	No. 6
70	No. 4	No. 4
100	No. 1	No. 3
140	No. 2/0	No. 1/0
200	250 MCM	No. 3/0
400	750 MCM	600 MCM

When using fused service-entrance equipment of a size larger than the minimum required, it is not contrary to the Code to use service wires smaller in capacity than the rating of the switch, provided that the fuses in the main switch are not rated higher in amperes than the ampacity of the wires. But if you are using a wire with an ampacity such that there is no standard fuse of that ampere rating, you may use a fuse of the next higher standard rating. Thus if you use wire with 95-amp ampacity, use a 100-amp fuse, for there is no standard 95-amp fuse. In spite of all this, it makes sense to use service-entrance wires of such capacity that the full rated capacity of the switch or circuit breaker can be utilized.

One additional caution may be necessary: The service switch

or circuit breaker does not need to be rated at the total number of amperes you would reach by adding up all the individual amperages of all the individual branch circuits. There never will be a time when every circuit in the house will be loaded to its maximum capacity.

To determine the size of the service entrance, follow Code Sec. 220-4. If it is decided in advance that the entrance will be 100-amp or larger, the Code permits a short-cut method. However, we shall discuss the original, or long, method first. The total load that must be carried by the entrance can be broken down into four groups:

1. Lighting.
2. Small appliances.
3. Heavy appliances.
4. Motors.

Lighting. The total power that the entrance must carry for lighting (and that includes the receptacle outlets for supplying items like radio, television, clocks, vacuum cleaner, and similar portable devices, but not kitchen appliances) is outlined in Sec. 220-2(a): 3 watts per square foot of area, the same figure you used in determining the number of circuits required.

3 watts per sq ft

Small Appliances. The Code includes in "small appliances" all irons, toasters, coffee makers, and similar portable appliances ordinarily used in the kitchen, as well as washing machines and the like used in the laundry, but excludes all permanently installed appliances like clothes dryers and the like. To allow for their use, add to the wattage for lighting, as determined by the previous paragraph, 3,000 watts. This corresponds to an average load of 1,500 watts on each of the two special 20-amp appliance circuits required by Sec. 22-3(b) for such appliances.

3,000 W + 35% in excess of 3,000 including lighting

Demand Factor. The larger the house, the less likelihood that it will *all* be lighted at the same time. Considering that fact, the requirement of 3 watts per sq ft plus 3,000 watts for small appliances might be considered excessive from a *safety* standpoint, which is the chief concern of the Code.

Accordingly, the Code in Sec. 220-4(a) establishes a "demand factor" of 35% for that portion of the wattage which exceeds 3,000 watts, computed as above outlined for lighting and small appliances (but excluding fixed appliances and motors). If the computed total is 3,000 watts or less, count all of it. If it is over 3,000 watts, count only 35% of the portion above 3,000 watts. Examples will be given later in the chapter.

It should be remembered that this demand factor applies only in determining the service-entrance equipment and not in determining the number of circuits. The individual circuits must be so planned that any *portion* of the house can be lighted to the point which requires 3 watts per sq ft, but there is no likelihood that the *entire* house will ever be so lighted that the full 3 watts per sq ft will be required throughout the entire area.

Heavy Appliances. The major heavy appliance is the electric range, which will be discussed separately. Other heavy appliances are such permanently installed appliances as water heater, clothes dryer, automatic laundry, bathroom heater, and the like. Each of these must be counted at its full rating in watts. No demand factor applies.

Range. The wattage consumed by a range when all burners and the oven are turned on to maximum heat will vary considerably with the size, type, and brand of the range. It may be as high as 15,000 watts or even more. But since it is not likely that all burners and the oven will be turned on at the same time while everything else in the house is also turned on, the Code permits an arbitrary minimum of 8,000 watts for a range in calculating the service entrance.

If you are installing a separate wall-mounted oven and also counter-mounted cooking units, add the total wattage of the two together and then use 80% of this total for calculating the entrance.

Electric Heating. In some localities electric heating is becoming quite common. The Code rules are fairly complicated, but in general, per Sec. 220-4(e), you must allow for the total wattage consumed by all the heating elements at the same time. If, however, the circuits are so arranged that not all the elements can be turned on at the same time, count only that wattage that can be in use at one time.

Air Conditioning. Determine the horsepower of the motor on the equipment, then allow the wattage outlined in the next paragraph for a motor of that size. But if the house is to have both electric heating and air conditioning, the two obviously will not be in use at the same time. Count the larger of the two loads.

Motors. The Code devotes considerable space to the proper installation of motors, and the subject is complex. For the purpose of calculating the service-entrance equipment *for homes,* allow the wattages shown below, and the Code requirements will be more than met:

⅙ hp	450 watts
¼ hp	700 watts
⅓ hp	850 watts
½ hp	1,000 watts
¾ hp	1,350 watts
1 hp	1,500 watts
1½ hp and larger	1,200 watts per hp

The wattages shown above are considerably above the actual wattages consumed by the motors, but since alternating-current motors have relatively low power factors, the amperages are considerably more than merely watts/volts. Also, motors can be overloaded to deliver considerably more than their name-plate horsepower and will then consume more than their rated amperage.

If there are several motors but no likelihood that all will ever operate at the same time, estimate the proper demand factor. For example, if a home workshop is to have four motors, it is not likely that more than one will be used at a time. Count only the largest of them.

Calculating a 2,000-sq-ft House. Assuming a house of 2,000 sq ft area (determined in the same way as outlined for determining number of circuits) without a range and with no motors, the calculations will be as follows:

	Gross computed watts	Demand factor, per cent	Net computed watts
Lighting, 2,000 sq ft at 3 watts.	6,000		
Small appliances (minimum)	3,000		
Total gross computed watts.	9,000		
First 3,000 watts	. . . . . .	100	3,000
Remaining 6,000 watts.	. . . . .	35	2,100
Total net computed watts.	. . . . .	. . . . .	5,100

Since there are more than two circuits, the service must be the 3-wire 115/230-volt type. The amperage involved is 5,100/230, or 22.2 amp. Since No. 10 wire has an ampacity of 30 amp, it would appear to be large enough, but the Code in Sec. 230-71 requires a service with a minimum of 60-amp rating with a switch, 50-amp with a circuit breaker. Our calculation then merely confirms that the house as planned can be served by the 50- or 60-amp service and meet the Code minimum requirements. The owner of the house would not long be satisfied by such an installation.

Assume now that an electric range is to be added and also a permanently installed bathroom heater. The calculations will then be as follows:

	Gross computed watts	Demand factor, per cent	Net computed watts
Lighting, 2,000 sq ft at 3 watts......	6,000		
Small appliances (minimum)........	3,000		
Total gross computed watts.......	9,000		
First 3,000 watts...............	.....	100	3,000
Remaining 6,000 watts...........	.....	35	2,100
Bathroom heater.................	1,500	100	1,500
Range (arbitrary minimum)........	.....	...	8,000
Total net computed watts......	.....	...	14,600

At 230 volts, the amperage is 14,600/230, or 63.5 amp. Therefore, a 70-amp service would appear to be large enough. But the Code specifies that if there are over 10,000 computed watts, a 100-amp service is the minimum required.

Let us now go a step further and figure a somewhat larger 3,000-sq-ft house on a more generous basis. Add a water heater consuming 3,500 watts. Add two ¼-hp motors, one for the furnace and one for its blower. Add a clothes dryer rated at 4,000 watts. Assume that now it is a suburban home with a ½-hp motor on the water pump. The calculations then will be as follows:—

	Gross computed watts	Demand factor, per cent	Net computed watts
Lighting, 3,000 sq ft at 3 watts......	9,000		
Small appliances...................	3,000		
Total gross computed watts.......	12,000		
First 3,000 watts................	......	100	3,000
Remaining 9,000 watts............	......	35	3,150
Range (arbitrary minimum).........	......	...	8,000
Fixed appliances:			
Bathroom heater................	1,500	100	1,500
Water heater....................	3,500	100	3,500
Clothes dryer...................	4,000	100	4,000
¼-hp motor, oil burner...........	700	100	700
¼-hp motor, blower on furnace....	700	100	700
½-hp motor, water pump.........	1,000	100	1,000
Total net computed watts......	......	...	25,550

At 230 volts, this is equivalent to 25,500/230, or about 111 amp. The 100-amp service is now too small, and you would then install a 140-amp service with circuit breakers or a 200-amp service with fuses.

Alternate Method. If you decide in advance that your house will have a 100-amp or larger service, you may use the short-cut method permitted by Sec. 220-7. Using this method, you must show the full name-plate rating of the electric range. The calculation for the 3,000 sq-ft house is shown on the next page.

The total wattage indicates a theoretical service of 20,960/230, or 91 amp, and the calculation then merely confirms that the 100-amp service tentatively established in advance will meet the Code minimum requirement. It is quite likely, however, that this minimum will not long be sufficient, and it would be wise to go to a larger size.

Do note that if you use this short-cut method, the 40% demand factor applies to all the load above 10,000 watts, with the exceptions of the next paragraph.

If you are going to have electric heating and there are *four or more* separately controlled units, you may include them in your total above. If there are three or less units, you may *not* include

	Gross computed watts	Net computed watts
Lighting, 3,000 sq ft at 3 watts................	9,000	
Small appliances............................	3,000	
Range, maximum rating......................	14,000	
Fixed appliances:		
Bathroom heater...........................	1,500	
Water heater.............................	3,500	
Clothes dryer.............................	4,000	
¼-hp motor, oil burner....................	700	
¼-hp motor, blower on furnace..............	700	
½-hp motor, water pump...................	1,000	
Total gross computed watts...............	37,400	
First 10,000 watts at 100% demand factor....	......	10,000
Remaining 27,400 watts at 40% demand factor...................................	......	10,960
Total net computed watts...............	......	20,960

them in your calculations until you have figured the net computed watts as in the example above; add them to that total without applying a demand factor. Likewise the wattage of air-conditioning motors may *not* be included in the tabulation, but must be added afterward to the net computed watts without applying the demand factor.

These sample calculations, regardless of whether you use the old method or the new short-cut method, will serve merely as examples. It will be well for you to calculate other houses in the same fashion; for example: (1) the house in which you live as it is now wired, (2) the same house as you would like to have it wired, and (3) the "ideal" house in which you would like to live. But always remember that the answers you reach by these Code methods tell you only the *minimum* size of wire the Code considers necessary for *safety*. The actual size of wire you will want to use will be larger than the minimum, to allow for convenience and practicability and above all for the future electrical appliances that you will surely add as time goes on.

Disconnecting Means and Overcurrent Protection. A device must be provided at or near the point where the service wires enter the building, to disconnect or isolate the entire building from its source of supply. Likewise it is necessary to have devices which disconnect a single circuit at a time from the source of supply. This is a safety factor, for there are times when it is most necessary to disconnect, or "kill," parts or all of the wiring, as in case of fire or when working on parts of the system.

Likewise it is necessary to provide overcurrent protection which protects the installation as a whole, or parts of it (individual circuits), against short circuits or overloads.

Usually the disconnecting means and the overcurrent protection come in the form of a single metal cabinet that houses all the necessary components. The Code requirements when fused equipment is used are a bit simpler in some respects than when circuit breakers are used, so will be covered first.

Fused Equipment. The "service switch" consists of a main switch by means of which the entire installation can be disconnected at one time plus main fuses to protect the installation as a whole plus as many individual branch-circuit fuses as are required to protect those branch circuits. Occasionally the branch-circuit fuses are in a separate cabinet.

According to Code the switch must be "externally operable," which condition is fulfilled if the switch can be operated without the operator being exposed to live parts. Older switches used an external handle as shown in Fig. 13-3. Most switches today don't have hinged switch blades in the usual sense at all. Instead, the main fuses are mounted on a small block of insulating material which can be pulled out of the switch. When this block is removed, with the fuses, the switch is

FIG. 13-3. The simplest type of switch. Occasionally it is used as a service switch for very small installations. It is more frequently used for other purposes. (*Clark Controller Co.*)

dead, just as if blades had been operated with a handle. Such switches once installed have no exposed live parts, whether the block with the main fuses is in place or removed, for the prongs on the removable block project into the switch through very small openings. A switch of this kind is shown in Fig. 13-4;

the pull-out block shown at the bottom holds the main fuses and fits into the upper left portion of the switch.   A second similar pull-out block at the upper right holds a pair of cartridge fuses to protect a range or similar load.   At the bottom are four plug fuses to protect four branch circuits.

Solid-neutral Switches.   For a 115-volt installation, use a 2-pole *solid-neutral* switch with one main fuse.   Such installations may not have more than two branch circuits.   In all other cases the

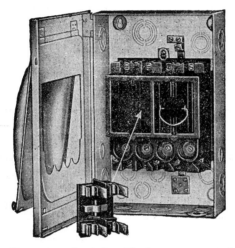

FIG. 13-4. A pull-out type of switch.   The fuses are mounted on an insulating block.   When the block is pulled out, no live parts are exposed.   Inserting block upside down in its holder turns switch off.   (*Clark Controller Co.*)

installations will be 115/230-volt type, for which use a 3-pole *solid-neutral* switch with two main fuses.   You have already learned that the neutral or grounded wire is never interrupted by a switch[3] or fuse.   "Solid neutral" then means that the neutral wire in the switch is not interrupted by switch or fuse; instead it runs to a "neutral bar" in the switch.   This neutral strap or neutral bar is merely a copper strip with a number of terminal

[3] If we wish to be precise, it must be stated that the grounded neutral *may* be interrupted by a switch blade or circuit breaker (but never a fuse) provided the device is so designed that it is impossible to open the grounded wire without simultaneously opening all the ungrounded wires.   Such devices are not used in homes.

lugs to which the neutral wire of the incoming wires, the neutral wires of all the branch circuits, and also the ground wire are connected. The "3-pole solid-neutral" switch then has two blades plus two main fuses to disconnect and protect the two hot wires, the third or neutral wire running to the neutral strap.

In this connection, Sec. 230-70(a) of the Code may prove confusing. This section reads that "Means shall be provided for disconnecting *all* conductors in the building from the service-entrance conductors." Section 230-70(i) reads "If the switch or circuit breaker does not interrupt the grounded conductor, other means shall be provided . . . for disconnecting the grounded conductor." One statement apparently contradicts the other, and both may seem contrary to the statements of the previous paragraph that the neutral wire always runs directly to the neutral bar without interruption by a switch.

The answer lies in the fact that *all* connections inside the switch must be by means of *solderless* connectors as required by Sec. 230-72 of the Code. Being so made, the connections can be opened using ordinary tools, and that satisfies the Code requirement. If such wires were *soldered* to the terminal bar, this would not be true.

Ratings of Service Switches. Service switches are rated at 30, 60, 100, 200, 400, and 600 amp with no in-between ratings. In residential work the 30-amp size is never used except possibly in a small summer cottage or similar building. The 60-amp size was formerly the most common but has proved too small in most cases. The 100-amp is the minimum size now specified by Code in most cases, as already explained. The 200-amp size is becoming fairly common and is already specified as minimum in some local codes.

Selection of Specific Switch. Switches are available with main fuses plus other fuses for 2 to 20 or more branch circuits. One fuse is needed for each 115-volt branch circuit; two fuses for each 230-volt branch circuit. Plug fuses are suitable for either voltage, but cartridge fuses are necessary if the rating is over 30 amp. Remember that all plug fuses are mechanically interchangeable. Cartridge fuses rated at 35 to 60 amp all have the same dimensions and fit the same holders. Those rated 65 to 100 amp are larger and are of the knife-blade type.

The so-called "range combination" shown in Fig. 13-4 was once very popular. Rated at 60 amp and with 60-amp main

fuses plus a pair of cartridge fuses for a range or other load within the 230-volt 35- to 60-amp size, plus fuses for four 115-volt circuits, it was considered big enough for the average house. Time has shown that it was much too small. Today a 100-amp switch is considered minimum; a typical one is shown in Fig. 13-5. Besides the 100-amp main fuses it provides two pairs of cartridge fuses for range or similar 230-volt loads, plus 12 plug fuses for 115-volt circuits. Other 100-amp switches are available with still more fuses for branch circuits. In larger houses and on

FIG. 13-5. Typical 100-amp service switch with many fuses for branch circuits. (*Clark Controller Co.*)

farms similar but larger switches are used, with 200-amp mains, plus two to six pairs of cartridge fuses for 230-volt branches, plus many plug fuses for 115-volt branches.

Remember that while any one plug fuse will protect a 115-volt circuit, two plug fuses (one on each of the two hot wires, or "legs," in the switch) will protect a 230-volt circuit of not over 30-amp rating.

Many of these switches have a pair of lugs for wires running to a water heater. Wires from these lugs are usually *not* protected by fuses; consequently a separate fused switch of the general type shown in Fig. 13-3 must be used in the circuit to the heater.

For your final selection, choose a switch that has the necessary number of fuses to protect the number of circuits that you have decided are necessary for your house, with a few spares for future circuits.

After having selected the exact switch you want, it is wise to discuss your selection with your power company. Be prepared with the manufacturer's number of the switch you have in mind. Some power companies are very particular about the switches on

their line and have "approved lists" of brands and specific catalog numbers that are acceptable.

Circuit Breakers. Remember that an individual circuit breaker
looks like a switch. On overload, the circuit breaker opens itself;
restore service by flipping the handle, like closing a switch (see
Fig. 13-6). One single-pole breaker protects a 115-volt circuit;
one two-pole (double-pole) breaker protects a 230-volt circuit.
The two-pole breaker in some brands has a single handle; in
some other brands it looks like two separate single-pole breakers
side by side, each with its own handle, but with the two handles
mechanically tied together to become one single handle, so far
as the Code is concerned. A two-pole breaker is dimensionally
twice as large as a single-pole.

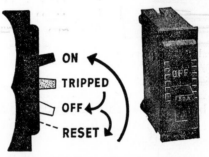

Fig. 13-6. A typical circuit breaker. If breaker trips because of overload,
force the handle *beyond* the "off" position, then move it to "on." (*General
Electric Co.*)

Circuit breakers are rated in amperes, just like fuses, but the
particular ratings are not exactly the same as those for fuses.
Breakers are rated at 15, 20, 30, 40, 50, 70, 100 and 200 amp to
correspond more or less to the ampacities of Nos. 14, 12, 10, 8, 6,
4, 2 and 4/0 wire.

Circuit-breaker cabinets come in two types: those containing
only branch-circuit breakers, and those that contain in addition
also one or two main breakers to protect the entire load. Cabinets to contain only branch-circuit breakers are usually sold
without the breakers, but contain an arrangement of bus-bars
into which the user plugs whatever assortment of breakers he
needs: single-pole or two-pole, of such amperages as desired.
The cabinet also contains terminals for the incoming wires, and

a neutral bar for the grounded neutrals of all the 115-volt branch circuits. If main breakers are also involved, they are already installed in the cabinet as purchased.

The 1959 and 1962 Codes contained a requirement that the cabinets and the plug-in breakers be so designed that once a breaker had been installed, another breaker of a larger amperage capacity could not be installed in its place. This proved to be impractical from several standpoints, and the 1965 Code did away with the requirement.

 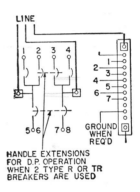

Fig. 13-7. A breaker cabinet with four branch circuits. If any of the breakers are 15- or 20-amp this cabinet cannot be used for service entrance unless a main breaker is installed ahead of it. (*General Electric Co.*)

Under the 1962 and earlier Codes, it was permissible to use a circuit-breaker cabinet *without* a main breaker, provided all the circuits could be disconnected with *not over six* movements of the hand, regardless of the ampere ratings of the individual breakers. Because of a change in the 1965 Code [Sec. 384-16(a)] this is now permitted only if all the breakers are rated at *more than 20 amp*. But in residential wiring, many of the circuits are rated at 15 or 20 amp, which means that this scheme can no longer be used. The circuit-breaker cabinet shown in Fig. 13-7, which was formerly acceptable, can no longer be used, unless protected by another breaker ahead of it in the feeder to the cabinet.

The simplest solution is to use a circuit-breaker cabinet with a main breaker; throwing this one breaker disconnects the entire

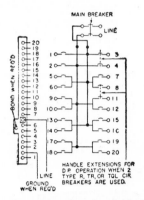

Fig. 13-8. This breaker cabinet has a main circuit breaker ahead of all the branch-circuit breakers. Combinations of breakers other than those shown may be used. (*General Electric Co.*)

load. One is shown in Fig. 13-8. The main breaker would be rated at 70, 100 or 200 amp as required.

A similar circuit-breaker cabinet containing *two* main breakers is shown in Fig. 13-9. Each breaker protects a portion of the branch circuits, which may be of any rating. While this illustration shows a cabinet with only eight branch-circuit breakers, it must be understood that cabinets accommodating a larger

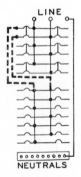

Fig. 13-9. This breaker cabinet has *two* main breakers, each protecting separate groups of branch-circuit breakers in the lower part of the cabinet. (*General Electric Co.*)

Fig. 13-10. Diagram for a typical "split-bus" breaker cabinet. One of the six breakers in the upper part of the cabinet, becomes the main breaker for the branch-circuit breakers in the lower part of the cabinet.

number are available. The rating of the total cabinet is the sum of the amperage rating of the two main breakers.

Another widely used scheme involves the "split-bus" type of breaker cabinet, the wiring for which is shown in Fig. 13-10. In the upper half of the cabinet are not more than six two-pole breakers each rated at 30 amp or more. Five of them protect individual 230-volt circuits such as range, water heater, etc. The sixth one becomes the main breaker for the remaining 15- or 20-amp circuits, each of which is protected by one of the breakers in the lower part of the cabinet. These breakers may be of any rating, and may be either single-pole for 115-volt circuits, or two-pole for 230-volt circuits.

Alternately, two of the larger breakers in the upper part of the cabinet, could be used to protect *two* groups of smaller breakers in the lower part of the cabinet. Note that in either case, the entire load can be disconnected by turning off the six breakers in the upper part of the cabinet, with not over six movements of the hand, thus becoming acceptable without having a single main breaker for the entire load.

Installation of Service Entrance. The equipment having been selected, it must now be installed. The details are covered in Chap. 17.

Chapter 14

GOOD LIGHTING

In the early days of electric lighting even one lamp[1] hung in the center of a room was such an improvement over the ordinary kerosene lamp or even the gaslight then in use that apparently little time was spent in considering whether the new illuminant provided really sufficient light for good seeing. This type of thinking persisted too long, and even today too little thought is given to providing good lighting. As a result, entirely too many homes and other buildings that are electrically lighted have not one-half or even one-quarter the illumination that is necessary for good seeing.

This chapter will be devoted to a discussion of the fundamentals of lighting, as well as the selection, installation, and use of lighting fixtures and the lamps that go with them, in order to provide good lighting. Many volumes have been written on the subject, some of them covering but one single small aspect of the science, and on some points there is a good deal of disagreement among the authorities. The author does not flatter himself therefore that he can begin to cover the subject in a single chapter. He does propose, however, to set forth some of the fundamentals involved, together with what are today considered standards, so as to give some degree of working knowledge to the reader.

Dozens of factors can be enumerated that go to make up a good lighting system. The more important ones are that the lighting system must:

---

[1] Is it a "lamp" or a "bulb"? The complete "light bulb" is properly called a lamp; the glass part of a lamp is the bulb. In fluorescent lamps the glass part is called the tube.

1. Provide sufficient quantity of light.
2. Provide light free from glare.
3. Provide light free from objectionable shadows.
4. Provide the right kind of light.

Good lighting is important in many ways. It contributes to personal comfort and reduces eyestrain. It leads to greater efficiency in all activities. It tends to promote safety by preventing accidents due to poor visibility.

Extent of Defective Vision. Broad surveys have shown that an amazing percentage of all people today have defective vision. One survey shows the percentage of defective vision to be:

Under 20 years	23%
20 to 30 years	39%
30 to 40 years	48%
40 to 50 years	71%
50 to 60 years	82%
Over 60 years	95%

Another survey shows that of all students in the elementary grades of school 9% have defective vision, in high school 24% and in colleges the figure has risen to 31%.

A different type of survey shows that the percentage of defective vision varies considerably by occupations. Those who work relatively little under artificial light and those whose work is not of an exacting nature suffer relatively little. For farmers and common laborers the proportion is under 20%, while for carpenters and painters it has risen to between 20% and 40%. For machinists and printers the figure is over 40%, whereas for draftsmen and stenographers it is over 80%.

It used to be generally accepted that poor lighting is one of the *causes* of defective vision; medical authorities now question that conclusion. Whichever theory is correct, it remains a fact that many people do have defective vision; the proportion increases with age. The important point is that those who do have defective vision need better lighting than those with normal vision. Since there are few families or other groups of people among whom there isn't at least one person with defective vision, it follows that lighting should be designed, not for those with perfect vision, but for those with impaired vision.

How Light Is Measured. Inasmuch as the candle was the common method of illumination when this science was first studied, it is not surprising that standards sprang up based on candle light, so that today there are such terms as "candlepower" and "footcandles." Since a big candle naturally gives more light than a little candle, there developed a standardized candle, the definition of which, however, need not concern us here.

Candlepower. This term does not measure the *total* amount of light emitted by the source, for the light may be brighter in one direction than in another. The standardized candle mentioned in the previous paragraph emits 1 candlepower of light in a particular direction; in other directions it may emit more or less than 1 candlepower. Because of this, the term "candlepower" is of relatively little value because the direction must always be taken into consideration when the term is used. For this reason lamps are no longer rated in candlepower. However, many times the term "candlepower" is still used when the term "horizontal candlepower" or "mean spherical candlepower" is meant.

Mean Spherical Candlepower. If a source of light gives off 1 candlepower in *every* direction, it is said to have 1 mean spherical candlepower; if it gives off 10 candlepower in every direction, it has 10 mean spherical candlepower. If it gives off 5 candlepower in one direction, 10 in another, and 12 in a third, but *averages* 10 candlepower, it has 10 mean spherical candlepower. Automobile lamps are still rated in candlepower; the mean spherical candlepower is meant, but this apparently is too long a term for ordinary commercial use, so that the words "mean spherical" are dropped but are implied.

Beam Candlepower. When a reflector is placed behind a source of light, the emitted light rays which ordinarily go off in all directions are crowded into a relatively narrow beam. The brightness of this beam in candlepower is called the "apparent beam candlepower." For example, an ordinary automobile lamp of 21 candlepower, if used in a good reflector, will provide an apparent beam candlepower of 100,000, within a very narrow beam. This simply means that there is enough candlepower within the beam to produce the same intensity of light at the point of observation as would be produced at that same point by a light source of 100,000 *mean spherical* candlepower, without a reflector, when located at the position of the smaller lamp and reflector.

Lumens. The term "candlepower" measures only the light in a given direction, not the total amount of light emitted. The total quantity is measured in lumens.[2] Assume a light source producing 1 candlepower in every direction, located in the center of a sphere which is exactly 2 ft in diameter; this means that the light source is then exactly 1 ft from every point on the inner surface of the sphere. Assume that there is an opening in the sphere and that this opening is exactly 1 sq ft in area (see Fig. 14-1). The lumen is defined as *the amount or quantity of light*

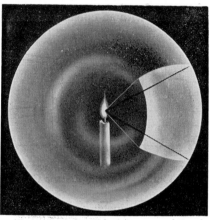

Fig. 14-1. A candle is in the exact center of a sphere which is 2 ft in diameter. An opening with an area of exactly 1 sq ft has been cut out of the sphere.

emitted through an opening of 1 sq ft located at a distance of 1 ft from a light source which emits 1 candlepower in every direction. Note that this opening must be part of a sphere; if the opening is a hole 12 in. square in a sheet of paper, there is no way of placing the paper so that every point is exactly 1 ft from the light source. This definition is important; study it well.

Simple geometry tells us that the total area of a sphere 2 ft in diameter is 12.57 sq ft ($4\pi \times R^2$). Since by the definition above 1 lumen of light falls on *each* square foot of area in the sphere, the *total* light falling on the interior of the sphere must be 12.57 lumens. This was produced by a light source of 1 mean spheri-

[2] Derived from the Latin word *lumen* meaning light.

cal candlepower.   Therefore to find the lumens emitted by a lamp
of which the mean spherical candlepower is known, multiply by
12.57; if the lumens are known, divide by 12.57 to determine the
mean spherical candlepower.

Law of Inverse Squares.   The candlepower and lumens of a
light source are absolute or constant; other circumstances being
the same, they do not change.   A candle produces the same
amount of light when the observer is 2 ft away from it as when
he is 5 ft away from it.   Nevertheless it is much easier to read a
newspaper 2 ft distant from the candle than it is when 5 ft distant.
Assume again a light of exactly 1 mean spherical candlepower enclosed in the 2-ft sphere with an opening exactly 1 sq ft in area

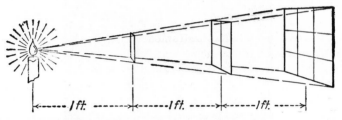

Fig. 14-2. The illumination on an object varies inversely as the square of its
distance from the light source.   (*General Electric Co.*)

A newspaper placed at the opening will have 1 sq ft of print illuminated by the 1 lumen of light escaping through the opening.
Now move the newspaper so that it is located 1 ft from the sphere
or 2 ft from the lamp.   The 1 lumen of light that escapes through
the opening will now illuminate an area 2 ft on each side, 4 sq ft
altogether.   Move it to 2 ft from the sphere or 3 ft from the lamp.
The area illuminated will now be 3 ft on each side, 9 sq ft altogether (see Fig. 14-2).

The area illuminated was first 1 sq ft, then 4, then 9, yet the
total amount of light involved remained the same, 1 lumen.   Obviously it will be harder to read at the 3-ft distance than the 1-ft
distance, because there is only one-ninth the illumination—the
total amount of light has been spread nine times as thin, if we may
use the expression.   *The illumination of a surface varies inversely
as the square of the distance from the light source.*   This is known
as the "law of inverse squares."   If a single light source gives

satisfactory illumination for a given job when it is located at a distance of 5 ft, a light source giving four times as many lumens will be required if it is moved to a distance of 10 ft, other conditions remaining the same. To determine the relative amount of illumination, simply divide the square of one distance by the square of the other. For example, comparing the relative illumination of an object 7 ft from a light source as compared with one 4 ft away,

$$\frac{4 \times 4}{7 \times 7} = \frac{16}{49} = 33\% \text{ (approx)}$$

The absolute degree of illumination at any given point, without regard to the power of the source from which the light comes, is measured in footcandles.

Law of Inverse Squares Is Treacherous. Later in this chapter there is described a simple instrument for measuring footcandles. Assume that such an instrument held 1 ft from a lighting fixture shows 160 footcandles. If it is held 2 ft away, according to the law of inverse squares, it should read 40 footcandles; 4 ft away it should read 10 footcandles; 10 ft away it should read 1.6 footcandles. It does not. Does that mean the law is no law at all, only a theory that does not work? Not at all.

The law is correct when all the light there is comes from one source and that source is dimensionally small (for example, a candle or a very small lamp) and further that none of the light from the source hits a surface and is then reflected back into the lightmeter. The trouble is that such conditions are rarely found. The meter measures not only the light from the fixture that you are thinking about but also light from other fixtures. It measures not only the light that comes directly from the fixture but also light that is reflected from ceilings and walls. Generally speaking the law of inverse squares can be confirmed by a footcandle meter only if the distance from light source to meter is at least five times the maximum dimension of the light source.

All that does not detract from the usefulness of the footcandle meter; it is a very convenient device and serves many useful purposes. More will be said about that later.

Footcandles. The footcandle is defined as the degree of illumination produced by a light source of one candlepower on a surface exactly one foot distant from the light source. Remembering the 2-ft sphere of earlier discussions, since every point on the inside is exactly 1 ft from the light source of 1 candlepower, it should be obvious that the surface will be uniformly illuminated to the extent of 1 footcandle.

Since this light source of 1 candlepower emits a total of 12.57 lumens of light and the 2-ft sphere has an area of exactly 12.57 sq ft, it should be equally obvious that it requires 1 lumen of light to produce a uniform illumination of 1 footcandle over an area of 1 sq ft. This is a most important relation to bear in mind: *One lumen of light per square foot produces illumination of one footcandle.* Likewise, 10 lumens per sq ft produce 10 footcandles; 100 lumens per sq ft produce 100 footcandles, and so on.

One point that often is misunderstood is the fact that the illumination in footcandles remains the same, no matter what the distance from the light source, as long as the number of lumens of light falling on each square foot does not change. This at first glance appears to be a complete contradiction of the law of inverse squares, but the following consideration should clarify it. Assume a reflector so perfect that it condenses *all* the light produced by a lamp producing 100 lumens into a narrow beam so that it illuminates a spot *exactly* 1 *sq ft in area* on a sheet of paper 10 ft from the lamp. The illumination on the spot will then be 100 footcandles. If now the sheet of paper is moved to a point 20 ft away, the beam will illuminate a spot 4 sq ft in area and the illumination will be only 25 footcandles. If, however, a different reflector is then substituted, producing a much narrower beam, so that at the new 20-ft distance the entire 100 lumens will again illuminate a spot only 1 sq ft in area, the illumination on the spot will again be 100 footcandles. As long as *all* the light produced by a source delivering 1 lumen falls on an area of 1 sq ft, that area is illuminated to 1 footcandle no matter what the distance. It is impossible in practice to concentrate light to this degree, for reflectors are not perfect, absorbing some light and allowing some also to spill in various directions. As a starting point, however, the relation can be considered correct. It is a most important rule, and most of this chapter up to this point has been written to help in a clear understanding of this fundamental: 1 *lumen of light on 1 sq ft of area produces 1 footcandle.*

To illustrate the utility of this rule, assume that an area 12 by 12 ft is to be lighted to 15 footcandles. Since the total area is 144 sq ft, it will require 144 lumens to provide 1 footcandle. Fifteen footcandles will require 144 × 15, or 2,160 lumens.

The approximate lumens produced by general-purpose incandescent lamps are as follows:

Watts	Lumens	Watts	Lumens
15	140	150	2,700
25	270	200	3,800
40	470	300	6,000
60	840	500	9,900
75	1,150	750	16,700
100	1,640	1,000	23,000

A 150-watt lamp delivering 2,700 lumens in a room 12 by 12 ft should therefore produce about 19 footcandles if all the light produced by the lamp could be directed to the floor and none allowed to fall on the ceiling or the walls. This is entirely a theoretical figure; the actual footcandles attained depend altogether on additional factors such as the reflector used with the lamp, the reflecting ability of ceilings and walls, the type of fixture used, and other factors which will be discussed later.

Do note, too, that fluorescent lamps produce more lumens per watt than ordinary incandescent lamps. Naturally, then, 150 watts of fluorescent lighting will produce more footcandles of illumination than 150 watts of ordinary lamps. This will be discussed in more detail later in this chapter.

Note that brightness and footcandles of illumination are not the same. A black sheet of paper illuminated to 10 footcandles will not seem so bright as a white one illuminated to 5 footcandles, because the white paper *reflects* a goodly portion of the light falling upon it while the black *absorbs* most of it.

A Few Yardsticks. To provide some starting point of known values in footcandles, bright sunlight on a clear day varies from 6,000 to 10,000 footcandles. In the shade of a tree on the same day there will be somewhere in the neighborhood of 1,000 footcandles. On the same day the light coming into a window on the shady side of a building will be of the order of 100 footcandles, while 10 ft back it will have dropped to something between 7 and 15 footcandles. At a point 4 ft directly below a 100-watt lamp without a reflector, and backed by a black ceiling and walls which have negligible reflecting power, there will be approximately 8 footcandles.

Measurement of Footcandles. Candlepower and lumens are not measurable in a simple fashion. Fortunately footcandles can

Fɪɢ. 14-3. This instrument reads footcandles of light directly on its scale. (*General Electric Co.*)

be measured as easily as reading a voltmeter. In Fig. 14-3 is shown a direct-reading footcandle meter, commonly known as a "lightmeter." Simply set the instrument at the point where the illumination is to be measured, and the footcandles are read directly on the scale. The device consists of a photoelectric cell, which is a device that generates electricity when light falls upon it. The indicating meter is simply a microammeter,[3] which measures the current generated, the scale being calibrated to read in footcandles. The use of this instrument is invaluable, especially in commercial work, as it takes the guesswork out of many lighting problems.

[3] A microampere is one-millionth of one ampere.

Footcandles Required for Various Jobs. It must be remembered that there can be no absolute standard. First of all, the requirements for different individuals vary. Furthermore, what was considered adequate yesterday is insufficient today; what we by compromise accept today will be considered too little tomorrow. Accordingly all that can be given are the commonly accepted standards of today. The more critical the task, the higher the level of illumination required. The more prolonged the task, the greater the amount of light needed; for example, you can quite easily read a paragraph of a newspaper in the relatively poor light of the dusk of evening, but it is almost impossible to read an entire page.

Today's standards are considerably higher than those of ten years ago. In homes, a minimum of 10 footcandles should be maintained in halls, on stairways, in the general areas of living rooms and dining rooms, and in similar locations. But that isn't enough for locations in those parts of rooms where reading or similar activities are pursued. For casual reading of newspapers, magazines, and books 30 footcandles should be provided; if there is much reading of handwriting, the minimum should be 50 footcandles. For prolonged studying, 75 footcandles would be a wise minimum. Sewing requires from 50 to 200 footcandles; the finer the work and the darker the material, the more light is needed.

In the kitchen and laundry consider 30 footcandles the minimum, with about 50 footcandles in areas where cooking, dishwashing, and ironing are done. The bathroom should have 30 footcandles for general illumination and at least 50 footcandles at the mirror for make-up and shaving.

In nonresidential locations the requirements vary greatly from one type of work to another. In offices the recommended minimum varies from 50 to 200 footcandles, depending on the particular type of work; in stores it varies from 50 to 500 footcandles, depending on the particular area under consideration. This will be discussed in more detail in later chapters concerning various types of buildings and kinds of work.

Will these levels be considered correct ten years from now? Probably not. Much progress has been made in recent years in bringing the general level of illumination upward. Many thousands of offices, for example, now provide 50 footcandles, but still more thousands struggle along with lower levels. Those who have changed have discovered that the added cost is many times offset by increases in efficiency of the work force.

Glare. Because so much space has been devoted to the amount or degree of illumination, do not for a moment think that this is the one all-important factor in good lighting. It is only one of four factors. Another important factor is that the light must be free from glare.

Glare, generally speaking, is caused by a relatively bright area within an area illuminated to a lower level. An exposed lamp in the lobby of a motion-picture theater is not particularly noticeable when one enters during daylight, because the eyes are accustomed to the outdoor brightness; when one leaves, after the eyes are accustomed to the relatively dark interior, the lamp will appear very bright, will glare and hurt the eyes. Similarly a lighted automobile headlight is barely noticeable in daylight but may be blinding at night. General Electric Co. in their pamphlet "Fundamentals of Illumination" (from which many of the illustrations of this chapter have been borrowed) define glare as "any brightness within the field of vision of such a character as to cause annoyance, discomfort, interference with vision, or eye fatigue."

Glare is usually caused by exposed lamps so placed that they can be seen while we look at the object we primarily want to see; the lamp may not be directly visible, but even if it is so placed that it can be seen by merely moving the eyes without moving the head, it still produces glare. Bright automobile headlights constitute a good example of this type of glare. Figure 14-4 shows an example of extreme glare found when using exposed lamps, while Fig. 14-5 shows what can be accomplished by modern lighting. Note the absence of glare and shadows.

Glare of an equally objectionable type may be caused by reflection, for example from glass tops on desks. Glass is a good reflector, and the reflected image of a lamp may appear almost as bright as the lamp itself. For this reason glass tops have largely disappeared from the desks of executives. Likewise fewer and fewer highly polished and plated parts are being used on typewriters, office machinery, and other devices because manufacturers have learned that glare causes the evils recounted above.

Fig. 14-4. Exposed lamps cast harsh shadows and cause extreme glare. Efficient work is not possible with such lighting. (*General Electric Co.*)

with resultant lower efficiency. For this reason, too, printers have learned to avoid papers that are extremely glossy, reflecting too much undiffused light (see the examples shown in Fig. 14-6).

How to Avoid Glare in Lighting. Everyone has tried reading in direct sunlight and found it difficult. On the other hand it is not difficult to read in the shade of a tree on a bright day, even

Fig. 14-5. The shop of Fig. 14-4 now reequipped with modern glare-free lighting. (*General Electric Co.*)

if there the footcandles are much lower than in the direct sunlight. Therefore the answer cannot lie only in the footcandles of illumination prevailing at any given moment.

The answer does lie in the fact that direct sunlight comes essentially from a single point, the sun, and causes glare. In the shade of a tree the light comes from no point in particular but rather from every direction—north, south, east, west, and above. Not coming from one point, it does not cause harsh shadows or glare. It is *diffused light*.

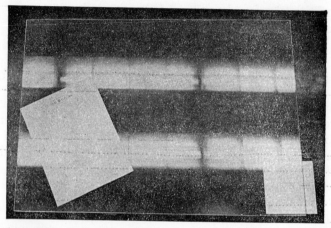

Fig. 14-6. Glass desk tops and glossy paper are both sources of glare. (*General Electric Co.*)

In lighting a home or office, the more the lighting can be made to duplicate the conditions of the shade of a tree, the better the lighting will be. Someday in the future there will be a way of having at least the ceilings of rooms give off light of low intensity but sufficient total volume to eliminate the need for lighting fixtures. A reasonable approach to that solution is the "luminous ceiling" consisting of translucent plastic squares or rectangles, with fluorescent tubes properly spaced above them so that there is uniform, even light from the entire ceiling.

Surface Brightness. When looking at an exposed 300-watt lamp of the clear-glass type, you see a concentrated filament less than an inch in diameter. The lamp itself is a little over 4 in. in diameter, but because the filament is so bright, the glass bulb itself is almost invisible. That is why practically all lamps today are frosted—the filament is not seen, but rather the entire bulb. Since the bulb has a diameter of about 4 in., there is exposed to the eye an apparent area equivalent to the area of a circle of the same diameter, or about $12\frac{1}{2}$ sq in. The same total amount of light, which in the case of the clear-glass bulb was concentrated in an area of about 1 sq in., is now distributed over a much larger area of about $12\frac{1}{2}$ sq in. Obviously, then, while the total amount of light is the same, the brightness of the larger area is greatly reduced—the "surface brightness" is lower. It is still uncomfortably bright if looked at directly.

Put the lamp inside a globe of translucent, nontransparent glass about 8 in. in diameter; this has an apparent area of about 50 sq in. altogether instead of the $12\frac{1}{2}$ sq in. observed before. The total amount of light is still the same, but it is far more comfortable to the eye because the surface brightness of the light source has been reduced still more. Consider the most common fluorescent lamp: It is the 40-watt type and is 48 in. long. The surface brightness is very low because the total surface area of the tube is very large for the amount of light emitted and there are no bright spots.

For comfortable lighting, use light sources that have low surface brightness.

Direct and Indirect Lighting. When light in a room is produced by fixtures that do not let any of the light fall on the ceilings and walls but instead throw all the light directly on the area to be lighted, the method is called direct lighting. When the light is produced by fixtures that throw all the light on the ceiling, which reflects it to the areas to be lighted, the method is called indirect lighting.

An extreme but completely impractical example of *direct* lighting would be to mount automobile headlights on the ceiling, shining down toward the floor. Such lighting would create extreme glare, sharp shadows, and uneven levels of light and would be very poor lighting—direct lighting of the worst kind. But it should not be supposed that direct lighting can't be made quite effective in stores and similar locations, particularly with flush fixtures in the ceiling, provided that objects below and the floor are of a light color so as to reflect the light upward, and provided that the ceiling is of a light color.

An extreme and again totally impractical example of *indirect* lighting would again involve automobile headlights, now mounted high enough on the wall so that they could not shine directly into your eyes, and with their beams thrown against the ceiling, to be reflected downward. It would provide very bright spots on the ceiling and very uneven lighting in the area below—it would be indirect lighting of the worst kind. Indirect lighting of all kinds is very inefficient, but in establishments other than homes can be made quite effective by properly designed fixtures that distribute the light properly on the ceiling, which must be of a light color.

Good lighting in homes is neither completely direct nor completely indirect. Most light sources let some of their light fall on the ceiling, some on the areas below. Indeed that is what we are looking for in good lighting. In general, the entire area of a room (including ceilings and walls) must be lighted to a reasonable degree; smaller areas must be lighted to much higher intensities for reading and other activities that require more light for comfort and efficiency. In some rooms ceiling fixtures provide light for general seeing and floor and table lamps provide the light for reading and similar work; in other rooms only such lamps are used. Such lamps, however, do not throw all their light downward; a considerable part goes upward to the ceiling. Whatever the light source, a reasonably even distribution of light is important for comfort and a room of pleasing appearance: no very dark areas, nor areas of extreme brightness as compared with other nearby areas.

Fixtures for Homes. When a room is lighted with fixtures using exposed lamps, of the general type shown in Fig. 14-7, most people think of it as direct lighting. It is a combination of direct and indirect, for a good deal of the light produced falls on the ceiling and is then reflected. But for most purposes it is not good lighting because the exposed lamps have high surface brightness, leading to great contrast with their immediate surroundings and much glare. Because the light comes from one point, such fixtures do not produce diffused shade-of-the-tree light that is so comfortable to the eyes.

The simple one-lamp fixture of Fig. 14-7 on the other hand is justifiable in attics, halls, and other little-used areas, where light is used for casual illumination and not for reading or other work where good lighting is essential.

FIG. 14-7. Fixtures with exposed lamps do not provide good lighting. They are acceptable for such locations as halls.

In general, fixtures so designed that you can *not* see the lamps are to be preferred. Naturally the room in which the fixture is to be used will determine the general type of the fixture. For kitchens and bedrooms, fixtures with one to three lamps are often used, ceiling-mounted. These can be of the general type shown in Fig. 14-8, with shaded lamps. Some of the light falls directly

FIG. 14-8. Fixtures on which the lamps can not be seen provide light that is more diffused, which is better for the eyes.

on the ceiling, some is reflected from the glassware to the ceiling, and some of the light goes directly downward. The combination eliminates dark areas on the ceiling, eliminates extremely bright spots on the fixture, and produces generally diffused light which is easy on the eyes. Whether any given fixture produces enough light in any given area will depend on the wattage of the lamps used in the fixtures.

In larger rooms, again, fixtures with a number of lamps may be used, of the general type shown in Fig. 14-9, but be sure the lamps are shaded from direct view.   One-lamp fixtures of the general type of Fig. 14-10 are quite popular.   In this type of fixture perhaps half of the light goes downward through the glass or plastic shade; it is diffused as it goes through, so that with well-designed units there are no dark spots below the fixture, nor any extremely bright spots on the shade to produce glare.   Much of the light is reflected to the ceiling, thence is reflected throughout the room, thus approaching the desired shade-of-the-tree type of light. Fig-

Fig. 14-9. On this fixture the lamps are shaded, and provide diffused light.

Fig. 14-10. Fixtures using a single large lamp produce more light *per watt* than fixtures with a number of smaller lamps.

ure 14-11 shows why the light seems to fill the room instead of coming from one point.   Note the path of individual rays of light.   The solid lines show what their paths would be if ceilings and walls were absolutely smooth like a mirror.   While a plaster wall may seem very smooth, it will, if examined under a magnifying glass, be found to be uneven, full of hills and dales.   Therefore the rays, as they strike any one point, strike these hills and dales and are reflected in every direction; what would otherwise be individual rays split up into a multitude of rays (as shown in the dotted lines) giving truly diffused lighting.

All that has been said refers to fixtures using ordinary incandescent lamps.   In kitchens and other areas where their appearance is acceptable, fluorescent fixtures will provide up to three times more light per watt; be sure to select a type which permits part of the light to strike the ceiling so that there will not be any dark, dismal areas on the ceiling.

Sometimes, of course, efficiency and good lighting can be overlooked, as when the fixture is selected for its decorative value rather than as a light-producing means. The use of a beautiful crystal chandelier in a dining room is entirely justifiable, especially since it without a doubt produces better lighting than the wax candles sometimes preferred by our wives.

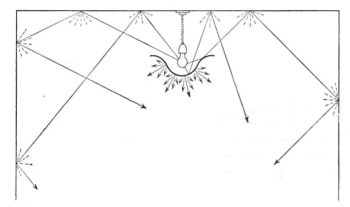

Fig. 14-11. This diagram illustrates how light becomes diffused as it is reflected from ceiling and walls.

Reflection. If the ceiling and walls of the room were mirrors, obviously a very great percentage of the light striking the ceiling and walls would be reflected downward. However, there would be direct reflections of the lamp, and the glare would be as bad as from an exposed lamp. On the other hand, if the ceiling were black, most of the light would be absorbed and little reflected, and the lighting would be inefficient indeed. Accordingly, for best results, the ceiling and walls should be a color that reflects as much light as possible, and at the same time the finish should be dull or flat rather than glossy, so as to avoid the mirror effect, with bright spots producing glare.

Experiment has shown that various colors of paint reflect light

in various degrees, the percentages reflected being of the order of
the following:

White	80 to 85%
Ivory	70 to 80%
Cream	65 to 75%
Buff	55 to 65%
Gray	35 to 50%
Light blue	35 to 50%
Light green	30 to 40%
Dark green	15 to 25%
Red	15 to 25%
Dark blue	10 to 20%
Brown	8 to 12%
Black	2 to 5%

Woods in natural finish seldom reflect over 50%, and the darker
woods may fall as low as 15%.

Shadows. When we read in direct sunlight, the extreme glare
makes reading uncomfortable. Moreover, the reader's own
shadow on the reading material is extremely sharp; the contrast
between bright light and sharp shadow is most annoying and
tiring. In the shade of a tree the footcandle level is much lower,
but reading is more comfortable: The light is diffused; shadows
are soft and not objectionable. Two sources of light, for example a floor lamp and an overhead fixture, lead to greater comfort
in reading. Use fixtures or lamps that provide diffused light, light
that seems to come from many points, as in the shade of a tree.

Color of Light. Sunlight has come to be accepted by most
people as a standard, although the color and the quantity vary
greatly, depending on the hour of the day and on the season. It
may seem strange to speak of the "color" of sunlight, which appears colorless, yet sunlight is composed of a mixture of all colors.
The rainbow is simply a breaking down of sunlight into its separate colors.

What makes one object red and another object blue when this
mixture of all colors which we call sunlight hits these objects?
The explanation is simple. When "white" light strikes certain
objects, the component colors are all reflected equally, and we call
such objects white. When white light hits other objects, the light
instead of being reflected is absorbed and we see no light; we
then say that such objects are black.

Still different objects may absorb some of the colors of the spectrum, reflect the others. For example, they may absorb all except the red and reflect that. We then see only the red part, so we say such objects are red. So with every other color: whatever the color of the object, that is the color that the object can reflect; all the other colors are absorbed and destroyed.

Everybody has observed that the color of an object appears different when observed in natural light as compared with artificial light. What causes this? Light produced by incandescent lamps does not have the same proportion of colors as exists in natural light; it has more orange and red and less of the blue and green. It is not surprising, then, that efforts have been made to produce special lamps that more nearly duplicate the mixture and proportions of colors existing in natural light. The effort has led to lamps that approximate the light from a northern sky rather than direct sunlight. Such lamps are called "daylight type" and in one brand are called "coloramic sky blue." Use such lamps when color comparisons are important; don't use them for general lighting because they are not as efficient as ordinary lamps—they produce less light per watt. In the fluorescent type the "de luxe cool white" is best suited for the purpose.

Life of Lamps. The life of ordinary filament lamps is from 750 to 1,000 hr. It is a simple matter to make lamps that last longer, but in doing so their efficiency is reduced; the lamp will produce less light, fewer lumens per watt. A 60-watt lamp costing 25 cents uses 60 kwhr of energy during its 1,000-hr life. At 3 cents per kilowatthour, the cost of the energy used is therefore $1.80, as compared with the 25-cent cost of the lamp itself. If, then, to obtain longer life in a 25-cent lamp, we reduce the efficiency, an extra 50 cents may be spent for electric power to produce the same amount of light, and expense rather than economy results.

Where no great amount of light is needed and the lamp serves merely as a signal, for example in pilot lights, the lamp may be designed to last 2,000 hr or more; on the other hand, where a great deal of light is needed and where it is important to limit the heat, for example in lamps for motion-picture projectors, the lamp may be designed for a relatively short life but with corresponding increase in efficiency, thus permitting smaller wattage lamps producing less heat to be used. For example, a 1,000-hr 1,000-watt lamp produces about 23 lumens per watt, but a 50-hr lamp of the same wattage produces about 28 lumens per watt, while a photoflood lamp of the same approximate wattage, but only 10-hr life, produces roughly 31 lumens per watt.

Effect of Voltage on Lamp Life. If a lamp is operated at a voltage below that for which it was designed, its life is prolonged considerably, but the watts, the lumens, and the lumens per watt drop off rapidly. If it is operated at a voltage above normal, its life is greatly reduced, although the watts, the lumens, and the lumens per watt increase. For lowest over-all cost of illumination use lamps on a circuit of the voltage for which they were designed.

Careful study of the following table will confirm these statements. If a lamp is burned at the voltage for which it is designed, it will have characteristics shown in the line labeled 100%. If it is burned at a voltage higher or lower than its design voltage, the various factors will change to a new value shown as a percentage of normal. . . . .

Circuit voltage as percentage of rated voltage of lamp	Total average life, hours	Total output, lumens	Actual watts	Lumens per watt
85%	800%	58%	78%	72%
90%	400%	68%	85%	80%
95%	200%	83%	93%	90%
100%	100%	100%	100%	100%
105%	58%	118%	108%	109%
110%	37%	140%	116%	120%
115%	18%	162%	124%	131%

As an example, an ordinary 100-watt lamp designed for use on a 120-volt circuit will when burned at 120 volts have a life of about 750 hr, produce 1,640 lumens, and consume 100 watts, resulting in 16.4 lumens per watt. If burned at 108 volts (90% of 120 volts), it will have a life of about 400%, or 3,000 hr; produce

68% of 1,640 lumens or 1,115 lumens; and consume 85% of normal, or 85 watts, resulting in 80% of normal efficiency, or about 13.1 lumens per watt.

Occasionally there will be applications where it is entirely in order to use lamps on a voltage considerably above that for which they were designed. There may be conditions when a great deal of light is needed, but for only short periods, as, for example, in temporary floodlights for athletic fields. By using 115-volt lamps on a 130-volt circuit (or 110-volt lamps on a 125-volt circuit), the amount of light secured *per watt* is increased by about

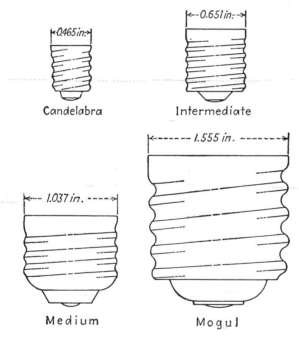

Fig. 14-12. The screw-shell bases used on lamps are standardized to the dimensions shown. The illustrations are actual size.

25%. The fact that the lamp will last only about 220 instead of 1,000 hr is immaterial when weighed against the extra cost of larger reflectors, floodlights, and larger temporary power lines to accommodate the larger lamps that would otherwise be needed.

Bases. There are various standardized sizes of bases in use, matched to the watts and the physical size of the lamp. In the

screw-shell type the largest is the mogul, used mostly on lamps
from 300 watts upward; its dimensions are shown in Fig. 14-12,
together with the dimensions of other standard bases. The medium is used on ordinary household lamps. Smaller lamps use
the intermediate and the candelabra. Flash-
light and similar lamps use the miniature,
which is still smaller.

Another base used on high-wattage lamps
is the bipost of Fig. 14-13. The prefocus
base of Fig. 14-14 is used mostly on lamps for
projectors and maintains the lamp in one particular position which gives maximum light
in one direction. Both of these types are
available in two sizes: medium and mogul.

Fig. 14-13. The bi-
post type of base is
used on some
larger lamps. (Gen-
eral Electric Co.)

A three-light lamp is merely a lamp with two separate filaments,
say 100 and 200 watts, with a special base so arranged that either
filament alone or both at the same time can be used, producing
100, 200, or 300 watts as desired. The construction is shown in
Fig. 14-15.

Fig. 14-14. The
prefocus base is
used on lamps for
projection pur-
poses. (General
Electric Co.)

Lamp Designations. The mechanical size
and shape of a lamp are designated by standardized abbreviations such as A-19, PS-35,
F-15, etc. The letter designates the shape in
accordance with the outlines shown in Fig.
14-16. The numeral designates the diameter
in eighths of an inch. Thus an A-19 lamp has
the simple A shape and is 1%, or 2%, in. in
diameter.

Lumiline Lamps. This type of lamp, shown in Fig. 14-17, was
once quite common; today it is used mostly for replacement purposes. Instead of having a base with two contacts, it has a single
contact cap at each end, with a continuous filament from end to
end. This makes the lamp usable only in a fixture designed for it.

Reflector Lamps. Special lamps with a silver reflector on the
outside or inside of the bulb are available for floodlighting and
spotlighting purposes. While used in homes for lighting walks,
yards, and so on, they are more generally used in commercial and
industrial lighting, and therefore they will be described in
Chap. 30.

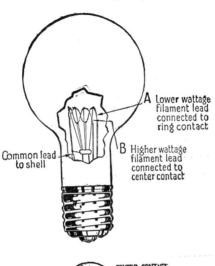

Common lead to shell

A Lower wattage filament lead connected to ring contact

B Higher wattage filament lead connected to center contact

SHELL

CENTER CONTACT

RING CONTACT

END VIEW OF BASE

FIG. 14-15. Construction of 3-light lamp. (*General Electric Co.*)

Efficiency of Various Sizes of Lamps. Larger lamps produce more light per watt, so that generally speaking, when there is a choice, it is desirable to use one large lamp rather than several smaller ones. Study the table below, which is based on general-purpose lamps of present manufacture.

Size of lamp, watts	Total lumens	Lumens per watt
25	270	10.8
40	470	11.8
60	840	14.0
75	1,150	15.3
100	1,640	16.4
150	2,700	18.0
200	3,800	19.0
300	6,000	20.0
500	9,900	19.8

Study of this table will show that one 150-watt lamp gives as much light as ten of the 25-watt size; one 300-watt lamp gives as much light as seven of the 60-watt size.

Efficiency of the Various Colors of Lamps.   There is no difference in efficiency between a lamp with a clear-glass bulb and one of the inside-frosted type.   The latter provides light that is better diffused than is the case in the clear-glass type.   A new trend is away from the inside-frosted type to a still newer type

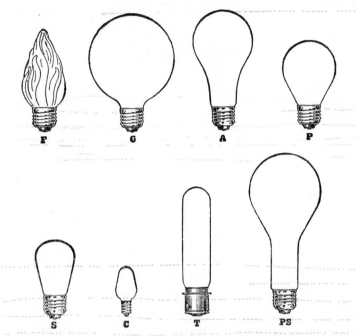

Fɪɢ. 14-16. The shape of lamps is well standardized.   (*General Electric Company.*)

Fɪɢ. 14-17. Lumiline lamps have a contact at each end.   (*General Electric Co.*)

with a translucent, milky-color internal silica coating that diffuses the light still more, resulting in less glare with no appreciable difference in efficiency.

However, incandescent lamps that produce colored lights are very inefficient. The coloring material simply absorbs most of the light produced by the lamp; only that portion which matches the color of the bulb is transmitted. For this reason colored lamps should not be used except for their decorative value.

Fluorescent Lighting. This form of lighting is relatively new, having been introduced commercially in 1938. The fluorescent installation is familiar to all, but few understand its method of operation, which is quite complex as compared with that of an ordinary incandescent (filament-type) lamp.

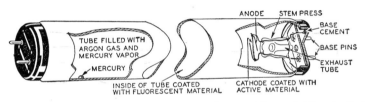

Fig. 14-18. Construction of a fluorescent lamp. (*General Electric Co.*)

In the ordinary incandescent lamp, a filament made of tungsten wire is heated by an electric current flowing through it until it reaches a high temperature, when it emits light. It operates by its terminals being connected to two wires of an electric circuit of the proper voltage.

The fluorescent lamp consists essentially of a glass cylinder called the "tube," with a filament at each end. The filaments are not connected to each other in the lamp. Each filament is brought out to two pins on the end, as shown in Fig. 14-18. The inside of the glass tube is coated with a whitish or grayish powder, called a "phosphor." The air has been pumped out of the tube, and a carefully determined amount of a gas called argon is introduced. A very small amount of mercury is also put into the tube. That is the basic machinery of a fluorescent lamp, but if it is connected directly to the ordinary 115-volt circuit, it will not operate.

If a fluorescent lamp is connected to a source of high-voltage current, the lamp will light up but will be quickly destroyed. If it is connected to a source of high-voltage current and just at the instant of starting the voltage is reduced to 115 volts, it will still be destroyed. Apparently then some special accessories are required to make the fluorescent lamp operate.

Figure 14-19 shows the basic scheme. The secret of operation consists of two devices: a ballast or choke coil, and an automatic switch, called a starter. Any coil of wire wound on an iron core has two peculiarities: (1) When connected to an alternating-current circuit, it tends to resist any change of current flowing through it, and (2) when a current flowing through it

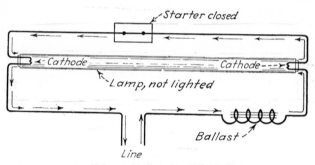

FIG. 14-19. Flow of current in a fluorescent lamp circuit at the instant when the light is first turned on.

is cut off, it delivers momentarily a voltage much higher than the voltage applied to it. The ballast for a fluorescent lamp is just such a coil. The automatic switch is so designed that it is ordinarily closed (while the lamp is turned off), but when the lamp is turned on, the switch opens a second or two after the current starts to flow and then stays open until the lamp is turned off again.

Visualize then what happens. Start with Fig. 14-19, which snows the circuit just as the lamp is turned on. Current flows as indicated by the arrows, through the ballast, through one filament, or "cathode" as it is called in the case of the fluorescent lamp, through the automatic switch or "starter," through the other filament or cathode, and back to the line. During this period the lamp glows at each end but does not light. Then the automatic switch opens, and the ballast does its trick—it delivers a high voltage as mentioned in the previous paragraph, a voltage considerably above 115 volts and high enough to start the lamp. The current can no longer flow through the switch because it is open; it then flows through the tube, jumping the gap and forming an arc inside the glass tube, following the arrows of Fig. 14-20 (in both Figs. 14-19 and 14-20 the current flows first in the direction indicated by the arrows, then in the opposite direction, because the current involved is alternating current). The ballast then performs its other function: It limits the current flowing through the lamp to a predetermined safe value.

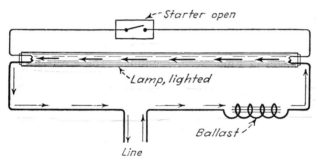

Fig. 14-20. Flow of current through a fluorescent lamp after it has started. The automatic "starter" has now opened, and the current cannot flow through it.

How does the current jump from one end of the tube to the other? It is a complicated story, and yet it is, in some ways, simple. The filaments or cathodes of coiled tungsten wire are coated with a chemical which when heated emits electrons, particles so small that billions of them laid side by side would still be invisible, being actually basic negative charges of electricity. They shoot out into space as popcorn does in a corn popper; they travel more easily through argon gas than through a vacuum, which is the reason that gas is introduced. A stream of these particles constitutes an electric current, which heats the argon, which heats the mercury to become mercury vapor, which then becomes the path for a heavier electric current.

If a fluorescent lamp such as just described had a wall of clear glass, an insignificant amount of light would be visible, and yet the fluorescent lamp as installed produces a great deal of visible light. The answer lies in the fact that the electric arc through the mercury vapor produces only a slight amount of *visible* light but a great deal of *invisible* ultraviolet light.

The inside of the tube is covered with a layer of chemicals that become fluorescent or light-producing when exposed to ultraviolet light. In other words, invisible ultraviolet light striking fluorescent chemicals makes the chemicals glow brightly, producing visible light. The particular chemical used determines the color of the light.

The exact scientific principles that govern the emission of electrons from a heated coated filament, the creation of the arc, the production of ultraviolet light by the arc, and the creation of visible light when invisible ultraviolet light strikes certain chemicals had best be left to the chemists and engineers.

Advantages of Fluorescent Lighting. The greatest single advantage of fluorescent lamps lies in their efficiency. Per watt of power used, they produce two to three[4] times as much light as ordinary incandescent lamps. Their life is much longer than that of incandescent lamps. Being more efficient, they produce much less heat, which is important when larger amounts of power are used for lighting, especially if the lighted area is air conditioned.

Another major advantage is that the lamp, being of relatively large size (in terms of area in square inches compared with the total light output), has relatively low surface brightness, which in turn leads to less glare, less shadow; all contributing to better seeing, and less eyestrain. The surface brightness being low, there is less need for enclosing glassware; thus the cost of installation and upkeep is reduced.

Disadvantages of Fluorescent Lighting. Ordinary incandescent or filament-type lamps operate in any temperature. Fluorescent lamps are somewhat sensitive to temperature. The ordinary type used in homes will operate in temperatures down to about 50°F. For industrial and commercial areas other types are available that will operate at lower temperatures, some as low as −20°F.

In the case of filament lamps, as the voltage is reduced, the

[4] In the case of certain colors, the fluorescent lamp produces over 100 times as much light per watt as an incandescent lamp.

light output drops off much faster than the voltage. However, even at greatly reduced voltages the filament still glows, producing some light. In the case of fluorescent lamps, as the voltage is reduced, the light output also drops off, but not so fast as in the case of the filament lamps. However, if the voltage is greatly reduced, the lamps go out completely, long before a filament lamp ceases to glow. Therefore, ordinary fluorescent lamps cannot be used where there are frequent violent fluctuations in voltage. Special voltage-regulating ballasts are available for such locations, however, so that fluorescents need not be ruled out completely.

Life of Fluorescent Lamps. The life of ordinary *incandescent* lamps is from 750 to 1,000 hr; it does not make an appreciable difference whether the lamp is burned continuously or turned on and off many times during its life. A *fluorescent* lamp that is turned on once and never turned off until the end of its useful life will probably last far in excess of 10,000 hr. If it is turned on and off every 5 min, it may not last 500 hr. The answer lies in the fact that there is a specific amount of electron-emitting material on the filaments or cathodes; a specific part of it is consumed each time the lamp is started; when it is all gone, the lamp is inoperative. It is not possible to predict the exact number of starts the lamp will survive, and ordinary operation between starts also consumes some of the material, but the fact remains that the oftener a fluorescent lamp is turned on, the shorter its life will be. Under ordinary operation, its life will probably be at least six or seven times that of the incandescent lamp.

Rating of Fluorescent Lamps. An ordinary *incandescent* lamp marked "40 watts" will consume 40 watts when connected to a circuit of the proper voltage. A *fluorescent* lamp rated at 40 watts also will consume 40 watts within the lamp, but actually an additional wattage is consumed by the ballast; this additional wattage is 15 to 30% of the wattage consumed by the lamp proper and must be added to the wattage of the lamp to arrive at the total wattage of the combination.

Power Factor of Fluorescent Lamps. Ordinary *incandescent* lamps have a power factor of 100%. A single *fluorescent* lamp connected to a circuit has a power factor of somewhere between

50 and 60%. Assume 100 lamps rated at 40 watts, connected singly to a 115-volt circuit. The ballast for each lamp can be expected to consume approximately 8 watts. The total for each combination is 48 watts, and for 100 such lamps, the total is 4,800 watts. The amperage consumed by these 100 lamps and their ballasts is, however, not 4,800/115, or 42 amp, as might be expected, but rather (assuming a power factor of 60%) 4,800/(115 × 0.60), or 4,800/69, or approximately 70 amp. Therefore the wiring serving this load must be capable of carrying 70 amp rather than a theoretical 42 amp.

Fortunately this is not so serious as it sounds. The common method is to have either two or four lamps per fixture and, in addition to the usual ballast, to use power-factor-correction devices built into the same case with the ballast, which bring the power factor up to about 90% or better.

Unfortunately, however, not all two- or four-light fixtures on the market are of the high-power-factor type. The subject is introduced so that due caution may be exercised when making a purchase to make sure the high-power-factor type is procured. This is especially important when making commercial or industrial installations, where the power company exacts an entirely justifiable penalty when the power factor of an installation is low.

Sizes of Fluorescent Lamps. The lamps most commonly used in homes are those listed below. Note that the wattage consumed by the ballast is *not* included in the column headed "watts."

Designation	Length, inches	Diameter, inches	Watts	Total lumens	Lumens per watt
T-8	18	1	15	750	50
T-12	24	1½	20	1,030	52
T-8	36	1	30	1,900	63
T-12	48	1½	40	2,800	70

In addition to those listed above, the Circline lamps of the type shown in Fig. 14-21 are frequently used in fixtures and lamps where a long, straight lamp would not fit. They are available in three sizes: 22-watt, 8¼ in. outside diameter; 32-watt, 12 in. diameter; and 40-watt, 16 in. diameter.

Other Types of Fluorescent Lamps. The lamps just discussed are the kind commonly used in homes, and, of course, they are used in other locations too. For nonhome use there are several other types of fluorescent lamps, and these will be discussed in Chap. 30. Let it be noted too that the circuit of Figs. 14-19 and 14-20 is that of a single lamp. More complicated circuits are used when the fixture has two or more lamps.

Color of Light from Fluorescent Lamps. Everyone has noticed that the colors of flowers, clothing, and so on look different under

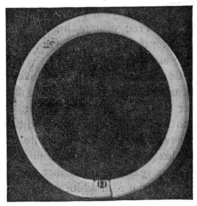

Fig. 14-21. The "circline" fluorescent lamp comes in three diameters and finds application in floor lamps and lighting fixtures. (*General Electric Co.*)

ordinary filament lamps than in natural sunlight. Ordinary filament lamps produce light that is rich in red.

The color of the light produced by fluorescent lamps is determined entirely by the chemical and physical composition of the "phosphor" or powder which is deposited on the inside surface of the tube. The most ordinary color is "white," but there are many varieties of it, among them de luxe warm white (also called "Homeline"), warm white, white, cool white, and de luxe cool white. The differences lie in the proportion of red and blue in the light produced by the respective lamps. The "warm" varieties emphasize the red and green (like light from ordinary incandescent lamps), while the "cool" varieties emphasize the blue (more like natural sunlight). The kind of "white" to use depends on the effects desired.

If you look at a "black-and-white" printed page under each of the "white" colors in turn, you will see little difference. But if you look at a colored page, colored fabrics, or food under each kind in turn, you will see much difference.

Under de luxe cool white, people's complexions will appear much as in natural light, but the Homeline or de luxe warm white will flatter them a bit, adding a ruddy or tanned appearance (much as is done by ordinary incandescent lamps). The cool white gives quite a good appearance also, but with a slight tendency toward paleness.

As to home furnishings, if your preference leans toward those that have warm colors (red, orange, brown, tan), use Homeline or de luxe warm white; if you prefer the cool colors (blue, green, yellow), use the de luxe cool white.

It must be mentioned here that the "de luxe" varieties are not nearly so efficient as the others; they produce about 25% less light per watt of power used. If then you want maximum efficiency and are willing to sacrifice good color rendition a bit, use the warm white in place of the de luxe warm white, and the cool white in place of the de luxe cool white. This difference in efficiency is probably the major reason for the fact that about 75% of all fluorescents sold are of the cool-white variety.

Most sizes of fluorescent lamps are available also in such colors as blue, green, pink, gold, and red. Their efficiency in colors is extraordinarily high; for example, the fluorescent lamp produces about 100 times as much green light per watt as is produced by incandescent or filament lamps. These colored lamps find a particular application where spectacular color effects are needed, for example, in theater lobbies, lounges, stage lighting, advertising, and similar purposes.

Luminescent Lighting. This paragraph could equally correctly be headed "The Light of the Future" or "Things to Come." A new kind of lighting called "electroluminescent" is under development. No bulbs or tubes are involved. It has been found that if two conducting surfaces (one of them transparent) are laid parallel and very close together and the space between filled with the correct chemical powder, the powder will glow and produce light when an alternating-current voltage is applied to the two surfaces. See Fig. 14-22, which shows the basic construc-

tion.   Flat light-producing areas of considerable size can be made
in this way.   The color and intensity of the light can be controlled by changing the voltage and the frequency of the applied power.

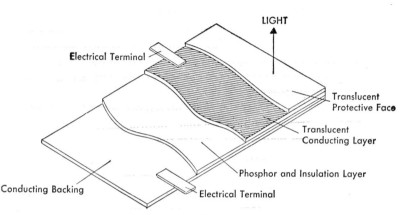

Fig. 14-22. Cross section of luminescent panel. (*General Electric Co.*)

However, it is not likely that this new method will come into
common use in the near future, for the cost of the material is very
high and its efficiency exceedingly low.   If you were tempted to
install such lighting for general use in a room, you would find the
initial cost from twenty to fifty times as much as for a good fluorescent installation and your power bill at the end of the month
would probably be fifty times as high as for the fluorescent lighting.   Nevertheless, this kind of lighting is used where only a
minute quantity of light is needed, as, for example, on clock faces
or radio dials.

Chapter 15

RESIDENTIAL AND FARM MOTORS

A working man can deliver no more than $\frac{1}{10}$ to $\frac{1}{8}$ hp continuously over a period of several hours. If the man is paid $2 an hour, it costs at least $16 for a horsepower for an hour. At average rates an electric motor will deliver a horsepower for an hour for 5 cents. The motor costs little to begin with. It will operate equally well on a hot day or a cold day. It never gets tired, and costs nothing except while running. It uses electricity only in proportion to the power it is called upon to deliver. With reasonable care, it will last for many years.

A later chapter will cover the wiring of industrial motors; this chapter will cover only ordinary wiring of the type needed in homes and on farms. However, a discussion of the characteristics and limitations of the types in common use should be in order here.

How Motors Are Rated. A motor is rated in horsepower. This means that (except for special-purpose motors) it will deliver the horsepower stamped on its name-plate hour after hour, all day and all week without a stop, if necessary.

Starting Capacity. Motors deliver far more power while starting than after they are up to full speed. The proportion varies with the type of motor; some types have starting torques four or five times greater than at full speed. Naturally the watts consumed during the starting period are much higher than while the motor is running at full speed. That means the motor will heat up quickly if it does not reach full speed because of too heavy starting load. Therefore the right kind of motor must be used for each machine, depending on how easy or how hard it is to start that machine. This will be explained later in this chapter.

Overload Capacity. Almost any good motor will for short periods develop from 1½ to 2 times its normal horsepower without harm. Thus a 1-hp motor is usually able to deliver 1½ hp for perhaps a quarter of an hour, 2 hp for a minute, and usually even 3 hp for a few seconds without harm. Of course, no motor should be deliberately overloaded continuously, but this ability of a motor to deliver more than its rated horsepower is most convenient. For example, in sawing lumber, ½ hp may be just right, but when a tough knot is fed to the saw blade, the motor will instantly deliver, if needed, 1½ hp, dropping back to its normal ½ hp after the knot has been sawed. A water-pressure system in a suburban home or on a farm may be properly equipped with a ½-hp motor. When the motor is first turned on, with no pressure in the water tank, the pump may require a good deal less than ½ hp. As the pressure in the tank builds up, the horsepower required also gradually increases. Just before the automatic pressure switch cuts off the motor as a 40-lb pressure is reached in the tank, the motor will be delivering a good deal more horsepower than in the beginning of the running cycle, possibly as much as ¾ hp. The motor with its overload capacity automatically takes care of the problem.

Gasoline Engines vs. Electric Motors. A gasoline engine is rated at the maximum power it can deliver *continuously*. Thus, an engine rated at 5 hp can deliver 5 hp continuously, but unlike an electric motor, it cannot, even for a short time, deliver more than 5 hp. This explains why it is often possible to replace a 5-hp engine with an electric motor sometimes as small as 2 hp. If the engine being replaced always runs smoothly with little effort, if it seldom labors and slows down, it can be replaced with an electric motor of much smaller horsepower. If, on the other hand, the engine is always laboring at its maximum output, then the motor that replaces it should be of the same horsepower as the engine, because no motor should be expected *continuously* to deliver more than its rated horsepower.

Power Consumed by a Motor. The watts drawn from the power line by a motor are in proportion to the horsepower it is delivering. The approximate figures for a 1-hp motor are as follows:

While starting	4,000 watts
While idling	200 watts
While delivering ¼ hp	400 watts
While delivering ½ hp	600 watts
While delivering ¾ hp	800 watts
While delivering 1 hp	1,000 watts
While delivering 1½ hp	1,500 watts
While delivering 2 hp	2,000 watts
While delivering 2½ hp	2,600 watts
While delivering 3 hp	3,300 watts

Motors are designed to operate at greatest efficiency when delivering their rated horsepower; while they are delivering more or less power, the efficiency usually falls off. In other words, it costs a little more per hour to run a 1-hp motor at half load than it does to run a ½-hp motor at full load. The 1-hp motor, while delivering only ½ hp, as per table above, consumes about 600 watts; a ½-hp motor delivering ½ hp consumes about 525 watts. In the long run therefore, especially if the motor must run many hours, it will be less costly to have a small motor for a small load than to run a small load with a big motor that you may happen to have handy.

Speed of AC Motors. The most common 60-cycle AC motor runs at a theoretical 1,800 rpm but at an actual speed of 1,725 to 1,750 rpm while delivering its rated horsepower (the horsepower stamped on its name-plate). When the motor is overloaded, the speed drops further. If the overload is increased too far, the motor will stall; it will burn out if not quickly removed from the line. Low voltage also reduces the speed.

Motors of other speeds are built, running at theoretical speeds of 900, 1,200, and 3,600 rpm, actual speeds a little lower. These cost more; in case of motor failure, they are hard to replace quickly because they are seldom stocked, which makes it necessary to change pulleys and belts and leads to similar inconveniences. Use an 1,800-rpm motor wherever it is at all possible. If a very slow speed is needed, use a motor which runs at 1,800 rpm but has built-in gears which cut the speed of the drive shaft to a much lower figure.

The speed of ordinary alternating-current motors *cannot be controlled* by rheostats, switches, or similar devices. Special variable-speed motors are obtainable, but they are very expensive special-purpose motors and will not be discussed here.

Temperature Rise in Motors. All electrical devices heat up in use; motors are no exception. However, if a well-designed motor is run continuously, delivering its full rated horsepower (the horsepower stamped on the name-plate), the temperature of the motor will not increase by more than 40°C or 72°F [1] over and above room temperature. On a hot summer's day the temperature of the air in an enclosed pump house, for example, may be as high as 110°; add to this the 72° rise and you have a total of 182°, not far below the boiling point of water. This will feel decidedly hot to the hand but will be entirely safe as far as the motor is concerned. Install motors so that air can get at them for cooling.

Types of Single-phase Motors. There are three common types of motors designed for single-phase work, and these will be described separately in the following paragraphs.

Split-phase Motors. This type of motor operates only on single-phase alternating current. It is the most simple type of motor made, which makes it relatively trouble-free; there are no brushes, no commutator. It is available only in sizes of ⅓ hp and smaller. It draws a very heavy amperage while starting. Once up to full speed, this type of motor develops just as much power as any other type of motor, but it is not able to start heavy loads. Therefore it should never be used on any machine which is hard to start, such as a deep-well water pump or an air compressor that has to start against compression. It can be used on any machine which is easy to start or on one where the load is thrown on after the machine is up to full speed. It is entirely suitable for washing machines, grinders, saws and lathes, and general utility use. It can be used on paint sprayers which do not start against compression but not on those that start against pressure.

Capacitor Motors. This type of motor also operates only on single-phase alternating current. In construction it is quite simi-

[1] Do not confuse *change* in readings of thermometers with their *actual* readings. When a centigrade thermometer reads 40°, a Fahrenheit thermometer reads 104°. While a centigrade thermometer changes by 40°, the Fahrenheit changes by 72°. Thus, if the centigrade changes from 40 to 80°, the Fahrenheit changes from 104 to 176° (by 72°).

lar to the split-phase type, with the addition of a "capacitor" or a "condenser" which enables it to start much harder loads. There are several grades of capacitor-type motors available, ranging from the home-workshop type, which starts loads from $1\frac{1}{2}$ to 2 times as heavy as the split phase, to the heavy-duty type, which will start almost any type of load whatever. Capacitor motors usually are also more efficient than split phase, using fewer watts per horsepower. The amperage consumed *while starting* is about half that of the split-phase type. Capacitor motors are made in any size but are commonly used only in sizes up to $7\frac{1}{2}$ hp.

Repulsion-start, Induction-run Motors. Most people call this type of motor simply an R-I motor. It operates only on single-phase AC current. It has a very large starting ability and should be used for the heavier jobs; it will "break loose" almost any kind of hard-starting machine. The starting current is the lowest of all types of single-phase motors. It is available in sizes up to 10 hp.

Dual-voltage Motors. Most AC motors rated at $\frac{1}{2}$ hp or more are so constructed that they can be operated on either of two different voltages: 115 or 230 volts. Single-phase motors of this type have four leads; Connected one way, the motor will operate at 115 volts; connected differently, the motor will operate at 230 volts (see Fig. 15-1).

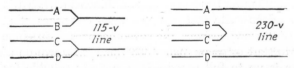

FIG. 15-1. Many motors are so constructed that they may be operated at either 115 or 230 volts, depending upon the connection of the four leads as shown in the diagrams above. It is always wise to operate such motors at 230 volts if possible.

If the motor is of the dual-voltage type, that is, if it will operate on either 115 or 230 volts, two different voltages and amperages are shown on the name-plate. For example, it may be marked: "Volts 115/230, Amps 24/12." This simply indicates that, while delivering its rated power, it will consume 24 amp if operated at 115 volts or 12 amp if operated at 230 volts.

Three-phase Motors. This type of motor, as the name implies, operates only on 3-phase alternating current. Three-phase motors in sizes ½ hp and larger cost less than any other type, so by all means use them if you have 3-phase current available. Do not assume that because you have a 3-wire service you have 3-phase current; more likely you have 3-wire 115/230-volt single-phase current. If in doubt, see your power company.

Direct-current Motors. Direct current is found in the downtown sections of such larger cities as New York and Chicago and also in a few small towns. All 32-volt farm lighting plants are direct current, as are a few of the 110-volt models. There are numerous types of direct-current motors, such as the series, the shunt, the compound, and others. However, too few direct-current motors are in use to warrant a detailed discussion of each type here.

One important difference in operating characteristics between an alternating-current and a direct-current motor should be discussed. An ordinary alternating-current motor is designed to run at a specific speed, usually between 1,725 and 1,750 rpm, even with considerable fluctuations of voltage and load. Regardless of voltage, the motor will not run faster than its design speed. Its speed cannot be controlled either by a rheostat or by any other device.

A direct-current motor on the other hand, even if designed for 1,800 rpm, will run at that speed only with a particular combination of voltage and load. If the voltage changes, the speed changes; if the load changes, the speed changes. Excess voltage will make it run at more than 1,800 rpm. Moreover, its speed can easily be controlled by a rheostat, although once adjusted, it will again change with any change in voltage or load.

Universal Motors. This type of motor operates on either direct current or single-phase alternating current of 60 cycles or any other frequency. However, it does not run at a constant speed but varies over an extremely wide range. Idling, a universal motor may run as fast as 15,000 rpm, while under a heavy load the same motor may slow down to 500 rpm. This, of course, makes the motor totally unsuitable for general-purpose work. It is used only when built into a piece of machinery where the load is constant and definitely predetermined. For example, you will find this motor on your vacuum cleaner and your sewing machine, on some types of fans, on electric drills, etc.

Reversing Motors. The direction of rotation of a repulsion-induction motor can be changed only by shifting the position of the brushes. On other types of single-phase alternating-current motors it is changed by reversing two of the wires coming from the inside of the motor. If a motor must be reversed often, a special switch can be installed for the purpose.

Problems with Large Motors. The largest single-phase motor easily available has a rating of 7½ hp, although larger ones up to and including 20 hp are in use in a few localities. But before buying a motor of 5 hp or larger size, check with your power company or REA to make certain whether that motor is usable on your power line.

The maximum size of motor that can be used depends on the size of the transformer serving your farm. Whether your power company will furnish you with a transformer big enough to operate a 10-hp motor will probably depend on how many hours a year you plan to use the motor. They will probably object to installing the larger transformer if you intend to use the motor only a comparatively few hours, just as the farmer would object to buying a 10-ton truck just because 10 tons had to be hauled occasionally, with the usual load only a ton or two.

What then is the farmer to do? The answer is to use smaller machines. For example, instead of a large hammer mill which requires 10 or 15 hp to operate, use a smaller mill which requires only 3 to 5 hp. Small hammer mills which are very efficient are now available, having more capacity *per horsepower* than the larger mills. Even ear corn can be ground with as little as 2 hp. The smaller machine may have to be operated more hours altogether, but it may require fewer men to operate, costs less to begin with, and costs less to operate because the smaller machine has more capacity per horsepower.

Care of Motors. Motors require very little care. The most important is proper oiling of the bearings. Use a very light machine oil, such as SAE No. 10, and use it sparingly—most motors are oiled too much. Never oil any part of the motor except the bearings; under no circumstances put oil on the brushes, if your motor has brushes.

If your motor has a commutator and brushes, occasionally while the motor is running, hold a very fine piece of sandpaper (never emery) against the commutator to remove the carbon that has worn off the brushes. *Be sure you are standing on something absolutely dry to avoid shock.*

Bearings. In most commonly used motors, there is a choice of sleeve bearings or ball bearings. If the motor is to be operated with the shaft in the ordinary horizontal position, there is no need for ball bearings. If the motor is to be operated with the shaft in an up-and-down position, ball bearings should be used because the usual sleeve-bearing construction lets the oil run out. Ball bearings are also better able than sleeve bearings to absorb the weight of the rotor. Ball bearings of some types are filled with grease and permanently sealed, thus doing away with the nuisance of greasing. If this type is purchased, be sure the bearings are double-sealed, that is, with a seal on each side of the balls. Some bearings are sealed on only one side, so that the grease can still get out on the other side.

Pulleys and Belts. Even though the figuring of proper pulley ratios is not a wiring problem, a short discussion of this subject should not be amiss. In such calculations four factors are involved:

Motor pulley diameter.
Machine pulley diameter.
Motor speed.
Machine speed.

If any of the four is unknown, it is a simple matter to figure it from the three known factors, using the formulas below:

$$\text{Machine pulley diam} = \frac{\text{motor pulley diam} \times \text{motor speed}}{\text{machine speed}}$$

$$\text{Machine speed} = \frac{\text{motor speed} \times \text{motor pulley diam}}{\text{machine pulley diam}}$$

$$\text{Motor pulley diam} = \frac{\text{machine pulley diam} \times \text{machine speed}}{\text{motor speed}}$$

$$\text{Motor speed} = \frac{\text{machine speed} \times \text{machine pulley diam}}{\text{motor pulley diam}}$$

In making the calculations indicated above, remember that there is always some belt slippage for which allowance must be made. For motor speed use the actual speed that the motor will develop under full load.

The ratio between the diameters of the driving and the driven pulleys should be kept within reasonable limits. If one pulley is a great deal larger than the other, especially if they are close together, the belt will make contact with but a small portion of the total circumference of the smaller pulley and slippage will be increased. The ratio should not exceed 12 to 1 in small motors; for a 1-hp motor, 10 to 1 is usually considered the practical limit, decreasing to 8 to 1 in the case of a 5-hp motor and 5 to 1 in the case of a 25-hp motor.

Especially for small fractional-horsepower motors the use of V belts is very common. They have the advantage of being relatively inexpensive, have little slip even on small pulleys, and carry substantial loads on even the smallest size. As the load increases above ½ hp, it is often the custom to use two or more such belts side by side on multiple-groove pulleys. Avoid the use of very small diameter pulleys. Their use leads to excessive belt slippage, short belt life, and loss of power.

A common mistake is to run belts too tight. This only increases the load on the motor, causes excessive bearing wear and short belt life.

The table on the next page should be used in determining pulley sizes for any given machine. It is based on a motor speed of 1,750 rpm, and some allowance has been made for belt slippage. Figures show speed of machine with each combination of pulley diameters.

Wiring for Motors. The Code sections that govern the installations of motors are extremely complicated, for they cover all motors from the tiniest to those developing hundreds of horsepower. The wiring of motors *for homes and farms,* however, can be covered by a few simple rules. Three points especially must be observed:

1. Overcurrent protection.
2. Disconnecting switch for motor.
3. Wire sizes.

Table of Machine Speed.

Diam motor pulley	Diameter of pulley on machine, inches														
	1¼	1½	1¾	2	2¼	2½	3	4	5	6½	8	10	12	15	18
1¼	1,725	1,435	1,230	1,075	950	850	715	540	430	330	265	215	175	140	115
1½	2,075	1,725	1,475	1,290	1,140	1,030	850	645	515	395	320	265	215	170	140
1¾	2,400	2,000	1,725	1,500	1,340	1,200	1,000	750	600	460	375	315	250	200	165
2	2,775	2,290	1,970	1,725	1,530	1,375	1,145	850	685	530	430	345	285	230	190
2¼	3,100	2,580	2,200	1,930	1,725	1,550	1,290	965	775	595	485	385	325	255	215
2½	3,450	2,870	2,460	2,150	1,900	1,725	1,435	1,075	850	660	540	430	355	285	240
3	4,140	3,450	2,950	2,580	2,290	2,070	1,725	1,290	1,070	800	615	515	430	345	285
4	5,500	4,575	3,950	3,450	3,060	2,775	2,295	1,725	1,375	1,060	860	700	575	460	375
5	6,850	5,750	4,920	4,300	3,825	3,450	2,865	2,150	1,725	1,325	1,075	860	715	575	475
6½	8,950	7,475	6,400	5,600	4,975	4,480	3,730	2,790	2,240	1,725	1,400	1,120	930	745	620
8	....	9,200	7,870	6,900	6,125	5,520	4,600	3,450	2,750	2,120	1,725	1,375	1,140	915	765
10	....	....	9,850	8,620	7,670	6,900	5,750	4,300	3,450	2,650	2,150	1,725	1,430	1,140	950
12	....	....	....	....	9,200	8,280	6,900	5,160	4,130	3,180	2,580	2,075	1,725	1,375	1,140
15	....	....	....	....	....	....	8,635	6,470	5,170	3,970	3,230	2,580	2,150	1,725	1,425
18	....	....	....	....	....	....	....	7,750	6,200	4,770	3,880	3,100	2,580	2,070	1,725

Overcurrent Protection in Motor Branch Circuit. Bear in mind the fundamental fact that any motor consumes more amperes while *starting* than while *running*. For example, an ordinary washing-machine motor may consume 25 amp while *starting*, but only 5 amp while *running* and delivering its normal horsepower. It is capable of delivering for short periods considerably more than its rated horsepower, but if it is overloaded to do so, it will consume correspondingly more current. If considerably overloaded, it may draw as much as 10 amp. It will not be harmed if it delivers normal horsepower (consuming 5 amp) all day long, nor will it be harmed if it delivers considerably in excess of its normal horsepower (and consuming 10 amp) for short periods, but it will burn out if it is required to deliver considerable overloads (and consuming 10 amp) for a considerable period of time.

The wire to the motor must then be big enough to carry its *starting* current momentarily, its running current continuously, and its normal running current plus a considerable overload for short periods. It must be protected accordingly. Consider then a washing-machine motor which normally consumes about 5 amp. While starting, it consumes about 25 amp. The ordinary branch circuit is wired with No. 14 wire and is protected with 15-amp fuses. This fuse will frequently blow on 25 amp while the motor is starting. Therefore, for those circuits which serve motors, it is wise to use circuit breakers, or time-delay fuses of an amperage rating determined by the size of the wire in the branch circuit. Fuses of this type were shown in Figs. 5-2 and 5-10. As a matter of fact, the Code in Sec. 430-42(d) requires the use of this type of fuse when motors are on the circuit.

Components of Motor Circuit. In addition to the overcurrent protection in the branch circuit serving the motor, three additional components are required.

1. *Controller:* to start and stop motor. This can be a manually operated device, such as a switch, or an automatically operated one, such as a pressure switch on a pump, a thermostat on a refrigerator or furnace, and so on.

2. *Running-overcurrent protection:* to protect the motor against overload. The circuit breaker or fuse in the branch circuit that serves the motor protects the circuit, not the motor; its rating depends on the size of the wire in the circuit. Consider a washing-machine motor normally consuming about 5 amp. Suppose the belt on the motor is too tight or the bearings "freeze" for lack of oil. Either condition requires extra power, and the motor, instead of consuming 5 amp, may consume 10 amp or even more. The 15-amp overcurrent protection in the branch circuit will not protect the motor, and it will burn out. Therefore it is wise to provide separate protection for the motor. The Code requires it on

a. All motors larger than 1 hp.
b. All motors 1 hp or less if automatically started.
c. All manually started motors if the motor cannot be seen from the controller or if it is located more than 50 ft from the controller.

3. *Disconnecting means:* to disconnect the motor totally from the circuit. This becomes necessary when working on the motor or the machinery which it drives, to guard against accidental starting, which would be dangerous.

Two or all three of these requirements are often combined into a single device. The Code requirements for these things are quite complicated and a separate chapter, Chap. 31, will discuss them for all motors. For the ordinary motors found in homes and on farms, the essential points will be discussed here.

Automatically Started Motors. The controller will be built into the machinery that the motor drives. Sometimes the overcurrent protection will also be built in. Provide a disconnect switch of the general type shown in Fig. 15-2. If the motor is smaller than 2 hp, the switch may be one rated in amperes, but the ampere rating must be at least *twice* the amperage of the motor. For larger motors use a similar switch rated in horsepower, not less than the horsepower rating of the motor. For a 115-volt motor, use a switch with one fuse; for a 230-volt motor, use one with two fuses.

FIG. 15-2. A switch of this type may be used with small motors. If the switch has two fuses, it is for a 230-volt motor; if it has only one fuse, it is for a 115-volt motor. (*Clark Controller Co.*)

If the motor has built-in overcurrent protection, the fuses in this switch may be of the same rating as the fuses protecting the branch circuit. If the motor does not have built-in overcurrent protection, the fuses must be of a rating not more than 125% of the amperage stamped on the name-plate of the motor. However, if the calculation results in a fuse of a nonstandard rating, this may be increased to 140%. In any event use time-delay fuses.

A circuit breaker may be used instead, of an amperage rating determined in the same way as for fuses.

The switch (or circuit breaker) then serves as the disconnecting means and also as running overcurrent protection.

Manually Started Motors. The simplest arrangement is to use an ordinary switch of the general type shown in Fig. 15-2. Determine its type, rating, and the amperage of the fuses in it exactly as in the case of the automatically started motor just discussed. The switch will then serve as controller, overcurrent protection, and disconnecting means. A circuit breaker may be used instead.

A separate controller or starter of the general type shown in Fig. 15-3 is generally used. For fractional-horsepower motors the small starter shown is used; it is operated by moving the handle just as on an ordinary toggle switch. As a matter of fact, it isn't much larger than an ordinary switch. For larger motors, use the larger starter shown in the same illustration. Start and stop buttons are built into the cover; they can also be placed at a distance from the starter. The principles of operation will be discussed in Chap. 31.

Starters of this type have the running-overcurrent protection built into them; each starter must be selected to match the amperage of the motor with which it is to be used. However, they will not serve the purpose of the disconnecting means, so a switch of the general type of Fig. 15-2 must be installed ahead of the starter. Such a switch may be unfused, but unfused switches are

Fig. 15-3. Controls of the type shown not only start and stop a motor but also protect it against overloads. (*Allen-Bradley Co.*)

sometimes hard to locate, so use a fused switch with fuses of an amperage not exceeding that of the overcurrent protection in the branch circuit. A circuit breaker may be used in place of the switch.

Wire Sizes. First of all, extension cords made of ordinary No. 18 or 16 lamp cord should never be used, even on small fractional-horsepower motors. A short cord on the motor is in order, but if a longer extension is added, the voltage drop in the cord during the starting period while the amperage is high is apt to be so great that the motor never gets off its starting windings. A damaged motor may easily result. The wire must be heavy enough to carry the starting amperage, and the horsepower of the motor and the distance involved must also be taken into consideration.

The Code requires that the wire must have a carrying capacity
equivalent to at least 125% of the name-plate amperage of the
motor.

For convenience the table below has been worked out. Under
each size of wire is given the maximum distance for which that
size of wire should be used if maximum efficiency of the motor
is expected. This table is calculated for *single-phase* AC motors.
The table is not applicable to 3-phase motors.

Motor			Wire sizes								
Horse-power	Volts	Am-peres	14	12	10	8	6	4	2	1/0	2/0
1/4	115	5.8	55	90	140	225	360	575	900	1,500	1,800
1/3	115	7.2	45	75	115	180	300	450	725	1,200	1,590
1/2	115	9.8	35	55	85	140	220	350	550	850	1,100
3/4	115	13.8	25	40	60	100	150	250	400	600	800
1	115	16.0	—	35	50	85	130	200	325	525	650
1 1/2	115	20.0	—	25	40	65	100	170	275	425	550
2	115	24.0	—	—	35	55	85	140	225	350	450
3	115	34.0	—	—	—	40	60	90	160	250	325
1/4	230	2.9	220	360	560	900	1,450	2,300	3,600		
1/3	230	3.6	180	300	460	720	1,200	1,600	2,900		
1/2	230	4.9	140	220	340	560	875	1,400	2,200		
3/4	230	6.9	100	160	240	400	600	1,000	1,600	2,400	
1	230	8.0	85	140	200	340	525	800	1,300	2,100	
1 1/2	230	10.0	70	110	160	280	400	675	1,100	1,700	2,200
2	230	12.0	60	90	140	230	350	550	900	1,400	1,800
3	230	17.0	—	65	100	160	250	400	650	1,000	1,300
5	230	28.0	—	—	60	100	160	250	400	650	800
7 1/2	230	40.0	—	—	—	70	110	175	275	450	550
10	230	50.0	—	—	—	—	90	140	225	350	450

Figures below the wire sizes indicate the *one-way* distance in feet (not the number of feet
of wire in the circuit) that each size wire will carry the amperage for the size motor indicated
in the left-hand column, with 1½% voltage drop. A dash indicates that the wire size in
question is smaller than the minimum required by the Code for the horsepower involved,
regardless of circumstances. Figures are based on single-phase AC motors.

The table is based on 1½% voltage drop, and assumes that the
motor is not overloaded. Most motors are overloaded to some

degree during some portion of their normal running cycle, so that the drop will probably be more nearly 2% during part of the cycle. Moreover, all motors consume many more amperes while starting than they do while running at full speed. During the starting cycle the drop may be as much as 6 or 8%. Too much drop during the starting period prolongs the starting period, leading to excessive heating. If the motor must start exceptionally hard-starting loads, too much drop may prevent the motor from reaching full normal speed, which could lead to motor burnouts.

If in doubt as to the right wire size, use the next larger size.

Part 2

ACTUAL WIRING:
RESIDENTIAL AND FARM

Part 2 of this book explains the actual wiring of houses and farm buildings of every description. The author feels that it will be much easier for you to study first these relatively simple installations than it would be if one chapter pertaining to one particular phase of the work included everything from a simple cottage up to an elaborate project.

All the fundamentals covered by Part 2 will in practice also be used in the bigger projects. They are the foundation for the more complicated methods to be covered by Part 3, which covers the wiring of larger industrial and similar projects.

Chapter 16

PLANNING AN INSTALLATION

The plans for an electrical installation usually consist of outline drawings of the rooms involved, with indications where the various outlets for fixtures, receptacles, and other devices are to be located. Obviously a *picture* of a switch, a receptacle, or other device cannot be shown on the plans at each point where one is to be used. Standardized symbols are used instead.

Symbols. In Fig. 16-1 are shown the older symbols that were used for many years, and in Fig. 16-2 the revised symbols. It is necessary to be familiar with both, and since the differences are not great, no particular difficulty should be experienced. Each symbol must instantly indicate as much as if a picture of the device in question were shown. Throughout this book, where such symbols are required, the new recommended types are used rather than the old standard.

In plans using these symbols, wires are indicated only to connect switches with the outlets they control. Only a single line is drawn to represent all the wires that may be required. Unless otherwise specified, it is still the contractor's problem to determine which outlets go on each circuit and exactly how the different wires are to run.

Typical Plans. Consider first a very simple plan, covering a small three-room cottage with two circuits, involving one ceiling outlet controlled by a wall switch for each of the three rooms, with three receptacle outlets for the larger room and one for each of the smaller rooms. The service entrance is 2-wire 115-volt only. The plan for this installation is shown in Fig. 16-3.

To make it easier to interpret this plan, Fig. 16-4 shows the same layout in pictorial fashion, with all the wires shown in detail.

OLD STANDARD SYMBOLS FOR ELECTRICAL EQUIPMENT OF BUILDINGS

Ceiling outlet..................	⌀
Ceiling lamp receptacle—specification to describe type such as key, keyless, or pull chain..	Ⓡ
Ceiling outlet for extensions.....	Ⓔ
Ceiling fan outlet...............	∞
Floor outlet....................	⊕
Drop cord.....................	Ⓓ
Wall bracket...................	⌀
Wall outlet for extensions.......	Ⓔ
Wall fan outlet.................	⅋
Wall lamp receptacle—specification to describe type such as key, keyless, or pull chain.	Ⓡ-
Single convenience outlet........	⊝
Double convenience outlet.......	⊝₂
Junction box...................	Ⓙ
Special-purpose outlet—lighting, heating, and power as described in specification..............	Ⓐ
Special purpose outlet—lighting, heating, and power as described in specification..............	⊗
Special-purpose outlet—lighting, heating, and power as described in specification..............	⊖
Exit light.....................	⊗-
Floor elbow....................	○ᴱ
Floor tee......................	○ᵀ
Pull switch....................	⬥ₚ.ₛ.
Local switch—single-pole........	S¹
Local switch—double-pole.......	S²
Local switch—3-way............	S³
Local switch—4-way............	S⁴
Automatic door switch..........	Sᴰ
Motor........................	◎
Motor controller...............	M.C.
Lighting panel.................	▬
Power panel...................	▨
Heating panel.................	◣

Pull box......................	▨
Cable-supporting box...........	⊞
Meter........................	⊟
Branch circuit, run concealed under floor above............	───
Branch circuit, run exposed......	----
Branch circuit, run concealed under floor.................	─ ∙ ─
Feeder run, concealed under floor above.................	───
Feeder run, exposed...........	∙∙∙∙
Feeder run, concealed under floor......................	── ──
Pole line.....................	⊶⊷
Push button...................	▣
Buzzer.......................	◻
Bell..........................	⌂
Annunciator..................	◇
Interior telephone.............	◁
Public telephone..............	◀
Maid's plug...................	M
Clock (secondary).............	⊕
Electric door opener...........	▣
Watchman station.............	W
Watchman central station detector......................	W
Special outlet for signal system as described in specification...	⊠
Battery......................	⊦⊢⊦⊢⊦
Signal wires in conduit concealed under floor.................	───
Signal wires in conduit concealed under floor above............	───
This character marked on tap circuits indicates 2 No. 14 conductors in ½-in. conduit (see note).................	▯
3 No. 14 conductors in ½-in conduit....................	▯▮
4 No. 14 conductors in ¾-in. conduit unless marked ½-in..	▮ ▮
5 No. 14 conductors in ¾-in. conduit...................	▮▮▮

NOTE.—If larger conductors than No. 14 are used, use the same symbols and mark the conductors and conduit size on the run.

FIG. 16-1. Old symbols used in plans.

NEW STANDARD SYMBOLS FOR ELECTRICAL EQUIPMENT OF BUILDINGS

Ceiling Wall

GENERAL OUTLETS

Ceiling	Wall	
O	-O	Outlet.
Ⓑ	-Ⓑ	Blanked Outlet.
Ⓓ		Drop Cord.
Ⓔ	-Ⓔ	Electrical Outlet; for use only when circle used alone might be confused with columns, plumbing symbols, etc.
Ⓕ	-Ⓕ	Fan Outlet.
Ⓙ	-Ⓙ	Junction Box.
Ⓛ	-Ⓛ	Lamp Holder.
Ⓛₚₛ	-Ⓛₚₛ	Lamp Holder with Pull Switch.
Ⓢ	-Ⓢ	Pull Switch.
Ⓥ	-Ⓥ	Outlet for Vapor Discharge Lamp.
Ⓧ	-Ⓧ	Exit Light Outlet
Ⓒ	-Ⓒ	Clock Outlet. (Specify Voltage)

CONVENIENCE OUTLETS

Duplex Convenience Outlet.

Convenience Outlet other than Duplex. 1 = Single, 3 = Triplex, etc.

Weatherproof Convenience Outlet.

Range Outlet.

Switch and Convenience Outlet.

Radio and Convenience Outlet.

Special Purpose Outlet. (Des. in Spec.)

Floor Outlet.

SWITCH OUTLETS

S	Single Pole Switch.
S₂	Double Pole Switch.
S₃	Three Way Switch.
S₄	Four Way Switch.
Sₚ	Automatic Door Switch.
Sₑ	Electrolier Switch.
Sₖ	Key Operated Switch.
Sₚ	Switch and Pilot Lamp.
Sᴄʙ	Circuit Breaker.
Sᴡᴄʙ	Weatherproof Circuit Breaker.
Sᴍᴄ	Momentary Contact Switch.
Sʀᴄ	Remote Control Switch.
Sᴡᴘ	Weatherproof Switch.
Sꜰ	Fused Switch.
Sᴡꜰ	Weatherproof Fused Switch.

SPECIAL OUTLETS

Oₐ,ᵦ,c,etc / ₐ,ᵦ,c,etc / Sₐ,ᵦ,c,etc Any Standard Symbol as given above with the addition of a lower case subscript letter may be used to designate some special variation of Standard Equipment of particular interest in a specific set of Architectural Plans.

When used they must be listed in the Key of Symbols on each drawing and if necessary further described in the specifications.

PANELS, CIRCUITS, AND MISCELLANEOUS

Lighting Panel.

Power Panel.

Branch Circuit; Concealed in Ceiling or Wall.

Branch Circuit; Concealed in Floor.

Branch Circuit; Exposed.

Home Run to Panel Board. Indicate number of Circuits by number of arrows.

Note: Any circuit without further designation indicates a two-wire circuit. For a greater number of wires indicate as follows: ─╫╫─ (3 wires) ─╫╫╫─ (4 wires), etc.

Feeders. Note: Use heavy lines and designate by number corresponding to listing in Feeder Schedule.

Underfloor Duct and Junction Box. Triple System. Note: For double or single systems eliminate one or two lines. This symbol is equally adaptable to auxiliary system layouts.

Ⓖ	Generator.
Ⓜ	Motor.
Ⓘ	Instrument.
Ⓣ	Power Transformer. (Or draw to scale.)
⊠	Controller.
⊐	Isolating Switch.

AUXILIARY SYSTEMS

▪	Push Button.
◿	Buzzer.
◖	Bell.
─◇	Annunciator.
◀	Outside Telephone.
◁	Interconnecting Telephone.
◁	Telephone Switchboard.
Ⓣ	Bell Ringing Transformer.
D	Electric Door Opener.
FⒹ	Fire Alarm Bell.
F	Fire Alarm Station.
⊠	City Fire Alarm Station.
FA	Fire Alarm Central Station.
FS	Automatic Fire Alarm Device.
W	Watchman's Station.
W	Watchman's Central Station.
H	Horn.
N	Nurse's Signal Plug.
M	Maid's Signal Plug.
R	Radio Outlet.
SC	Signal Central Station.
▭	Interconnection Box.
⊣⊢⊣⊢	Battery.

Auxiliary System Circuits. Note: Any line without further designation indicates a 2-Wire System. For a greater number of wires designate with numerals in manner similar to ─── 12-No. 18W-3/4" C., or designate by number corresponding to listing in Schedule.

Special Auxiliary Outlets. Subscript letters refer to notes on plans or detailed description in specifications.

Symbols in accordance with American Standards Association Standard ASA Z32.9-1943.

FIG. 16-2. New symbols used in plans.

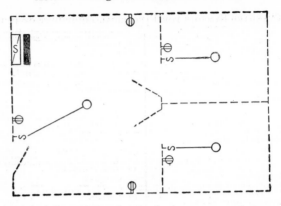

FIG. 16-3. Layout of a simple three-room project.

The neutral wire is shown as a light line; the "hot" wires as heavy lines. Note how the neutral wire runs without interruption from the point where it enters the building to each device where current is to be used. The black wires run from their fuses direct to each receptacle outlet and to each switch; an additional length runs from each switch to the light it controls, and that completes the wiring.

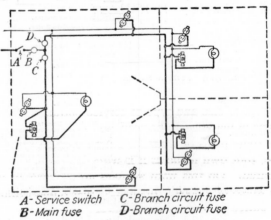

A- Service switch   C- Branch circuit fuse
B- Main fuse   D-Branch circuit fuse

FIG. 16-4. The layout shown in Fig. 16-3, but here indicated in pictorial fashion.

A represents the main switch. B represents the main fuse. C and D represent the two fuses, one for each branch circuit. The first branch circuit comprises all the wiring served by the current that flows through fuse *C*; the second circuit comprises all wiring served by the current that flows through fuse *D*.

The complete wiring plans for a larger house are shown in Figs. 16-5 to 16-8. These diagrams[1] may at first sight seem rather formidable, but with study they become simple. Such plans are supplemented by detailed written specifications which give such

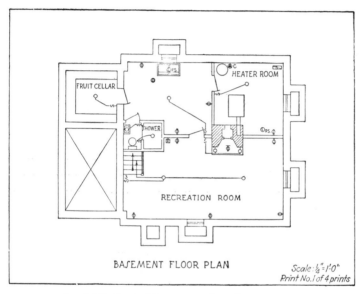

FRUIT CELLAR

HEATER ROOM

SHOWER

RECREATION ROOM

BASEMENT FLOOR PLAN

Scale: 1/4" = 1'0"
Print No.1 of 4 prints

FIG. 16-5. Typical basement plan of a residence.

information as size and type of service entrance, number of circuits, type of materials to be used, and similar data.

Make some plans of a similar nature of other installations, for example, your own home as it is wired and as you would like to see it wired. Do this until symbols are as clear to you as the printed words of a book. Remember that *round* symbols always denote outlets served by the full voltage of the wiring system; *square* symbols always denote outlets operating at low voltage, for example, bells, buzzers, etc. Solid lines denote wires in ceilings or walls; dotted lines denote wires under the floor.

[1] Reproduced by permission from the "Handbook of Interior Wiring Design," by the Industry Committee on Interior Wiring Design.

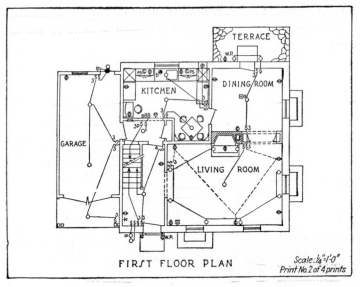

Fig. 16-6. Typical first-floor plan of a residence.

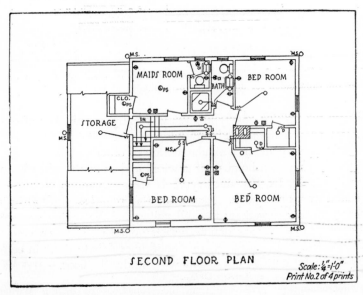

Fig. 16-7. Typical second-floor plan of a residence.

Making Plans. Often the electrician may be called upon to make the plans for a job instead of finding them ready-made. In that case include all those details found in plans of the type shown in Figs. 16-5 to 16-8. Likewise include in the specifications such things as the size of service-entrance wires and

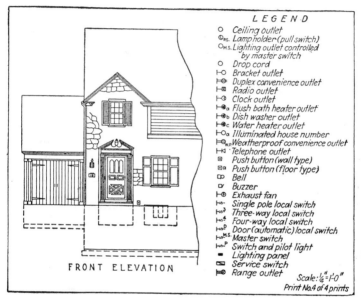

FRONT ELEVATION

FIG. 16-8. Typical front elevation, also legend of plan for a residence. Note the explanation for outlets *a, b, c.*

switch, the number of circuits, the location of circuit breakers or service switch and fuse panels, material to be used, and similar details.

In making such plans there is usually little choice except to follow the general ideas of the owner as to the number of outlets and similar details. On the other hand, the average homeowner knows very little about things electrical, with the result that his specifications may result in an installation that is far from adequate. Explain to your customer what advantages there are for him in an adequate installation, and it will mean a larger sale for you and a better satisfied customer.

Chapter 17

INSTALLATION OF SERVICE ENTRANCE
AND GROUND

Chapter 13 covered the selection of the proper service-entrance wires, the rating of the service switch, and similar essentials. This chapter will cover the actual installation of the materials selected. Many variations are possible in the selection of mechanical arrangement and the different parts; the service-entrance wires may come in through conduit, in the form of service-entrance cable, or underground; the meter may be outdoors or indoors; the branch-circuit overcurrent equipment may be circuit breakers or fuses; main overcurrent protection may or may not be required.

We shall now have to assume that you have already decided the question of 2- or 3-wire, the amperage capacity of the service and the size of the wire you are going to use, the number of branch circuits, whether circuit breakers or fused equipment is to be used, and similar details. We shall discuss first factors that pertain to all services. Then we shall discuss the entrance using conduit, then using service-entrance cable, and lastly using underground cable. Finally we shall discuss the ground.

Solderless Connectors. The Code in Sec. 230-72 prohibits the use of soldered joints in connecting wires to service-entrance switches or circuit breakers. The reason for this is not hard to understand. It is not particularly hard to learn how to make good soldered joints when using small wires; it is, however, quite an art to solder a joint when a heavy wire and a tubular solder lug are involved. In the smaller sizes of wire, solder joints are frequently made, giving the workman much opportunity for practice; in the heavier sizes they are infrequently made, affording little opportunity for practice. In connecting wires to service equipment, use only joints made with solderless or "pressure" connectors or similar clamp-style terminals using no solder. The same requirement holds with respect to connections involving the ground wire.

Uninsulated Wire in Service Entrance.   In the wiring of houses and farms, the neutral wire is grounded.   As was pointed out in an earlier chapter, this means that whenever you touch a water pipe or radiator, you touch the neutral wire.   That being t' case, why insulate the neutral?   The Code in Sec. 230-40 does permit uninsulated or bare wire for the grounded neutral wire of the service entrance, but only if the voltage *to ground*[1] is not over 300 volts, which condition is met with a 2-wire 115-volt, a 3-wire 115/230-volt, or a 4-wire 120/208- or 277/480-volt 3-phase service. Insulated wires are entirely acceptable, but you may use bare wire.   In case of a service using conduit, you may use a bare, uninsulated neutral wire.   In case of a service using service-entrance cable, the neutral wire will be automatically bare.

Size of Neutral Wire.   In a 3-wire 115/230-volt installation, the 230-volt loads are connected only to the two hot wires and impose no load whatever on the neutral wire.   Such loads will operate just as well whether there is a neutral wire or not.   Therefore on a 3-wire installation, when both 115- and 230-volt loads are installed, the neutral wire carries a smaller amperage than the two hot wires.   As a matter of fact, even if only 115-volt loads are installed, but properly balanced between the two legs of the service, the amperes carried will be less than the number of amperes in the hot wires (this will be discussed in detail in Chap. 20 in connection with Figs. 20-38 to 20-42).

That being the case, the neutral wire in the service may be smaller than the hot wires.   The rules for figuring the size of the neutral are a bit complicated (Secs. 220-4(d) and 230-41 of the Code), but as a practical matter, the *neutral* wire may be one size smaller than the hot wires. In other words, you may use:

> Two No. 6 with one No. 8
> Two No. 4 with one No. 6
> Two No. 2 with one No. 4
> Two No. 1/0 with one No. 2

[1] See Chap. 9 for definition of "voltage to ground."

Meter. The power company decides whether the meter is to be located indoors or outdoors. In most cases it will be the out-

FIG. 17-1. A detachable outdoor meter and the socket on which it is installed. Meters of this type are mounted exposed to the weather. (*Westinghouse Electric Corp.*)

door type shown in Fig. 17-1 with its socket. Both are installed exposed to the weather. The power company furnishes the

FIG. 17-2. A piece of steel pipe with teeth cut on one end with a hack saw makes a handy tool for occasional drilling through brick walls.

meter. The socket is sometimes furnished by the power company, sometimes by the owner; in any event it is installed by the contractor.

If the meter is to be the indoor type, provide a board, preferably plywood, big enough so that the meter plus the circuit breakers or fused equipment can be mounted on it.

Service-drop Wires. The Code defines service-drop wires as "that portion of overhead service conductors between the pole and the first point of attachment to the building." If the wires are not overhead, they are not classed as service-drop wires but become service-entrance wires, covered by the next paragraph. In general, the service-drop wires are supplied and installed by the power company, although the owner or contractor furnishes the insulators by which the wires are supported at the building.

Service-entrance Wires. The wires from the point where the wires supplied by the power company end, up to the service switch, are the service-entrance wires. They may be Type T or Type R wires brought in through conduit or wires made up into special cables designed for the purpose. Often service-entrance wires are run underground. The kind of wire to use for this purpose will be discussed later in this chapter.

Openings into Buildings. If the building is of frame construction, it is a simple matter to bore through the wall. If the opening must be through brick or concrete, hard labor will be involved. Use a star drill of the type that will be described in Chap. 22. For an occasional job especially if only brick is involved, cut some teeth with a hack saw on the end of a piece of water pipe (don't use conduit, it is too soft) as shown in Fig. 17-2, and use it as a star drill.

Entrance Using Conduit. A typical installation is shown in Fig. 17-3. The size of the conduit and the fittings will depend on the size of the entrance wires and has already been discussed in Chap. 11. Only galvanized conduit may be used.

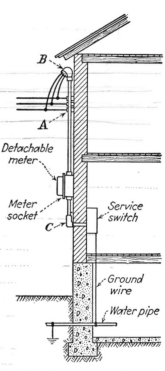

Fig. 17-3. Cross section of a typical service entrance. Locate the service head B *higher* than the insulators.

Service Insulators. Insulators for supporting the power company's wires where they reach the building (point *A* in Fig. 17-3) must be provided. These may be simple screw-point insulators, shown in Fig. 17-4; according to the Code they must be kept a minimum of 6 in. apart. More frequently, however, the type

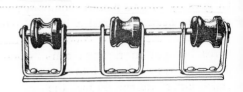

FIG. 17-4. Screw-point in-sulators of this type are used to support outdoor wires.

FIG. 17-5. A unit which comprises two or three insulators may be used instead of sep-arate insulators.

shown in Fig. 17-5 is used; choose one with the individual knobs 8 in.[2] apart. These are known as "service brackets" or "secondary racks."

These insulators should be mounted almost as high above the ground as the shape and structure of the building will permit. Do note that point *A* in Fig. 17-3 (the location of the insulators) must be *lower* by a foot or two than point *B* (the upper end of

FIG. 17-6. A typical service head, used at the top of the conduit through which the service-entrance wires enter the building.

the service conduit). This is to mini-mize the danger of water following the wires down into the conduit. The Code in Sec. 230-26 requires that the supported wires must be at least 10 ft above the ground or sidewalks and 18 ft above driveways, alleys, and public roads. However, the minimum is 12 ft above residential driveways. On farms the entire yard is more or less a "driveway," so the 18-ft clearance should be observed.

In wiring the ranch-house type of building, it is difficult to maintain these minimum clearances. Use a "mast," which will be described later in this chapter.

[2] In some localities a separation of 6 in. is permitted.

Service Head. At the top end of the service conduit (*B* in Fig. 17-3) the Code requires a fitting that will prevent rain from entering the conduit. A fitting of this type is shown in Fig. 17-6; it goes by various names such as service head, entrance cap, and weather head. It consists of three parts: the body, which is attached to the service conduit; an insulating block to separate the wires where they emerge; and the cover, which keeps out the rain and holds the parts together.

Entrance Ell. At the point where the conduit enters the building (*C* in Fig. 17-3) it is customary to use an entrance ell of the type shown in Fig. 17-7. With the cover removed, it is a simple matter to pull wires around the right-angle corner. This device also must be raintight.

Fig. 17-7. A typical entrance ell, used at the bottom of the conduit through which the service - entrance wires run, at the point where they enter the building.

Service Conduit. We shall have to assume that you have already installed the service insulators, that you have cut an opening into the building for the entrance conduit to enter, and have marked the location of the meter, about 5 to 6 ft above the ground. Cut a piece of conduit to reach from the meter location to a point a foot or two *above* the insulators. Cut a piece to reach from the service equipment inside the house to a point just outside the wall, where you will install the entrance ell (point *C* of Fig. 17-3). Cut a third piece long enough to reach from this ell to the meter socket.

Ream the cut ends carefully and thread them, as outlined in Chap. 11. Assemble the whole "stack" on the ground: service head at top, meter socket in the middle, ell at the bottom, then the short end to run into the house. Install the wires as outlined in the next paragraph. Then install the whole assembly on the side of the house: Push the short stub of conduit through the opening in the wall, and anchor the conduit to the side of the building, using pipe straps such as shown in Fig. 11-8, or similar.

Inside the building, the conduit must be anchored to the service switch, using the locknut and bushing procedure shown in Fig.

10-6, but instead of using an ordinary bushing, use a "grounding bushing," which will be described later in this chapter.

Pulling Wires. The conduit will contain three wires. The neutral if insulated must be white. The other wires may be black, but it is more usual to use black and red if the size of the wire you are using is available in red (heavier sizes come only in black). Cut three lengths to reach from the meter socket to the top, plus about 3 ft extra to stick out of the top. Cut three additional lengths to reach from the socket to the service equipment inside the house; don't forget to allow length to reach the neutral strap inside this equipment.

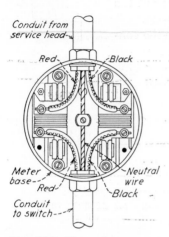

Conduit from service head

Red — Black

Meter base — Neutral wire
Red — Black

Conduit to switch

Fig. 17-8. How wires are connected to the meter base or socket. The neutral wire is always connected to the neutral center contact of the socket.

Pull the wires into the preassembled stack while it is still on the ground. First remove the covers from the entrance ell and the entrance cap. For occasional jobs you can push the wires from the top to the meter socket and the shorter pieces from the socket to the end of the run inside the house. At the ell there is a sharp bend, but you can manipulate the wires around the corner with a little effort. For easier pulling, first pull a fish wire into the conduit, anchor the three wires to the conduit, and pull all into place.

Connect the ends of the wires to the proper terminals in the meter socket as shown in Fig. 17-8. At the top end replace the cover on the entrance cap, letting each wire come out through a separate hole in its insulating block. At the bottom replace the cover on the entrance ell. Then install the preassembled stack on the side of the building.

Thin-wall Conduit. This material may be used instead of rigid conduit. The procedure is as outlined except that connectors are used at all ends of conduit, instead of threads. Entrance caps and ells of a slightly different type are used to clamp to the conduit. Caps and ells designed for threaded, rigid conduit may be used employing adapters that were described in connection with Fig. 11-13.

Service-entrance Cable. Instead of separate wires inside conduit, special service-entrance cable is very commonly used. The most usual type is shown in Fig. 17-9 and is known as Under-

FIG. 17-9. Service-entrance cable, Type SE, Style A. One of the wires is a bare wire wrapped concentrically around the insulated wires. Over all the conductors is a steel armor, and an outer braid. (*Crescent Insulated Wire & Cable Co.*)

writers' Type SE, Style A. It consists basically of two insulated wires, Type R, red and black. The bare, uninsulated neutral consists of many small strands of tinned copper wire spiraled around the insulated conductors. Next comes a wrapping of galvanized steel armor for mechanical protection (the "A" of Style A stands for "armored"), followed by a rubber tape for protection against moisture, with a final fabric jacket, usually painted gray.

All the fine wires in the neutral collectively are equivalent to the same wire size as the size of each insulated conductor or, alternately, one size smaller as permitted in service entrances. Both types are popular.

If the armor is left out of the assembly, it becomes what is known as Type SE, Style U (the "U" stands for "unarmored"). It is shown in Fig. 17-10. Whether to use the Style A or Style U

FIG. 17-10. Service-entrance cable, Type SE, Style U. This cable is like that shown in Fig. 17-9 except that the steel armor is omitted. (*Crescent Insulated Wire & Cable Co.*)

depends on local custom; check with your local inspector or your power company.

The ampacity of the wires in service-entrance cable is the same as for ordinary Type R wire, per Table 310-12 of the Code (see Appendix), unless the cable is marked "75°C," in which case use the column headed "Type RH."

FIG. 17-11. Service-entrance cable, Type SD. It is used mostly for overhead runs. When used on a building, it must be protected by conduit. (*Crescent Insulated Wire & Cable Co.*)

Still another type is shown in Fig. 17-11 and is known as Type SD. It has less insulation and may be used only in service drops (the span of wires ending at the insulators).

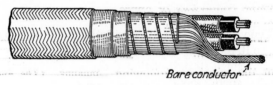

Bare conductor

FIG. 17-12. The concentric conductor is bunched together where it is to be connected to a terminal.

Regardless of type in use, all the fine wires of the neutral are bunched together, twisted, to become a single neutral wire, all as shown in Fig. 17-12. It is then handled just as if it had been an ordinary stranded conductor all the way through the cable.

Fittings for Entrance Cable. The service head for cable is slightly different from the type used for conduit in that it is fastened to the building instead of being supported by the conduit (see Fig. 17-13). The cable itself is secured to the building using one of the several

FIG. 17-13. A typical service head for service-entrance cable.

types of straps that were shown in Fig. 11-8 or the clip of Fig. 17-14, which has no exposed screws when the installation is finished.

Cable is anchored to the meter socket by means of watertight connectors, two types of which are shown in Fig. 17-15. These connectors incorporate soft rubber glands; as the locking nut or the locking screws are tightened, the rubber is compressed, making a watertight seal around the cable. In use, the connector is screwed into the threaded opening of the meter socket, the thread being treated with waterproofing compound. Next the cable is slipped through the rubber gland and the locking screws or nut taken up, making a complete watertight connection. Inside of buildings watertight connectors are not required; armored-cable connectors of appropriate size are used instead.

FIG. 17-14. Clips of this kind are handy for fastening service-entrance cable to the building. (*The Anchor Mfg. Co.*)

At the point where the cable enters the building, a sill plate is used to prevent the rain from following the cable into the inside of the building. One type is shown in Fig. 17-16; usually a soft rubber compound is supplied with it to seal any opening that might exist.

Service-entrance cable in most brands comes with a grayish paint finish, which permits painting to match the building on which it is installed.

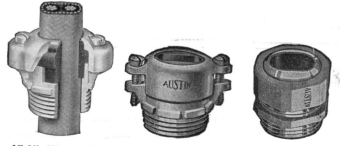

FIG. 17-15. Watertight connectors for service-entrance cable. The rubber gland inside the connector expands when the connector is tightened, making the installation watertight.

Service Wires on Side of Building. In residential work it is usually possible to plan the installation so that the service con-

duit or cable drops straight down from the insulators to the point
where it enters the building. But if that can't be done, make a
special effort to make the installation
neat. Conduit or cable running at an
angle is most unsightly. Try to run the
conduit or cable directly down from the
insulators, and then at a point level with
the point of entry, let it run horizontally
to the opening.

Underground Services. When the
service wires run underground, the wires
must be protected against moisture and
against mechanical damage. At one
time the common method was to use
lead-sheathed cable of the type shown in
Fig. 17-17. This consists of two or three
Type T or Type R wires encased in a
continuous sheath of lead. The Code
requires that it be enclosed in conduit

Fig. 17-16. A sill plate is
used at the point where
service-entrance cable enters the building. Soft
rubber compound seals
openings to keep out wa-
ter. (*The Anchor Mfg.
Co.*)

for mechanical protection. The lead is
soft and easily damaged, with the result
that when it is pulled into conduit, the
sheath is often damaged, even punc-
tured, defeating the purpose of the lead.
Moreover, it is a costly type of installation because the cable itself is expensive,

it must run inside conduit, and installation labor is high. For
these reasons, this method is little used today.

Fig. 17-17. Lead-sheathed cable is used where there is too much moisture
for ordinary wire. The lead is not intended as mechanical protection; it
serves only to keep moisture out. (*Crescent Insulated Wire & Cable Co.*)

Several styles of cable are available that can be buried directly
in the ground, no conduit being required. The carrying capacity
of buried wires is the same as for wires in conduit. See Code
Table 310-12 in the Appendix.

Type USE Cable. This material has a basic layer of insulation which is especially designed to be moisture-resistant, and over that comes another layer of insulation which is mechanically very tough and sturdy. It is generally used in the single-conductor

Fig. 17-18. Type USE. Wire of this type may be buried directly in the ground without further protection. (*Crescent Insulated Wire & Cable Co.*)

type shown in Fig. 17-18 but is also available in the multiconductor type shown in Fig. 17-19. The letters USE stand for underground service entrance.

Type UF Cable. The 1953 Code was the first to recognize Underwriters' Type UF cable. It is used mostly in the multicon-

Fig. 17-19. Type USE is also available in multiconductor type. (*Crescent Insulated Wire & Cable Co.*)

ductor type shown in Fig. 17-20 but is also available in single-conductor type. It greatly resembles Type USE except that the insulated conductors are embedded in a plastic compound which is at the same time very moisture-resistant and strong mechani-

Fig. 17-20. Type UF is used like Type USE, except it must be protected by fuses or circuit breakers. (*Crescent Insulated Wire & Cable Co.*)

cally. Use it as you would Type USE, except that it *must be protected by circuit breakers or fuses at the starting point.* Consequently it may *not* ordinarily be used for services except on farms in those cases where there is overcurrent protection at the starting point: the meter pole. However, it is useful for runs from one building to another as from house to garage or between farm buildings.

This material is to all intents and purposes identical with non-metallic-sheathed cable Type NMC, discussed in Chap. 6. If the cable is marked "Type NMC," it may not be buried in the ground; if it is labeled "Type UF," it may be buried but may not be used for general indoor wiring. Many brands now appear labeled "Type UF-NMC" and may then be used for either ordinary indoor wiring or buried in the ground. A continuous run can be extended from underground into the building and continued there.

Parkway Cable. Another cable that may be buried directly is parkway cable; there are many types, one of which is shown in

Fig. 17-21. Armored parkway cable is of very sturdy construction. It is used for street lighting and similar purposes. (*Crescent Insulated Wire & Cable Co.*)

Fig. 17-21. It consists of one or more conductors insulated with a particularly high grade of moisture-resistant compound, followed by additional layers of insulation, tapes, and similar materials for further moisture and mechanical protection. Often an interlocking steel armor is added for further mechanical protection; sometimes there is a lead sheath inside the armor for further protection against moisture. This is an expensive cable and is used mostly for street-lighting purposes but is used occasionally for residential work.

Installing Underground Cables. Bury these cables directly in the ground. No splices are permitted—use continuous lengths. Common sense suggests that you bury the cable at least 18 in. and in any event deeply enough so that it will not be disturbed or damaged by digging, ruts in roads, and so on. It is wise to place a board or similar obstruction on top of the cable as a warning should further digging become necessary in the area of the cable.

If you use individual conductors, bunch them rather than spreading them in the trench. Do not pull the cable tight from one end of the trench to the other; rather "snake" it a bit.

Underground conductors usually begin at the power company's pole. The Code requires that the cable be given good mechanical protection at all points above the ground. Run a length of conduit starting a minimum of 8 ft above the ground. At the top provide a service head. At the bottom install a bushing at the end of the conduit, which should end about halfway between the bottom of the trench and the ground level, and should

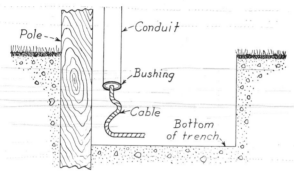

FIG. 17-22. Provide an "S" loop where an underground run ends, to protect against frost damage.

point straight down rather than in a horizontal sweep. Then be sure to provide an S loop in the cable. This will tend to prevent damage to the cable (especially in northern climates) due to movement of the earth in changes from winter to summer. All this is shown in Fig. 17-22.

At the house, if the meter is the outdoor type, follow the same procedure, using a piece of conduit from the meter socket down into the trench. But if the cable is to run through the foundation to an indoor meter, follow the procedure shown in Fig. 17-23. Provide a length of conduit as shown, and after the cable has been installed, fill the openings around the conduit and inside the conduit with asphalt compound to prevent rain water or melted snow from following the cable and running into the building.

Bare Underground Wires. If the entrance is made using conduit or cable, the neutral may be bare, uninsulated. If the service is underground and you are using multiconductor cable, the neutral may be bare. But if you are using *individual* underground conductors, the neutral must be insulated like the hot conductors.

Service Switch or Circuit Breakers. The service wires end at the service-switch or circuit-breaker cabinet. From this cabinet

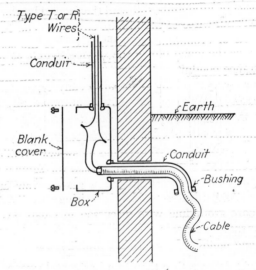

FIG. 17-23. If underground conductors cannot be run directly to entrance switch, use the construction shown in changing over from underground cable to the usual interior wiring.

you must run the ground wire, also all the wiring for the individual branch circuits.

The switch or breaker cabinet must be located as close as possible to the point where the wires enter the building. It may be mounted directly on the wall or preferably on a piece of plywood that has been installed for the purpose. If the meter is to be the indoor type, be sure the plywood is large enough to hold the meter also. Observe the local custom in your locality.

The neutral wire of the service runs directly to the neutral strap in the cabinet. The two hot wires run to the main lugs.

They are usually marked "Mains." The proper connections are usually shown on a wiring diagram that comes with the equipment.

Spend a few extra minutes to run the wires *neatly* within the cabinet. Instead of running them this way and that at random, bend them to run parallel to the sides of the cabinet. You can then take pride in your workmanship.

Grounding. The Code differentiates between two types of grounds: system grounds and equipment grounds. The system ground consists of grounding the white neutral incoming wire as well as the neutral wires of the branch circuits. The equipment ground consists of grounding the metal parts of the service entrance, such as the metal box of the service switch, as well as the service-entrance conduit or the armor[3] of service-entrance cable. If the branch-circuit wiring is metallic (any type of conduit or armored cable), the metal raceway is automatically grounded because it is anchored to the service switch. The equipment ground also includes motor frames, switchboard frames, and similar equipment, which, however, need not be considered in residential wiring because, if metal raceway is used for branch circuits, such equipment is automatically grounded. If you use nonmetallic sheathed cable in residential wiring, use the kind with the extra, bare grounding wire discussed in Chap. 11.

For residential purposes system and equipment grounds are combined and handled by a single grounding wire.

Method of Grounding. The usual ground connection is to a water pipe of a city water system. Use the cold-water piping, not the hot, because the former runs more directly to the ground. Make the ground connection as near as practical to the meter or, if at all possible, to the street side of the meter; on the other hand, keep the ground wire as short and direct as possible. Other things being equal, it is probably best to run the ground wire to the nearest cold-water pipe.

If there is no underground *city* water system, any underground

---

[3] According to Code definition "armored" service-entrance cable is a type not shown in this book and rarely used. The cable shown in Fig. 17-9 has a flat steel protective tape (which is not armor in the sense of the Code definition) which becomes automatically grounded when the neutral wire is grounded.

piping system at least 10 ft long may be used.   This will be discussed later in this chapter.   A metal well casing (but not a
drop pipe in a dug well) is considered part of such a piping
system.

In the absence of underground water pipe, the metal framework
of a building may be used or even gas piping.   The local inspector should be consulted.   In the absence of all such means, use
a "made electrode" (artificial ground) as described later.

Grounding Wire.   The ground wire does not need to be insulated, although there is no objection to using insulated wire.
It may never be lighter than No. 8, which serves the purpose
when the largest service conductor is not heavier than No. 2.   If
the largest service conductor is No. 1 or 1/0, use No. 6 wire.   If
the largest service conductor is No. 2/0 or 3/0, use No. 4 wire.
(For heavier service conductors, see Chap. 28.)   There is no objection to using a grounding wire larger than the minimum required by the Code.   Note, however, that when a "made electrode" (as described later) is used, the grounding wire never need
be larger than No. 6 (Code Sec. 250-94).

If No. 4 grounding wire is used, it requires no further protection
such as conduit; it may be run open or concealed; it may run
directly to ground without following the exact contour of the
building.   It may be stapled to the building, but this is not required.   Common sense, of course, dictates that it be guarded
against mechanical injury if in a location where it might be disturbed.

If No. 6 wire is used, it requires no further protection such as
conduit, provided that it closely follows the surface of the building and is rigidly stapled to it, assuming further that it is free
from exposure to mechanical injury.   If these conditions are not
met, as is quite usual, then it must be given mechanical protection
in the same way as No. 8, which the next paragraph covers.

If No. 8 wire is used (or No. 6 wire neither following the surface of the building nor stapled to it), it must be run inside of
conduit, or it may be the armored type of wire shown in Fig.
17-24, consisting of bare wire plus armor.   If the protection is
conduit, it must be attached to the service switch by locknut and
bushing; if it is armor, with a connector of the type used on armored cable.   At the water pipe end, either conduit or armor

is fastened to the same clamp by which the ground wire is attached to the pipe.

Fig. 17-24. Armored ground wire. The conductor is not insulated. (*Crescent Insulated Wire and Cable Co.*)

Ground Clamps. There are many varieties of ground clamps on the market, all serving the same purpose. Figure 17-25 shows a common clamp fitting ½-, ¾-, or 1-in. water pipe. For the smaller sizes reverse the lower jaw. Larger sizes are available for larger size pipe. Use it with bare ground wire without further protection.

The type in Fig. 17-26 is very similar except that there is an extra clamp to which the armor of armored ground wire is clamped. The type in Fig. 17-27 is also similar except that it

| Fig. 17-25. Ground clamp for bare wire without protective armor. | Fig. 17-26. Ground clamp for armored ground wire. | Fig. 17-27. Ground clamp for use with ground wire run through conduit. |

has a still larger fitting in which conduit is clamped if used as protection for the ground wire.

The type of ground clamp should be carefully selected. The ordinary metal-strap type is prohibited by Sec. 250-116. If the pipe to which the ground connection is made is iron pipe, the ground clamp should be made of iron. If the ground connection is made to copper or brass pipe or to a copper or copper-coated rod, the clamp should be made of copper or brass. Unless this point is observed, electrolytic action is likely to set in, result-

ing in a high-resistance ground, which is not much better than
no ground at all.

Solder Connections Prohibited. The Code in Sec. 250-115
prohibits joints that depend on solder, as far as grounding wires
are concerned. Use only joints dependent upon solderless or
"pressure" connectors; do not use solder.

Water Meters. It is not unusual for a water meter to be removed from a building, at least temporarily while testing. If
the ground connection is made to a water pipe between the meter
and some other part of the building, removing the meter then
leaves the system ungrounded, which leaves a temporary hazardous condition.

In some cases the joints between the water pipes and the
meter are very poor joints, electrically speaking—practically insulated. If the ground of the electrical system is between the
water meter and some other part of the building, it results in a
"ground" apparently meeting Code requirements but actually is
no ground at all. This is very dangerous. Therefore the Code
in Sec. 250-112 (a) requires that when the ground connection is not
made on the street side of the water meter, a jumper be installed
across the meter, as shown in Fig. 17-28. Two ground clamps are

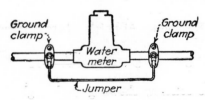

Fig. 17-28. A jumper must be placed around the water meter.

used; the size of the jumper wire is the same as used for the
ground proper.

A similar jumper is required around any other object in the
incoming water pipe if there is likelihood that the electrical continuity of the piping is or could be disturbed. For example,
water softeners are sometimes installed on a rental basis, and the
installation made with nonmetal hose to carry water into and out
of the softener. A jumper then is required around such an installation unless the ground wire is connected to the pipe at a point
between the softener and the street.

Most homeowners have not the slightest conception of the importance of a good ground. Ground connections have even been removed by some misguided or uninformed homeowners. This has prompted some wide-awake manufacturers to provide with their ground clamps printed tags intended to be permanently attached to ground clamps when installed, cautioning the occupant of the premises to leave ground connections intact for their own safety. It is recommended that such tags when provided be attached to ground clamps as they are installed.

Connections within Service Switch. The neutral of most service switches and breakers consists merely of a strap with a number of terminals. This terminal strap is usually not insulated from the steel cabinet but directly grounded to it; consequently the neutral wires are grounded to the cabinet when they are connected to these terminals. The service conduit is also fastened to the cabinet, as is the conduit or armor on the wires to the branch circuits. Therefore it would seem sufficient to run one ground wire from this neutral strap to ground, to ground the entire installation effectively. In practice, however, it has been found that the resistance created by the various locknut and bushing points is too high; therefore the Code requires further bonding together.

Grounding Bushings. At points where a service or grounding conduit enter the service switch or the cabinet housing the circuit breakers, use a grounding bushing of the type shown in Fig. 17-29 instead of an ordinary bushing. The setscrew shown goes through the bushing and bites into the metal cabinet, preventing the bushing from turning and at the same time ensuring that the joint will always be at least as good as when first made. In addition a bonding conductor can be connected under the setscrew and from there run to the neutral strap of the switch or, as is frequently the case, to a grounding terminal which is provided in some cabinets, separate and apart from the neutral strap. In that way all parts are completely bonded and effectively grounded.

Fɪɢ.   17-29.   A grounding bushing.

Many cabinets are of such size that there is not room to install all the different sizes of knockouts that might be needed in actual use. They are then provided with "concentric" knockouts as shown in Fig. 17-30. Remove as much of this complicated knock-out as required to provide the one size that is needed. Now such concentric knockouts are most convenient when installing the cabinet but provide very poor continuity of ground after installation. For that reason the Code in Sec. 250-72(d) requires extra means to provide good continuity; the ground-ing bushing is the simplest. If either the service conduit or the ground conduit enters the cabinet through one of these concentric knockouts, install a grounding bushing instead of an ordinary bushing. Run a jumper from the grounding bushing of the serv-ice conduit to the bushing on the grounding conduit; alternately run a jumper from each bushing to the grounding screw in the cabinet or to the neutral strap.

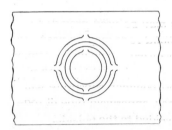

FIG. 17-30. Concentric knock-outs are convenient but need special attention when ground-ing a service.

If you use thin-wall conduit (EMT), install the grounding bushing in place of the locknut found on the connector used on the conduit.

If you use service-entrance cable, the grounding bushing is *not* required where the cable enters the cabinet.

Complete Ground. A complete ground for the average resi-dential job is shown in Fig. 17-31. For the sake of simplicity only the grounded or neutral wires are shown, the hot wires being omitted. Grounding bushings are used at points *A* and *B.* Sometimes the cabinet has at some convenient point *C* a terminal screw which is merely a screw in the cabinet of the box. The grounding jumpers are then run to this point and then on to the neutral strap. Alternately run the jumpers from the grounding bushings to the neutral strap.

Made Electrodes. When a city water system is not available, a substitute must be used. Early Codes called this an "artificial ground"; Codes since 1951 call it a "made electrode." Grounding to the pipe in a *dug* well is not recommended. Often this leads to exceptionally long ground wires; furthermore, wells sometimes go dry, resulting in no ground at all. On the other hand if the well is a driven well located close to the logical point of the ground connection, its casing makes an excellent ground.

The usual made electrode is a driven pipe or rod which must go at least 8 ft into the earth. Pipe may be used provided it is galvanized and at least ¾-in. size. Solid rods may be used and. if iron, must be at least ⅝ in. and galvanized. The most common form of ground rod is copper or an approved substitute and need be only ½ in. in diameter. The most common substitute which the Underwriters have approved is the Copperweld type of rod— a rod of steel with a layer of copper welded to the outside.

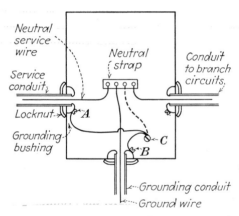

Fig. 17-31. Typical grounding scheme at entrance switch of residential job. Only the grounded neutral wires are shown. The detail used varies in different localities.

The Code requires that the ground rod or other made electrode be entirely independent of, and kept at least 6 ft from, any other ground of the type used for radio, telephone, or lightning rods.

When a made electrode is used, the ground rod is usually out of doors; therefore it is necessary to bring the ground wire out of the building. In many localities the inspector will require a special type of entrance ell similar to that shown in Fig. 17-7 but with an extra opening in the bottom for the ground wire. This is shown in Fig. 17-32, and its use should be clear from Fig. 17-33.

When service-entrance cable is used, a meter ring of the type shown in Fig. 17-34 is sometimes used. This is slipped between the service-entrance-cable connector and the meter socket.   The ground wire is connected to it and from there run to the ground.

The question often arises as to what to do if there is an underground pipe *less* than 10 ft long in the house where the ground is

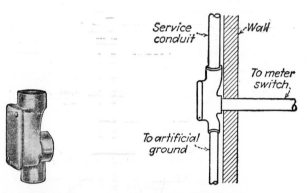

Fig. 17-32. A grounding elbow, generally used with artificial grounds when the entrance wires run through conduit.

Fig. 17-33. Installation showing use of the grounding elbow shown in Fig. 17-32.

to be installed.   The Code in Sec. 250-81 requires that you must ground to both a driven rod *and* this short underground pipe. This is a safety measure; do not overlook it.

Separate Meter for Water Heater.   In many localities the

Fig. 17-34. A meter ring, used with artificial grounds when service-entrance cable is used.

power company provides a separate meter and an automatic time switch for the water heater.   The automatic switch connects the heater to the line only during the "off-peak" periods. In other words the heater is disconnected during the periods when there is maximum demand for power, as, for example, in the periods before

meals when many electric stoves are in operation, during the early evening hours, and so on.

There are many ways of handling the wiring to the second meter.   Usually a pair of wires is tapped to the service-entrance wires where they enter the first meter.   They run on to the second meter, then to a fused switch or circuit breaker, which serves as overcurrent protection as well as the disconnecting means for the heater. The size of the wire from the first meter to the second is determined by the method outlined in Chap. 5 for taps under 25

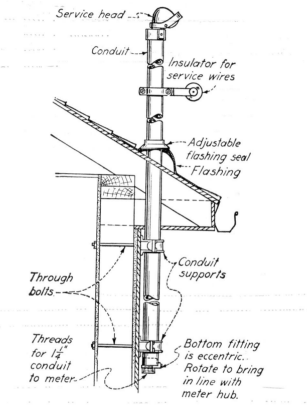

Fig. 17-35. Typical mast construction. (*M. & W. Electric Mfg. Co.*)

ft long. The size so determined is more than enough for the amperage required by the heater. The size of the wires from the second meter to the heater depends on the size of the heater and has already been discussed.

Service Masts. Many houses being built today are of the so-called ranch-house type. They are so low that it is impossible to run the service drop directly to the building and still maintain the minimum clearance required by Code above ground, sidewalks, and driveways.   The usual way of solving this problem is to use a service mast of the general construction shown in Fig. 17-35. The service conduit itself becomes the supporting member, but you must use 2 or 2½ in. to provide sufficient rigidity.   Some of the fittings are so designed that they will fit either size of conduit without threading.   Flashing is usually provided with each kit to make a watertight opening through the overhang of the roof.

Chapter 18

INSTALLATION OF SPECIFIC OUTLETS

In previous chapters installations of electrical devices were considered in rather general fashion; in this chapter the exact method of installing a variety of outlets using assorted materials will be discussed in detail. Only methods used in *new work* (buildings wired while under construction) will be explained. *Old work* (the wiring of buildings *after* their completion) will be described in a separate chapter.

When buildings are wired with conduit, the conduit is installed, all the outlet and switch boxes are mounted, and all similar details handled while the building is in the early stages. This is termed "roughing-in." The wires are not pulled into the conduit until after the lathing, plastering, papering, and similar work is finished, and obviously the switches, receptacles, fixtures, and other devices cannot be installed until the building is practically completed. However, to avoid repetition later, the pulling of the wires will be included in this chapter. If cable is used, the wires are automatically installed in the roughing-in process.

Each type of outlet will be treated separately. In the pictures each outlet will be shown in different ways, as follows:

1. As it would appear on a blueprint.
2. As it would appear in diagrammatic or schematic fashion.
3. In pictorial fashion using conduit.
4. In pictorial fashion using armored cable. The diagrams are also correct if nonmetallic-sheathed cable is used, but will not show the grounding wire of that cable, which must be properly connected. To avoid repetitious reference at each outlet in the remainder of this chapter, only a few references to the grounding wire will be made. If you *study* pages 167 and 168 you will have no trouble in connecting it properly.

287

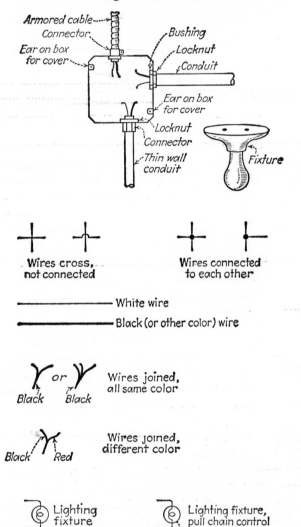

FIG. 18-1. Study these symbols well so that other diagrams in this chapter will be clear.

The same basic details shown in Fig. 18-1 will be used in other drawings, and since these will be smaller, the individual parts cannot be named as in the first picture, but you will easily recognize them.

In each case the two wires over which the current comes are labeled SOURCE. *The white or neutral wire always runs, without interruption by a switch or fuse or other device, up to each*

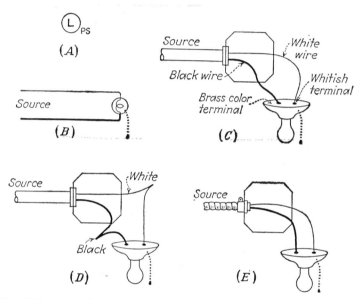

FIG. 18-2. A simple hookup of a pull-chain outlet, with wires ending at that outlet.

point where current is to be consumed. Joints are not interruptions. Switches consume no current; hence the white wire does not run to a switch (except when using cable, which will be discussed later). Black wires may be joined to black or red or other colors as the need requires, but not to white (except sometimes when using cable, which will be discussed later).

Ceiling Outlet, Pull-chain Control. This is the type of outlet generally used in closets, basements, attics, and similar locations, with the wires ending at the outlet. It is the simplest possible outlet to wire. Figure 18-2 pictures it. At *A* is shown its designation as found on blueprint layouts; the wire running up to it is not shown, for, in these blueprints, wires are shown only to connect switches with the outlets that they control.   At *B* is a wiring diagram for the same outlet; the light lines designate white wire, the heavy lines black wire or some color other than white.

Assume that you have already mounted the outlet box in the ceiling by one of the methods covered in a previous chapter; if conduit was used, you have provided a box with a plaster-ring cover of the type that was shown in Fig. 10-12.

Installing this outlet with conduit as in Fig. 18-2, *C*, assume that you have properly reamed the cut ends of the conduit, that you have properly anchored it to the outlet box with a locknut and bushing, and that you have pulled two wires, one black and one white, into the conduit with about 6 in. sticking out of the box. To complete the outlet all you have to do is to connect the wires to the fixture and mount the fixture in one of the ways discussed in the next chapter.

If the fixture is one which has two wire leads (instead of two terminals to which the wires from the outlet box can be connected), the wiring is still the same, except that a couple of splices must be made in the box, as shown in Fig. 18-2, *D*.

If you plan to use thin-wall conduit (EMT) instead of rigid conduit, follow the same procedure as with rigid conduit, except use the threadless fittings such as were shown in Figs. 11-10 and 11-11 instead of the locknuts and bushings used with rigid conduit.

Installing this same outlet with armored cable, as shown in Fig. 18-2, *E*, assume that you have properly cut the cable, inserted a fiber bushing between armor and wires, attached a connector solidly to the cable, and in turn rigidly anchored the connector to the box, all as explained in a previous chapter.   The cable must be anchored at intervals not exceeding $4\frac{1}{2}$ ft and also within 12 in. of the box.   Then there is nothing more to do except to mount the fixture.

If you plan to use nonmetallic-sheathed cable instead of armored cable, the only difference is that you use a slightly different style of connector and connect the grounding wire to the box.

If you plan to use flexible conduit, follow the procedure for armored cable, except that the wires are pulled into the conduit after completion of the job.

Same Outlet, Wires Continue to Next Outlet. This combination is as common as the first and practically as simple. From the first outlet the wires continue to the next; it makes no difference what may be used at that next outlet. The only problem is how to connect at the first outlet the wires running on to the second.

This combination is pictured in Fig. 18-3, and again *A* is its

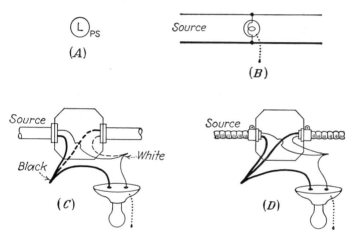

FIG. 18-3. The hookup shown in Fig. 18-2, but with the wires running on to another outlet.

designation as found on blueprint layouts. Comparing this with Fig. 18-2, *A*, you will find no difference. This may be confusing, but in blueprint layouts the wires between different outlets are not indicated except those wires between switches and the outlets they control. It is up to the one making the installation to use his own good judgment as to the exact fashion of hooking together different outlets. At *B* is shown the wiring diagram for the combination.

At *C* is shown the outlet using conduit. Compare it carefully with Fig. 18-2, *D*. The new outlet, Fig. 18-3, *C*, is the same as the former except for the addition of two new wires running on to the second outlet, at the right, and these two wires have been shown in dotted lines to distinguish them easily from the former wires.   Simply join all the black wires together, also all the white wires; solder, tape, and the job is finished.

Receptacle Outlet.   In Fig. 18-4 at *A* is shown the designation for this outlet as found on blueprint layouts; at *B* is a wiring diagram.   To wire this outlet, merely connect the wires to the receptacle.

At *D* is shown the same outlet wired with armored cable; the connections are so simple that no further clarification is needed. But when using nonmetallic sheathed cable, with the bare grounding wire now required, an extra wire must be run from the *green* grounding terminal of the receptacle (not shown in the picture) to the box; the bare wire in the cable must be connected to the box, and also to the bare wire in each other length of cable entering the box.   Study pages 165 to 168.

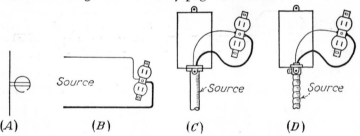

(*A*)   (*B*)   (*C*)   (*D*)

Fig. 18-4. Installation of a baseboard outlet.

Receptacle Outlet. Wires Continue to Next Outlet.   In Fig. 18-5, *A*, is shown the wiring diagram of the circuit in question. At *B* and *C* is shown the actual installation using conduit and cable; little explanation should be necessary.   Simply run the incoming white wire to one of the terminals of the receptacle, and from that terminal continue with another white wire to the next outlet.   Do the same with the black wire.

Because it is frequently necessary to do this, most receptacles are provided with double terminal screws so that two different wires can be connected to the same terminal strap, as shown in *A* of Fig. 18-6.   This is much simpler than connecting two differ-

ent wires under the same terminal screw, which the Code prohibits in Sec. 110-13. If conduit is used, you may find it far more
convenient to pull a continuous wire from SOURCE to box 1 to
box 2 to box 3 than to pull one length from SOURCE to 1, a second
length from 1 to 2, and another from 2 to 3. If you use one con-

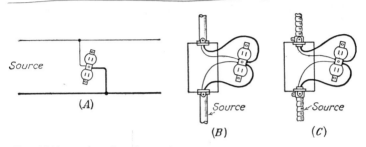

FIG. 18-5. Baseboard outlet, with wires running on to another outlet.

tinuous length, allow a loop of wire to project about 6 in. at each
box, as shown in Fig. 18-6, B. Remove the insulation, as shown
in B of the picture, and clamp the conductor under one of the
terminal screws, as shown in C. This method is the preferable
one. Remove just enough insulation from the wire so that the

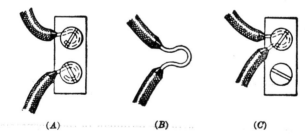

FIG. 18-6. Most duplex receptacles have double terminal screws, for convenience in continuing wires on to the next outlet.

bare uninsulated conductor will not be exposed after installation
for any distance from the terminal screw.

Outlet Controlled by Wall Switch. Naturally this is a very
common outlet and fortunately very simple to wire. Figure 18-7,
A, shows the blueprint symbol, and B shows the wiring diagram.
At C is shown the outlet wired with conduit. Run the white wire

directly to the fixture. Run two blacks from the outlet box to the switch box, and connect them to the switch; connect the upper

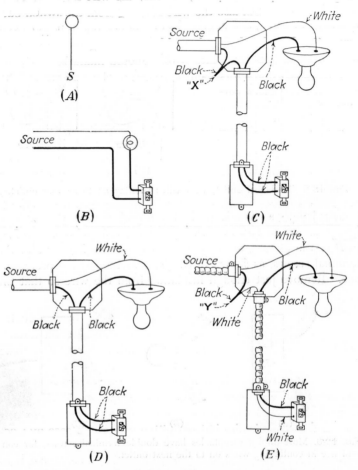

FIG. 18-7. Fixture controlled by wall switch (see also Fig. 18-10).

ends, one to the black incoming wire from SOURCE, the other to the fixture; and the job is finished. At *D* is shown the optional method whereby one continuous black wire is brought all the way through to the switch box instead of having a joint at point *X* in *C*.

When this outlet is wired with cable, either armored or non-metallic, as at *E*, a difficulty is encountered. According to everything learned up to this point, not only the wire from the outlet box to the switch but also the wire running from the switch back to the fixture should be black, since neither one is a grounded wire. On the other hand, the cable containing these two wires has one black and one white wire. Should manufacturers, distributors, and contractors then be forced to stock a special cable containing two black wires just for this purpose? That would be impractical.

The Code in Sec. 200-7 permits an exception to the general rule that the white wire may be used only as a grounded neutral wire and never as an ungrounded wire. In the case of a switch loop (as the wiring between an outlet and the switch which controls it is called) this section permits the use of a 2-wire cable containing one black and one white wire, even if its use does not fulfill the general rule. Under this exception the cable may be used provided that the black wire is made to run directly to the fixture. This leaves only one place to connect the white wire of the switch loop, and that is to the black wire in the outlet box. This is the only case where it is permissible to connect a black wire to a white wire, and it pertains only if cable is used.

Study this rule well: When cable is used for a switch loop, the wiring up to the outlet box upon which the fixture is mounted is standard, including connection of the white wire from SOURCE to the fixture. Connect the black wire of the switch loop to the fixture. The fixture will then have two wires connected to it: one black and one white. Then connect the white wire of the cable of the switch loop to the black wire in the outlet box contrary to the general rules but permitted in this one case by Code Sec. 200-7.

Combining Three Outlets. Three different outlets having been wired, you can combine them into one combination of three outlets, as shown in Fig. 18-8. As usual, *A* shows the blueprint symbols, *B* the wiring diagram, and *C* the three outlets as wired with conduit. All the points have been gone over in detail, and if they have been carefully studied, this combination should present no problem. If any point is not clear, go back to the idea of messengers chasing each other along the different wires, in on the white wire from source, along that wire up to every point where current is to be consumed, and from each such point back over the black wires through switches, if used, until they emerge at the black source wire.

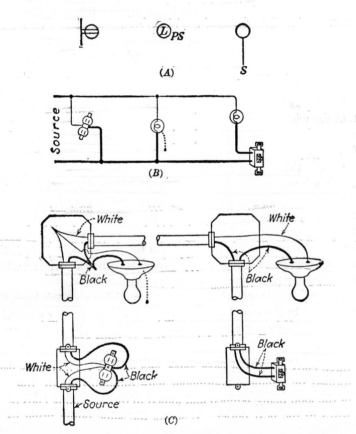

Fig. 18-8. Combining the outlets of Figs. 18-2, 18-4, and 18-7 into one three-outlet combination.

Taps.   At times an outlet box is used merely to house a tap where one wire branches off from another. Sometimes, especially in conduit work, it is difficult to pull wires into a long length of conduit, so a "junction box" is installed which will serve as an intermediate pulling point. Whenever a box is used only for connections, it is always covered with a blank cover.   The Code requires all junction or pull boxes to be placed in locations permanently accessible without removing any part of the building (Sec. 370-19).

Figure 18-9, A, shows how taps are indicated in blueprint layouts, and at B is shown the wiring diagram.   At C is shown the method using conduit; merely join all the white wires and then all the blacks.   At D is shown an optional method, when, instead of

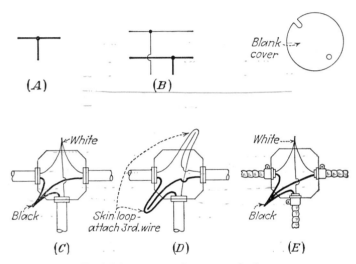

FIG. 18-9. A tap made in an outlet box.

three ends of wire of each color, one loop of each color is used, formed by pulling a continuous wire through the box, the ends of the loop being skinned and joined to the remaining ends of the wires to the next outlet.   E shows the same outlet using cable.

Outlet with Switch, Feed through Switch.   Switches are connected in different ways to the outlet which they control.   The source wires do not always run through the ceiling to the outlet box on which the fixture is installed and from there on to the switch, as in Fig. 18-7, already discussed.   Sometimes the source wires come in from below, run through the switch box and then on to the ceiling outlet, where they end, as in Fig. 18-10.   At A is shown the usual blueprint symbol, and B shows the wiring dia-

gram.   At *C* is shown the outlet using the conduit system, and
little explanation is needed.   At *D* is shown an optional method
of handling the wires at the switch box by pulling the white
wire straight through.   The black wire is also pulled straight
through but with a loop which is later cut, the two ends being
connected to the switch.

The diagram for this outlet when wired with cable is not shown

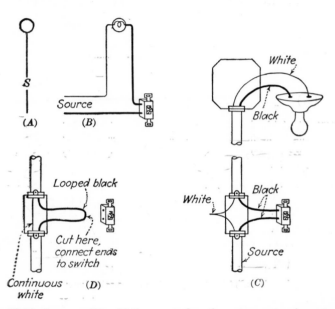

Fig. 18-10. Same as Fig. 18-7, except that the wires enter through the
switch box instead of through the outlet box on which the fixture is mounted.

because there is no new problem.   When the cable feeds through
the switch box, there is no difficulty with the colors of the wires in
the cable as in a previous example.   The wires can be run
through to completion of the outlet without the need of joining
black to white, exactly as when using conduit (*C* of Fig. 18-10).

Outlet with Switch, with Another Outlet.   This is simply a
combination of two outlets that have already been discussed
separately.   The wiring of an outlet with wall-switch control was
covered in connection with Fig. 18-7.   The wiring of an outlet
with pull-chain control was covered in connection with Fig. 18-2.

The two have been combined in Fig. 18-11, the left-hand portion of which is identical with Fig. 18-7; to it have been added in dotted lines the wires of Fig. 18-2, making the new combination as shown.   At D is shown an optional method of handling the wires through the outlet box, the wires from the fixture being connected

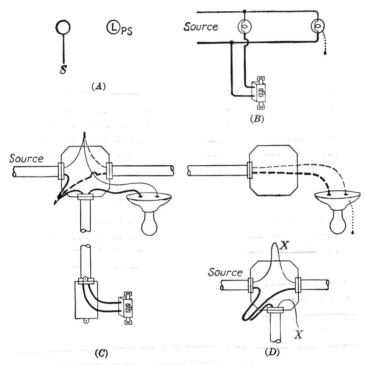

Fig. 18-11. The switch controls the first fixture; wires run on to a second fixture which is controlled by a pull chain.

at the points marked X.   No new problems are involved in the cable methods; for that reason they are not shown.

If the wires from SOURCE (instead of coming in through the ceiling outlet) come in from below through the switch box, the problem is different in that three wires instead of two must run from the switch box to the first outlet box, as shown in Fig. 18-12, B.   A good way to analyze this combination is to consider first the right-hand outlet with the pull chain.   Both a white and a black wire *must* run to this from SOURCE, uninterrupted by any switch, so that the light can always be controlled by the pull chain.   Then run the third wire from the switch to the left-hand outlet to control that.

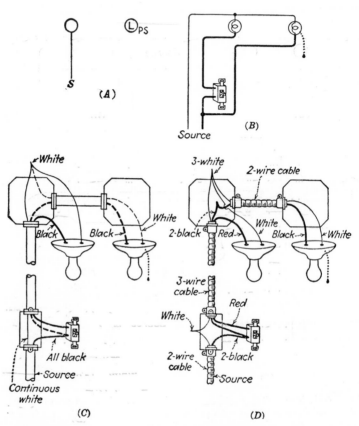

FIG. 18-12. This is the same as Fig. 18-11 except that the wires from SOURCE enter through the switch box.

Analysis of Fig. 18-12, *C*, shows that it consists of a combination of Figs. 18-10, *C* (wires in solid lines), and 18-2 (wires in dotted lines).

If instead of conduit you use cable, as in Fig. 18-12, *D*, the problem is equally simple.   If the wires are fed through the switch box, there is no problem in connection with the colors of the wires. Merely connect white to white in the switch box, and then continue the white to each of the two fixtures. The remaining colors are as shown in the picture.

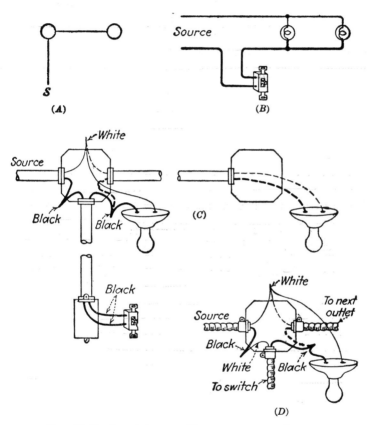

Fig. 18-13. A switch controlling two separate fixtures.

Switch Controlling Two Outlets. When a switch is to control two outlets at the same time, the connections are most simple. Merely wire the switch to control one fixture, then continue the white wire from the first fixture to the second, and do the same with the black.

As in the other pictures, in Fig. 18-13, *A* shows the blueprint symbols, *B* the wiring diagram, and *C* the combination using conduit. Compare this with Fig. 18-7, *C*; there is no difference except that these wires have been continued as shown in the dotted lines. To avoid all the joints shown in the outlet box for the first fixture, several of the wires may be pulled through as continuous wires, making a neater job.

If you use cable, there is again the problem of having to use in the switch loop a cable that has one black and one white wire, instead of the two blacks that should be used. Handle it as in Fig. 18-7, *D*. The white wire from SOURCE goes to each of the two fixtures. The black wire in the switch loop also goes to the first fixture, then on to the second. That leaves only two unconnected wires, the black wire from SOURCE and the white wire in the switch loop; connect them together as before, as permitted in the Code's exception.

— **Three-way Switches.** When a pair of 3-way switches controls an outlet, there are many possible combinations or sequences in which the SOURCE, the two switches, and the outlet may be arranged; a great deal depends on where the SOURCE wires come in. The most common are

> SOURCE—Switch—Switch—Outlet.
> SOURCE—Outlet—Switch—Switch.
> SOURCE—Switch—Outlet—Switch.

A fourth is the sequence where the SOURCE comes into the outlet box, from which point two runs are made, one to each switch.

These sequences are shown in Fig. 18-14, parts *A1*, *A2*, *A3*, and *A4*; the wiring diagrams are shown in *B1*, *B2*, *B3*, and *B4*. Comparing *B1*, *B2*, *B3* and *B4*, you will see little difference except the exact location of the light which the switches control.

Reviewing the subject of 3-way switches, remember that one of the three terminals on such a switch is a "common" terminal, corresponding to the middle terminal of an ordinary porcelain-base single-pole double-throw switch shown in Fig. 4-20; this terminal is usually identified by being of a different color from the other two. The exact location of this common terminal with relation to the other two varies with different brands; for the purposes of this chapter, where 3-way switches are shown in pictorial fashion, the terminal which is alone on one *side* of the switch will always be the common terminal.

Reviewing the subject a bit further, run the incoming black wire from source direct to the common or marked terminal of either switch. From the corresponding common or marked

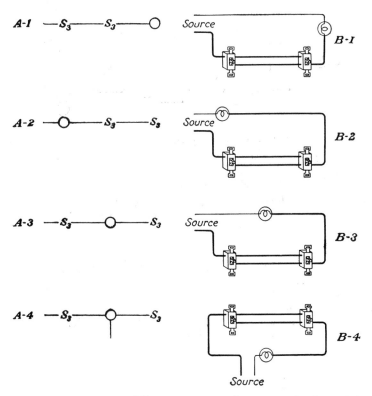

Fig. 18-14, Part 1.   Four different sequences of parts in a circuit consisting of a fixture and a pair of 3-way switches.

terminal of the other switch, run a black wire direct to the proper terminal on the fixture.   From the remaining two terminals on one switch, run wires to the corresponding terminals of the other switch, which are the only two terminals on that switch to which wires have not already been connected.   To complete the circuit, connect the incoming white wire from source to the fixture.

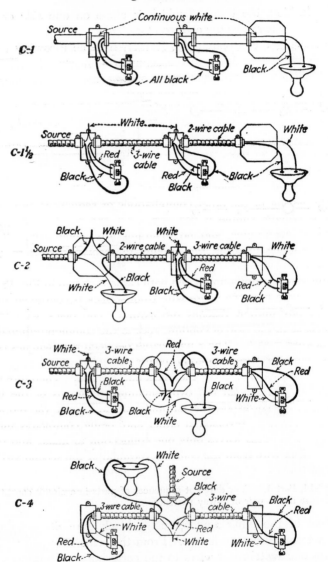

Fig. 18-14, Part 2.   Wiring methods of the combinations shown in Part 1 of this figure.

With these facts in mind, the wiring of any combination of 3-way switches with conduit becomes quite simple. Assuming that the boxes and conduit have been properly installed, as shown in Fig. 18-14, C1, which covers the sequence of A1, pull the white wire from SOURCE through the switch boxes up to the outlet where the fixture is to be used; run the black wire from SOURCE to the common terminal of the nearest 3-way switch. From the two remaining terminals of this switch, run two black wires to the corresponding two terminals of the second switch. From the common terminal of this switch, run a black wire to the fixture. All wires are black, but sometimes one red wire is used for identification purposes; any color may be used except white.

The wiring of the other combinations or sequences with conduit is equally simple if you remember the points of the two previous paragraphs, and no diagrams are shown. It will be good practice to draw the circuits in fashion similar to Fig. 18-14, C1.

This same combination wired with cable is shown in Fig. 18-14, C1½. Note how the white wire from SOURCE is continued from box to box until it reaches the fixture. The black wire from SOURCE, as in the case of conduit, goes to the common terminal of the nearest switch. The 3-wire cable between the switches contains wires of three different colors, of which the white has already been used, leaving the black and the red. Therefore run these two wires from the two remaining terminals of the first switch to the corresponding terminals of the second; the red and the black may be reversed at either end, being completely interchangeable. This leaves only one connection to make, and that is the black wire from the common terminal of the second switch to the fixture.

When some of the other sequences, such as A2, A3, or A4 in Fig. 18-14, are wired with cable, the usual difficulty in connection with the colors of the wires in standard 2-wire and 3-wire cables is met. The red wire of 3-wire cable is interchangeable with the black. Many times, however, you must take advantage of the Code's exception permitting, in switch loops, white wire to be connected to black.

C2 shows the sequence A2 and B2 of Fig. 18-14 wired with cable. The incoming cable from SOURCE contains one black, one white wire; run the white direct to the fixture. The Code requires that the other wire on the fixture may not be white; consequently the black wire of the 2-wire cable that runs to the first 3-way switch is attached to the fixture; connect the opposite end of it to the "common" terminal of the first 3-way switch. That leaves in the outlet box on which the fixture is mounted only two unconnected wires: the black wire from SOURCE and the white wire of the next run of cable. Connect them together, contrary to the general rule but permitted by the Code for switch loops. From the first 3-way switch to the second, 3-wire cable is used. Since one of these three wires is white, connect it to the white wire of the 2-wire cable and continue it on to the "common" terminal of the second switch. That leaves one black and one red wire between the two switches; connect them to the remaining terminals of each switch, completing the installation.

In wiring the sequence of A3 and B3 of Fig. 18-14, as pictured in C3, similar problems arise. There is a 2-wire cable from SOURCE entering the first switch box; from that point a length of 3-wire cable runs to the outlet box in the center, and from there another length of 3-wire cable runs on to the second switch box. Continue the white wire from SOURCE from the first switch box direct to the fixture, as the Code requires. Run the black wire from SOURCE direct to the common terminal of the first switch. Going on to the fixture, the second wire on the fixture may not be white; therefore make it black and continue it onward to the common terminal of the second switch. That leaves unconnected two terminals of each of the two switches, and your problem is to connect them to each other. There are yet two unused wires in each run of 3-wire cable, a black and a red in the one, and a white and a red in the other. Therefore make one continuous red wire out of the two reds, make a continuous white-black out of the other two, and connect the extreme ends to the two remaining terminals on each of the switches, respectively. This completes the connections.

In the case of the sequence of A4 and B4 of Fig. 18-14, as pictured in C4, the problems are similar, and you should have no difficulty in determining for yourself why each wire is of the color indicated. The fundamental rule is that the white wire from SOURCE must go to the fixture, and the second wire on the fixture may not be white.

Pilot Lights. In Fig. 18-15 is shown a frequently used combination toggle switch and pilot light, together with its internal wiring diagram. This is nothing more or less than a separate switch and a separate pilot light in a single housing. The arrangement of the terminals on another brand may be totally different from that shown in the picture. A pilot light is used at a switch which controls a light that is not visible from the switch, for example, at a switch in the house controlling the light in a garage; it is used simply as a reminder that another light is on.

In the same figure at C is shown the blueprint symbol for this combination and at D the usual wiring diagram. Compare this with Fig. 18-13, B; it is merely a case of one switch controlling two different lights, one of which happens to be located at the same point as the switch.

Using the conduit system, the connections are shown at E. Run the incoming white wire from SOURCE directly to the first fixture and extend it from there to the second fixture, which in this case happens to be the lamp in the combination device. Run the incoming black wire from SOURCE directly to the switch. From the other side of the switch, run a black wire to the first lamp and from there on to the second lamp, finishing the job. Note in the diagram that the two black wires have been labeled "No. 1" and "No. 2"; the two are not interchangeable at the switch end. This is a good example of a case where it is desirable to make the third wire red for identification purposes, in which case the incoming black wire from SOURCE would run directly to the switch terminal and red would be substituted for the black No. 2.

Wiring the combination with armored cable, as shown in Fig. 18-15, F, presents no problem. If the wires from SOURCE come in through the switch box, the problem is still simpler, as G shows.

Switched Receptacle Outlets. There is a growing trend toward controlling receptacle outlets with switches, so that all floor and similar lamps can be controlled at one time. No great problem is involved; simply consider the receptacles as so many fixtures, and connect the devices accordingly. Go through the process of connecting three receptacle outlets with a pair of 3-way switches. There can be a great many different sequences of outlets and switches; that shown in Fig. 18-16 at

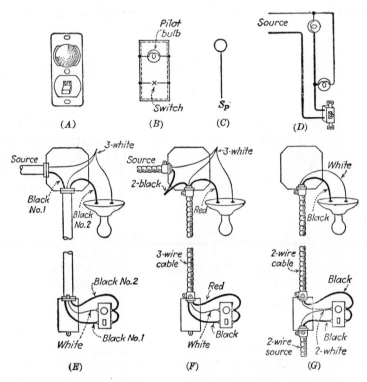

FIG. 18-15. A switch with a pilot light.

a and b is perhaps as common as any. When conduit is used, the problem is simple indeed. Run the white wire from SOURCE to each of the receptacles, connect the remaining terminal of each of the three receptacles together with black wire, and continue to the common terminal of one of the 3-way switches. From there run two wires over to the other 3-way switch. To the common terminal of this second switch, connect the black wire from SOURCE, and the job is finished. It is pictured in

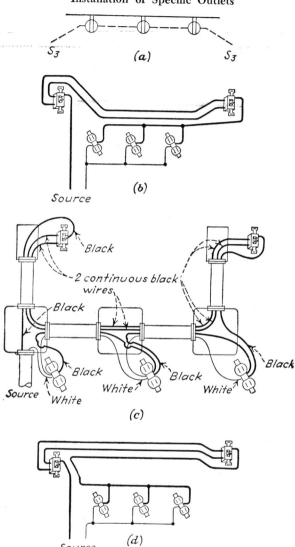

FIG. 18-16. Switched baseboard outlets.

Fig. 18-16, *c*. All the necessary wires in the boxes housing the receptacles will badly crowd the ordinary switch boxes, so the preferable method is to use 4-in. square boxes with raised covers designed to take a duplex receptacle (see Fig. 10-12, *A*).

To wire this same combination using cable is practically impossible with the particular sequence shown, because it requires four wires at some points and 4-wire cable is not stocked by dealers. Therefore when using cable, it is best simply to modify the sequence to that shown in Fig. 18-16, *d*, which requires nothing more than 3-wire cable.

Two-circuit Duplex Receptacles. When a receptacle outlet is controlled by a switch, there is the objection that it is impossible to run vacuum cleaners and similar devices without having the switch on, nor can electric clocks be used. One solution is to have a switch control some of the receptacles in the room, leaving others permanently connected. A better solution is to use duplex receptacles so designed that one half of each can be permanently live for clocks or appliances and the other half switched for floor lamps and similar devices. They differ little from ordinary receptacles in outward appearance, but careful examination will disclose that the contacts in the two halves have separate terminals (for details of construction, see Chap. 20, Fig. 20-42). Figure 18-17 shows the blueprint symbol in *A*. Note that there is no standardized symbol for such an outlet but that it is classed as a special outlet with a small subscript letter alongside it. The specifications will describe the outlet in detail.

The wiring of this combination presents no new problem. Run the white wire from source to one terminal of each half of the receptacle; frequently both halves are internally joined so that there is but a single terminal which would be alone on one side of the receptacle. Run the black wire from source to the terminal of one half of the receptacle, and from there continue it to the switch. From the switch run the black wire back to the terminal of the other half of the receptacle. All this is shown in *B* of Fig. 18-17.

If you use cable, again you meet the difficulty that one of the wires in the cable is white where both should be black; take advantage of the Code's special dispensation, and connect the white wire in the cable of the switch loop to the incoming black wire from SOURCE, as shown in C of Fig. 18-17.

If 3-way switches are used, the problem of getting the colors correct is more difficult but may be solved exactly as in the case of the outlets shown in Fig. 18-14.

Combining Outlets.   Just as in the early part of this chapter the outlets of Figs. 18-2, 18-4, and 18-7 were combined into one three-outlet combination of Fig. 18-8, so outlets may be combined

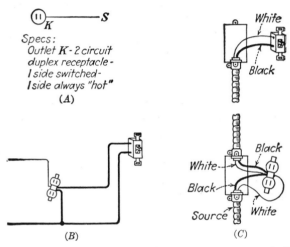

Specs:
Outlet *K* - 2 circuit
duplex receptacle -
1 side switched -
1 side always "hot"
(A)

Fig. 18-17. Wiring 2-circuit duplex receptacles so that one half of each outlet is permanently connected, the other half controlled by a wall switch.

into any desired combination with any desired total number of outlets, which then forms a circuit running back to the fuse cabinet.   To add an outlet at any point, connect the white wire of that new outlet to the white wire of the previous wiring, and the black wire of the new outlet to any previous wiring where the black wire can be traced back to the original SOURCE without being interrupted by a switch.   Simply connect the new outlet at any point on the previous wiring where a lamp connected to the two points in question would be permanently lighted.   Review Chap. 4 if this point is not entirely clear.

Installing Flush Fixtures.   The temperature inside flush fixtures is usually higher than it is in fixtures mounted in free air.   The terminals are likely to be the hottest part. Per Code Sec. 410-65, if the terminals operate at a temperature higher than 60°C or 140°F, the branch-circuit wires may not be Type T or Type R but must have an insulation suitable for the temperature involved, and may then run directly to the fixture; alternately, such high-temperature wire may run from the fixture to an outlet box located not closer than 1 ft from the fixture, through a metal raceway not less than 4 ft or more than 6 ft long. If this seems contradictory, the box located 1 ft from the fixture is connected through flexible conduit looped so as to be at least 4 ft long. Ordinary wire then is run in the branch circuit to the junction box.

A better method is to use fixtures designed to operate within the prescribed temperature limits, which permits using ordinary wire. A fixture so constructed and properly installed is shown in Fig. 18-18.

FIG. 18-18. A well-designed and properly installed flush fixture. (*The Kirlin Co.*)

Testing. When the roughing-in work has been finished, the installation must be tested. Then in case of error or mishap, the wiring is still accessible for correction. With conduit wiring, since the wires are not pulled in until after completion of the building, the test is made at that time.

Usually the test device consists of a doorbell or buzzer in connection with two dry cells connected in series, as shown in Fig. 18-19. Tape the bell to the cells; also tape the test leads to the cells so that, if the entire unit is lifted by the test leads, there will be no strain on the bell or on the dry-cell terminals.

Before proceeding to test, go around to each outlet, remove insulation from the ends of the wires, and twist together all those which will ultimately be permanently connected to each other. Leave those to which a fixture or receptacle is to be attached protruding freely out of the outlet. At all points where a switch is to be installed, temporarily twist together all the wires that will later be connected to any one switch. Be certain that no exposed bare wire is allowed to touch an outlet box or conduit or the armor of cable.

Testing Conduit Installation.   We must assume that the power has not yet been turned on.   We must assume that the appliances which will be controlled by thermostatic or similar means within the appliance (water heater, motor) have not yet been installed.   The transformer for doorbell or chimes must not be connected.

Connect one lead of your test bell to the neutral strap of your service equipment, and touch the other lead to each of the black wires to the individual circuits in turn.   The bell should *not* ring.   If it does ring, it indicates either a short circuit from the white to the black wire in the circuit under test, or a ground from

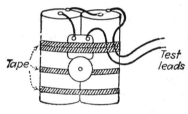

Fig. 18-19. Test outfit consisting of two dry cells and a doorbell.

the black wire to the conduit or a box, possibly at an outlet box where the black skinned wire has been allowed to touch the box.

If this test checks OK, make a different test.   If you are using circuit breakers, turn them all on.   If you are using fuses, be sure there is one in each fuseholder.   Then remove the bell from your batteries, and leave just the leads from the batteries. Connect one of these leads to the neutral strap in the service equipment, the other to *both* of the terminals in the service equipment to which the incoming service wires are connected. This will mean a temporary jumper from one terminal to the other which you must later remove—or you will have a direct short circuit at 230 volts.

Then take the bell to each outlet where a fixture or receptacle is to be installed.   Touch it across the black and white wires; in each case it should ring, just as the lamps in your fixture or floor lamp will later light when attached to the same wires. Of course, this assumes that previously all the wires which go to any one switch have been temporarily twisted together, thus duplicating the condition of all switches turned on. After each check across the black and white wire at each outlet, touch the bell across the black wire and the outlet box itself; the bell should again ring because through the conduit all the boxes are connected together and grounded and the white wire in turn is also grounded. The bell will probably not ring loudly because of higher resistance through the conduit than through the wire, but it should ring nevertheless. In making this test, if the conduit and boxes have black-enamel finish, it will be necessary to scrape off some of the enamel before touching the bell to the box, for the enamel is an insulation which might prevent the bell from ringing. If the bell rings feebly, a poor job has been done somewhere; probably the locknut on one or more boxes has not been run down tightly enough. Grounding is a safety precaution and must be properly done. If the bell rings at each point, the wiring is all right.

Testing Armored-cable Installation. Proceed exactly as with conduit.

Testing Nonmetallic-sheathed-cable Installation. If you have used metal boxes and cable with the bare grounding wire, properly installed, test as in the case of a conduit installation.

If you have used nonmetallic boxes (or metal boxes but cable without the bare grounding wire), naturally the bell cannot ring when touched to the black wire and the box. However the remainder of the test is the same as with the conduit system.

If all tests check, proceed to finish the installation as discussed in the next chapter.

Chapter 19

FINISHING: INSTALLATION OF SWITCHES AND OTHER DEVICES

In the previous chapter the roughing-in of a considerable assortment of outlets was discussed. Assume now that that work has been finished and that you are ready to install the switches and receptacles, the wall plates, the fixtures, and so on.

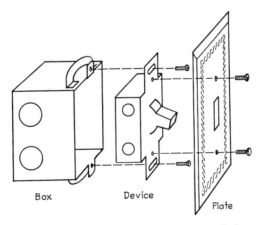

FIG. 19-1. The device is mounted on the switch box, and the wall plate is mounted on the device.

Installing Switches, Receptacles, etc. Every device of this kind is provided with a metal strap which has holes in the ends, so spaced as to fit over the holes in the ears of a switch box, on which it is mounted by means of machine screws that come with the device. The wall plate in turn is anchored to the device, not the box (see Fig. 19-1).

For a neat installation, the strap of the device must be flush with the front of the plaster. Since plastering is done after the switch boxes are installed, the front edges of the boxes are not always flush with the plaster; usually they are, and should be, a trifle below the surface of the plaster. Some means must therefore be used to mount the devices flush with the plaster. Most devices come equipped with "plaster ears" on the ends of the strap, as was shown on the switch in Fig. 4-7. These ears lie on top of the plaster, automatically bringing the device flush

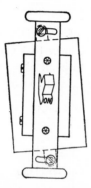

Fig. 19-2. The straps which support wiring devices have elongated holes in the ends, to permit vertical mounting even if the boxes are not mounted straight.

Fig. 19-3. A solder dipper is handy in soldering wires projecting out of ceiling outlets.

with the surface. The metal is scored near the end of the strap so that the ears can easily be broken off if they are not required. If your device does not have plaster ears, you can insert small washers between the box and the strap of the box.

Neatly installed devices must be absolutely straight up and down; often the boxes are not entirely straight. For this reason mounting holes in the ends of the mounting strap are not round but elongated, so that the device itself can be mounted straight even if the box is not straight. A glance at Fig. 19-2, which exaggerates the usual condition, should make this clear.

Before connecting wires to the terminals of switches and similar devices, cut off most of the excess wire protruding from the box, leaving only enough to make it easy to make connections to the terminals. But do not be too enthusiastic about cutting off the last fraction of an inch, for when much later a switch needs to be replaced, the terminals may be located somewhat differently from those on the original switch, requiring perhaps half an inch more wire. There is a happy medium of length: Cut off enough so that extra wire will not crowd the box, yet leave enough to make installation of the device easy.

Use care in preparing the wires for connection to terminals; skin off only enough insulation to make the connection. The insulation of the wire should extend up to the terminal. *There must be no bare wire exposed between the terminal and the end of the insulation.*

Soldering. At this point all the wires that need to be permanently joined must be soldered. The method used has already been covered in a previous chapter. For soldering wires at the ceiling, a solder pot of the type shown in Fig. 19-3 will be very useful. The solder in the pot is melted by means of the usual blowtorch. Use solderless connectors if you wish.

Installing Wall Plates. After the device has been installed in a switch box, a wall plate must in turn be installed by means of the screws that come with the plate. If the device has been properly mounted, the plate will fit snugly against both the device and the wall. If the device has been mounted slightly below the surface of the plaster, do not pull up too tightly on the screws holding the plate, for this will distort or damage the plates; it is not unusual to crack the bridge in the center of a bakelite duplex receptacle plate by pulling up too tightly. If the switches, receptacles, or other devices have plaster ears, the problem is automatically solved. If they do not have such ears, it is best to use spacing washers between the outlet box and the strap of the device in order to bring the device flush with the plate.

If the box is of the 2- or 3-gang type with a number of separate devices, the mounting of the plate will not be entirely simple because of the elongated holes in the mounting straps of the individual devices, as mentioned in an earlier paragraph. These elongated holes are a tremendous advantage in mounting devices in a single-gang box; they are a nuisance in multigang boxes,

because they permit mounting several devices so that they are
not entirely parallel with each other, as compared with the
absolutely parallel openings in a 2- or 3-gang plate. The only
thing that can be said about mounting devices in multigang
boxes is that extreme care must be used to see to it that all the
devices are absolutely straight up and down, that is, that they
are absolutely parallel to each other; then the holes for screws
in multigang plates will automatically match up with the tapped
holes in the straps of the individual devices mounted in the multigang boxes. Unless you are very careful in this detail, you will
waste a great deal of time in trying to insert screws through openings for them in plates, into corresponding holes in devices under
the plate, which holes, however, will be found to be displaced

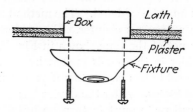

Fig. 19-4. Simple fixtures are mounted directly on the box.

far enough so that the mounting screws will enter with great
difficulty (which tends to crack the plates) or not enter at all—
there may be no visible holes for them to enter.

Wiring Lighting Fixtures. The fixture may have two terminals
for attaching the wires, in which case connect the white wire
to the whitish terminal, the black wire to the other terminal.
More often the fixture has two wire leads. If these are black and
white, there is no problem. Usually they consist of fixture wire,
as described in Chap. 6: one of them a solid color, the other of
the same color but identified with a colored tracer in the outer
fabric. The identified wire with the tracer is the neutral and
corresponds to the white wire in the outlet box. In case identification is not positive, trace the wires down into the fixture; the
one that connects to the outer screw shells of the individual
sockets is the neutral.

Hanging Fixtures. There are many ways of mounting lighting fixtures, all dependent on the style and weight of the fixture,

the particular box involved, and method of mounting the box in the ceiling or wall.

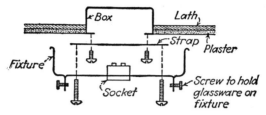

FIG. 19-5. Often larger fixtures are installed using a strap mounted on the box.

Simple fixtures sometimes mount directly on top of outlet boxes by means of bolts which fit into the ears on the boxes. This method is shown in Fig. 19-4 and requires no further description. At times the fixture is too large to permit direct mounting in this fashion, in which case a strap is used, as shown in Fig. 19-5. The strap is first installed on the outlet box, the fixture mounted on the strap. A detailed explanation should not be necessary.

FIG. 19-6. Fixture studs are installed on the bottom of boxes, to support fixtures.

Often a fixture stud, such as is shown in Fig. 19-6, is used in mounting the fixture. Mount the stud on the bottom of the switch or outlet box by means of bolts, through holes provided for the purpose. Some boxes have the stud as an integral part of the box. If you use a hanger of the types that were shown in Fig. 10-9, the stud that is part of the hanger goes

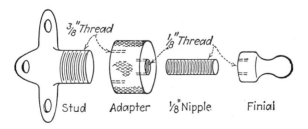

FIG. 19-7. A typical lockup unit for mounting small fixtures.

through the center knockout in the box, serves to anchor the box
to the hanger, and at the same time permits the stud to be used
for supporting the fixture. The outside of the stud is tapped to

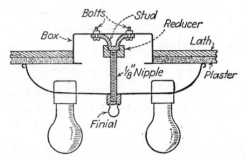

FIG. 19-8. This shows the parts of Fig. 19-7, being used to hold up a fixture.

fit ⅜-in. trade-size pipe; sometimes there is an inner female
thread fitting ⅛-in. trade-size pipe.

Figure 19-7 shows the fittings generally used, called the "lockup
unit." It consists of a reducer fitting over the fixture stud, a

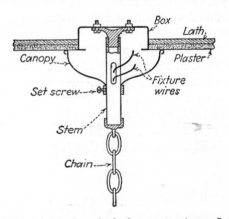

FIG. 19-9. The usual method of mounting larger fixtures.

length of ⅛-in. running-thread pipe, and a nut to hold the assembly together, the nut usually being of an ornamental nature
and then called a "finial." Figure 19-8 shows the same parts
used to hold up a simple fixture. It is a simple matter to drop

down the fixture while making connections, then to mount it on the ceiling.

If the fixture is a larger unit, such as the conventional five-light drop or a similar type, the mounting is similar, and Fig. 19-9 should make it clear. The top of the fixture usually consists of a hollow stem with an opening on the side through which the two wires from the fixture emerge. The top of the stem is threaded to fit on the fixture stud, and the mounting is as shown in the picture. While the connections are being made, drop the canopy down and then slip it back flush with the ceiling.

Sometimes the wires from the fixture come out of the end of

FIG. 19-10. A hickey, used between the fixture stud and the end of the stem on the fixture. (*Kwikon Company.*)

FIG. 19-11. In deep boxes it may be necessary to use an extension piece over the fixture stud. (*Kwikon Company.*)

the stem instead of through an opening in the side. In that case use a "hickey," shown in Fig. 19-10, between the end of the stem and the fixture stud. Sometimes the stud is too short or the box too deep, in which case use an extension piece, as shown in Fig. 19-11. Fixtures weighing more than 50 lb must be supported independently of the outlet box (Sec. 410-16 of the Code).

Mounting Wall Brackets. The method of mounting depends to a large degree on the type of box used. Many brackets are too narrow to cover up a 4- or even a $3\frac{1}{4}$-in. octagon box, so it has become customary to provide standard switch boxes on which to mount wall brackets. Sometimes a stud is mounted on the bottom of the box; in that case the mounting is completed with the lockup device that was shown in Fig. 19-7, the completed installation having the appearance shown in Fig. 19-13. More usually a fixture strap, such as shown in Fig. 19-12, is first mounted on the switch box, the fixture in turn being mounted on the strap, all as shown in Fig. 19-14.

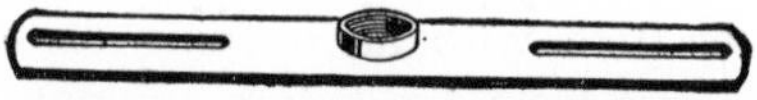

FIG. 19-12. Fixture straps are mounted on switch or outlet boxes, and the fixture is then supported by the strap.

Adjusting Height of Fixtures. A fixture with chain is adjustable as to the height above the floor and to compensate for ceilings of different heights. The height is simply controlled by removing as many chain links as required. The actual

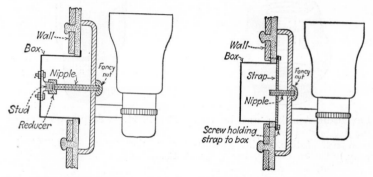

FIG. 19-13. Wall bracket mounted on switch box by means of fixture stud in bottom of box.

FIG. 19-14. Wall bracket mounted on switch box by means of fixture strap mounted on box.

height will be governed by personal preference and location. If the fixture hangs above a dining-room table, hang it at least 24 in. and preferably 30 to 36 in. above the table. Again this will be dependent upon the type of fixture, the ceiling height, and similar factors.

Chapter 20

MISCELLANEOUS WIRING

In the wiring of any house, there are problems and niceties of detail that could not readily be included in the discussions of previous chapters, so they will be grouped here in a separate chapter. Study this chapter well because from it you should get ideas that will help you to make your installation one that is better than just average.

Heavy Appliances. The installation of appliances such as range, water heater, clothes dryer, and so on will be covered in the next chapter.

Quiet Switches. Ordinary switches have an annoying click as they are turned on or off. Usually this click may not even be noticed, but in sickrooms, children's rooms, and similar locations the click can be decidedly annoying. In the dead of night, a switch turned on or off in the hall on the *outside* of a bedroom wall can sound very loud inside that room.

Two kinds of noiseless switches are available and are in common use. The original noiseless switch was the mercury type, in which a pool of mercury inside a glass tube takes the place of mechanical contacts. The more recent type is the "general-use AC-only" type of switch described in Chap. 4.

Touch-type Switches. In using the ordinary switch, moving the handle up turns it on, moving it down turns it off. Recently the touch type of switch has been introduced. Touching the handle and pushing it in slightly turns it on; touching it again turns it off. One of these is shown in Fig. 20-1.

Interchangeable Devices. Several switch boxes can be joined together to make one 2-gang or 3-gang or even larger box, permitting two or three or more switches, receptacles, and similar

devices to be used side by side.   However, the more devices used
side by side, the larger the wall plate becomes, until it arrives at
the stage where it becomes unsightly.   Sometimes there is not
sufficient room for a 3-gang plate at a particular point on a wall
where three switches are to be used.   Even if there is room, the

FIG.   20-1.   A   Tap-lite
switch.   Touching   the
one   button   turns   the
switch on; the next tap
turns it off. (*Minneapo-
lis-Honeywell   Regulator
Co.*)

holes in the mounting straps of the switches are, as already explained, oval, making it none too easy to mount three switches
in a 3-gang box so that a 3-gang wall plate will later fit easily and
neatly.   Therefore it is not surprising that there were developed
devices very small in physical size so that two or three can be
used in a single-gang switch box.

The basic devices, such as switches, receptacles, pilot lights,
and so on, are stocked separately; typical pieces are shown in
Fig. 20-2.   They are mounted by the user on the skeleton strap
of Fig. 20-3, and as shown in successive steps of the same illustration.

While a single strap with three devices can be mounted in a
single-gang switch box, or two straps with six devices in a double-
gang switch box, this does lead to some crowding of wires because
of the considerable number of wires involved.   For that reason it
is desirable to use a 4-in.-square box with a raised cover.   If the
cover which was shown in *A* of Fig. 10-12 is used, three devices
can be used; if the double type shown in *B* of Fig. 10-12 is used,
six devices can be used.

Plug-in Strip.   No matter how many receptacles there are provided in a home, there always seems to be a need for more.
Therefore, at least for better homes, consider the material known
as "plug-in strip," shown in Fig. 20-4.   This consists of a steel

channel with a cover providing outlets at regular intervals.   The
spacing varies, but for homes 18 in. is popular.   Many varieties
are available.   In some, the receptacles are wired by the installer;
in others, the receptacles come already connected to continuous
parallel wires at proper intervals to fit the covers.

FIG. 20-2. Separate devices of this style are assembled on the job into any
desired combinations.   (*Pass & Seymour, Inc.*)

FIG. 20-3. The devices of Fig. 20-2 are assembled on a skeleton strap as
shown in steps above.   (*Pass & Seymour, Inc.*)

The material is installed sometimes on top of the baseboard,
giving the effect of being part of it, sometimes in kitchens some
distance above the counter.   Connections are made to the back
of the channel with conduit or cable, as to an outlet box.

FIG. 20-4. Plug-in strip provides outlets at very frequent intervals, making
a most flexible and adequate installation.   (*National Electric Products
Corp.*)

Surface Wiring.   Where the wiring is to be permanently exposed as in some basements, attics, or garages, you have a choice
of several methods.   You may use cable or conduit with surface-
type boxes of the type that were shown in Fig. 10-19.   An alternate is to use the nonmetallic-sheathed cable, preferably Type
NMC, and special surface wiring devices which are combinations

of box plus device such as switch or receptacle.   Since such devices are more frequently used in providing additional outlets in

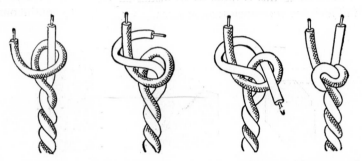

FIG. 20-5. In assembling drop cords, provide an Underwriters' knot at each end of the cord.

buildings that were previously wired, they will be described at the end of Chap. 22, concerning old work.

Door Switches.   A touch of luxury is a built-in door switch in closets.   Opening the door turns on the light; closing it turns the light off.   One was shown in Fig. 12-2. Switches of this kind are still expensive; when they become available at reasonable prices, they will receive the popularity they deserve.

FIG. 20-6. A trouble light of this kind is almost a necessity in any garage; provide an outlet for it. (*General Electric Co.*)

Telephones.   In ordinary residential work, too frequently no attention is paid to telephones, the problem of installation being left strictly up to the telephone people.   They do a good job, but still in many cases an exposed run of wire remains in view.   Therefore it is suggested that runs of conduit be installed, terminating in switch boxes, at the locations where the instruments are to be installed.   Usually the switch box is covered with a special wall plate with a single bushed opening for the telephone cord.

Drop Cords.   In making up a drop cord, assemble the parts so that their weight is supported, not by the copper conductor of the lamp cord used, but rather by the entire structure of the lamp cord, including the insulation and the braid. The simplest way of doing this is properly to install an Underwriters' knot at top and bottom. This knot is simply made, as Fig. 20-5 shows.

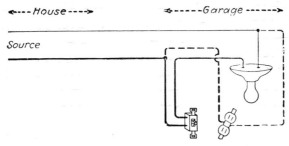

FIG. 20-7. Simple garage circuit. The light is controlled only by the switch in the garage.

The drop will be supported from the ceiling by a blank cover with a bushed hole in the center, mounted on any type of outlet box.

Garages. Garage lighting may consist of a single light, or it may incorporate a number of lights with an outlet for a trouble

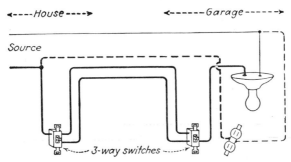

FIG. 20-8. The garage light is now controlled from either house or garage. The outlet is always on. This requires four wires between house and garage.

light of the type shown in Fig. 20-6 or for a battery charger or similar device. At least one of the lights should be controlled by 3-way switches at both house and garage.

If the light is to be controlled only at the garage, only two wires are required from the house to the garage. An outlet may also be installed, as shown by dotted lines in Fig. 20-7.

If the light is to be controlled by 3-way switches in house and garage, then three wires must be run, as shown in Fig. 20-8. If

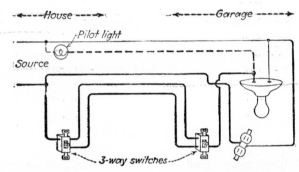

Fig. 20-9. The same circuit shown in Fig. 20-8, with the addition of a pilot light in the house to indicate whether the garage light is on or off. This requires five wires.

the wires shown in dotted lines are disregarded, this becomes identical with Fig. 4-22, the basic diagram for 3-way switches. If, however, an outlet is installed as shown in the previous diagram, the outlet will be disconnected with the light when it is

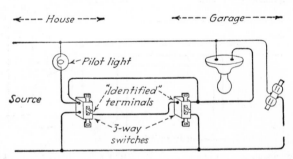

Fig. 20-10. This circuit using only four wires serves the same purpose as the circuit of Fig. 20-9, using five wires.

turned off at either end. This is undesirable because, for example, the outlet may be used for a charger which is to charge the battery in the car overnight, and the light should not burn all night. Therefore a fourth wire as shown in dotted lines in Fig.

20-8 is necessary, making the outlet strictly independent of the switches and the light controllable from either end. A "trick"

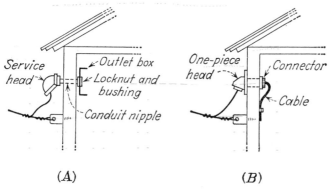

Service head

Outlet box

Locknut and bushing

Conduit nipple

One-piece head

Connector

Cable

(A)   (B)

FIG. 20-11. Two ways of having wires enter the garage. The same methods are used for other wiring; for example, farm buildings.

circuit permits using three wires instead of four, but it definitely violates Code requirements in several important respects and is an unsafe circuit.

Very desirable also is a pilot light at the switch in the house (see Fig. 20-9). If the dotted lines are disregarded, the result is the same as the former circuit of Fig. 20-8. To add the pilot light, run a fifth wire as shown in dotted lines.

Whereas the circuit shown in Fig. 20-9 is the usual one when 3-way switches are used, plus a pilot light at the house end, plus a permanently live receptacle at the far end, there is another circuit available which requires only four wires instead of five. It nevertheless meets Code requirements and therefore may be used. It is shown in Fig. 20-10. It requires a bit more care in installation to make sure all connections are correct.

FIG. 20-12. This wall-type entrance fitting is most convenient for bringing wires into outbuildings. (*Killark Electric Mfg. Co.*)

If the wires to the garage are to run overhead, they must be securely anchored at each end. Either of the insulators shown in Fig. 17-4 or 17-5 may be used. Where the wires enter or leave a building, either of the methods shown in Fig. 20-11 is suitable. A most convenient fitting to be used at that point is shown in Fig. 20-12 and shown installed in *B* of Fig. 20-11. Be sure the insulators are mounted at a point lower than the entrance of the wires into the building.

Underground Wires. Use any of the cables described in Chap. 17.

Outdoor Wiring. In most installations the outdoor wiring is limited to garage wiring, already described, and perhaps an out-

F<small>IG</small>. 20-13.   F<small>IG</small>. 20-14.   F<small>IG</small>. 20-15.   F<small>IG</small>. 20-16.

F<small>IG</small>. 20-13. Outdoor outlet. The cover closes automatically when the outlet is not in use. (*Killark Electric Mfg. Co.*)
F<small>IG</small>. 20-14. Install an ordinary switch in this housing for an outdoor installation. (*Killark Electric Mfg. Co.*)
F<small>IG</small>. 20-15. Typical weatherproof socket for outdoor use. (*General Electric Co.*)
F<small>IG</small>. 20-16. Insulating block for supporting streamers on "messenger wires"; required on runs longer than 40 ft. (*Pass & Seymour, Inc.*)

door outlet for Christmas-tree lights and similar purposes. A convenient unit for this purpose, shown in Fig. 20-13, is surface-mounted on the wall and has a flapper-type cover which covers the outlet when not in use. For outdoor switches, use the housing shown in Fig. 20-14. Install any kind of ordinary switch in the housing; it will be automatically protected from the weather. Outdoor wiring for farms will be discussed in Chap. 24.

Festoon Lighting. At times it will be necessary to install temporary decorative or other outdoor lights fed by overhead runs. This type of lighting is termed "festoon lighting" by the Code. The minimum size wire that may be used is No. 12 unless

supported by messenger wires as described below. The wires
must be supported on insulators at each end, and the sockets
must be of a type approved for outdoor use, usually of the type
shown in Fig. 20-15.

If the span is over 40 ft, the electrical wires alone may not be
depended upon for mechanical strength, but they must be supported by a messenger cable, which is usually a steel wire of some
kind. The electrical wires are supported from the messenger
cable at intervals by means of suspension cleats, one type of

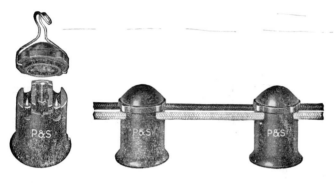

FIG. 20-17. Using this weatherproof socket, stranded wires are laid in the
grooves of the socket; the cover is then screwed on. The sharp points
puncture the insulation and make contact with the conductor. (*Pass &
Seymour, Inc.*)

which is shown in Fig. 20-16. The individual socket leads must
be soldered to the wires, and the points of attachment must be
staggered so that the soldered joint in one wire will not come
directly opposite that in the other wire. The wires must clear
the ground by a minimum of 10 ft in residential neighborhoods
and by 12 ft in all other localities.

A pin-point type of socket, as shown in Fig. 20-17, is very
handy for streamers, in that no soldering is necessary. The wires
are merely laid into the grooves in the device, and the cover is
screwed on. This causes the pin points to puncture the insulation and make contact with the conductor of the wire, making
the assembly shown. Only *stranded* wire may be used for the
purpose.

Low-voltage Wiring. In this term is included wiring for door-bells and other signals, thermostats, and similar devices operating at low voltages. Usually this means 30 volts or less.

The power for operating such circuits is usually derived from small transformers. Under no circumstances may low-voltage wires be run in the same conduit or armor or cable with other wires carrying full voltage. They must come no closer than 2 in. to other wires unless such wires are in conduit. Where the wires come closer than 2 in., use loom or porcelain tubes over the low-voltage wires. They may never enter an outlet or switch box carrying full-voltage wires unless a metal barrier of the same thickness as the walls of the box separates the two types of wiring.

Fig. 20-18. A transformer for operating doorbells and similar equipment. (*General Electric Co.*)

Transformers. If only the usual doorbells and buzzers are to be operated, ordinary doorbell transformers are used. One type is shown in Fig. 20-18. Mount the transformer near an outlet box. Connect the flexible leads to the 115-volt wires inside the box. Similar transformers are available mounted on a box cover, which is then installed on an outlet box. The screw terminals on the transformer deliver the low-voltage output of the transformer. Such transformers have a maximum capacity of about 5 watts and usually deliver somewhere between 6 and 10 volts. They are suitable only for operating a single device at a time.

Larger transformers are available which give a combination of voltages such as 6, 12, and 18, while again others are available in larger wattage capacity.

Transformers of this type are so designed that, even in case the secondary is short-circuited, the current flowing will be limited to the rating of the transformer. Such transformers are usually rated not over 100 volt-amp, and the type used for residential wiring is seldom over 25 volt-amp. Because of this limited current there is no danger of fire, and because of the low voltage there is no danger of shock. Therefore the Code has no limitations on the type wire used or the installation of it, except those points brought out in the previous paragraph.

The wires used for low-voltage work require and have little insulation. Ordinary bell wire or "annunciator wire," as it is formally called, consists merely of the bare copper with a layer of plastic or two layers of cotton, wrapped in opposite directions, then paraffined (see Fig. 20-19). Two or more of these wires

FIG. 20-19. Wire for low-voltage signal systems such as doorbells requires little insulation.

are often twisted together, with an over-all braid, forming what is known as "thermostat" cable; it is shown in Fig. 20-20. Each wire in the cable has a different color braid for ease in identification. Use of this cable makes a much neater installation than use

FIG. 20-20. Thermostat cable consists of a number of wires of the type shown in Fig. 20-19. (*Crescent Insulated Wire & Cable Co.*)

of two or more separate wires; there is also less danger of damage to the wires, which would be more a nuisance than a hazard. The usual size of the wire is No. 18, although No. 19 is also used, and the heavier sizes are available. The size must be chosen to match the length of the run, the load, and the voltage available. For ordinary residential use, No. 18 is universally used.

In use this wire is merely run over the surface or fished through walls without further protection. It is stapled to the surface over which it runs with insulated staples of the type shown in Fig. 20-21.

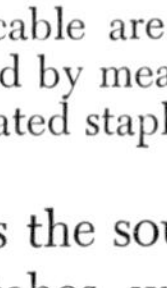

Low-voltage Circuits. It is a very simple matter to draw circuits for low-voltage work.

FIG. 20-21. Bell wire and thermostat cable are supported by means of insulated staples.

Simply consider the secondary of the transformer as the SOURCE for the circuit, and consider the push buttons as switches, which they are. The basic circuit is shown in Fig. 20-22. Disregard for the moment the dotted lines, and the circuit becomes most simple. If the bell is to be controlled from a number of different push buttons, merely add additional buttons as shown in the dotted lines.

Figure 20-23 shows a similar circuit but with both a bell and a buzzer, the former for the front door and the latter for the back door. Figure 20-24 shows the same circuit using a combination bell and buzzer. This device has three terminals. One of the three is usually a terminal screw that is fastened directly to the frame of the device, not insulated from it in any way. This is the terminal that runs direct to the transformer. Sometimes it is the middle terminal, as shown in the drawing; sometimes it is one of the other terminals. The two remaining terminals go directly to the two push buttons.

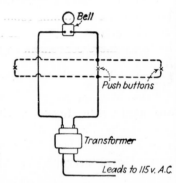

Fig. 20-22. The basic diagram for a doorbell is most simple.

Additional buzzer circuits may be operated from the same transformer, as required. Mount the buzzer where desired; run

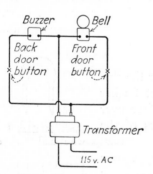

Fig. 20-23. This shows a bell and a buzzer operating from one transformer.

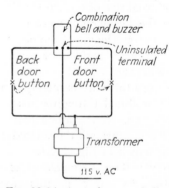

Fig. 20-24. A combination bell and buzzer has been substituted for the two separate devices shown in Fig. 20-23.

a wire from one terminal direct to the transformer or, for that matter, to any other handy nearby wire that runs direct to the secondary of the transformer; from the other terminal of the buzzer run a wire to the push button, and from the push button back to the other side of the transformer or, if handy, to a nearby wire that runs directly to the other side of the transformer.

A common use for such an auxiliary buzzer system is from a button under the dining-room table to the buzzer in the kitchen. The same buzzer used for the back door could be used, but it will be found more convenient to have a separate buzzer which will have a different tone so that it can be distinguished from the back-door buzzer.

Types of Push Buttons. Several types of buttons, both surface and flush mounting, are shown in Fig. 20-25; there is a great

FIG. 20-25. Push buttons are available in many styles. (*Nutone, Inc.*)

variety of sizes, shapes, and finishes to suit the user. For apartments the buttons are usually built into the combination mailbox, directory, and entrance telephone or speaking tube. A floor-tread button of the type shown in Fig. 20-26 is used under the rug at the dining-room table to operate the kitchen buzzer; being about 4 in. in diameter, it will operate regardless of the point where the pressure is applied.

Types of Bells. The ordinary bells and buzzers are none too attractive in appearance, for which reason a type has been developed which fits inside ordinary switch and outlet boxes, being then covered with lou-

FIG. 20-26. A floor-tread type of button. It is used under the rug, and operated by the foot. (*Edwards & Co., Inc.*)

vered covers far neater than exposed bells.

An assortment of the devices is shown in Fig. 20-27, while Fig. 20-28 shows an installation. Note the barrier separating the

115-volt wires up to the transformer from the low-voltage wiring to the devices.

Chimes. Instead of doorbells and buzzers, chimes are now generally used. These are available in many styles from the very simple to the very elaborate. Several are shown in Fig. 20-29.

FIG. 20-27. Flush concealed bells and similar devices are far neater than the ordinary type. (*Edwards & Co., Inc.*)

Most of them are so designed that they sound two notes for the front door, one note for the back door.

Wire them as you would a bell or buzzer. Do remember, however, that most chimes require a bit more power to operate than an ordinary bell or buzzer requires. For a good clear signal the transformer should deliver in the range of 12 to 20 volts, as

 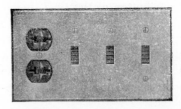

FIG. 20-28. An installation of the devices shown in Fig. 20-27. (*Edwards & Co., Inc.*)

compared with the usual 6 to 8 volts for bells. If you are replacing a bell with chimes, you will probably have to replace the existing transformer with one of higher voltage.

Remote-control Wiring System. If a light is to be turned on and off from a single switch, the wiring is very simple indeed. Even if it is to be turned on and off from two different points, the wiring is not especially complicated but often involves long runs of wire. If the light is to be turned on and off from three, four, or more different points, the wiring becomes decidedly complicated. It also becomes expensive because it requires 4-way switches, long runs of wire or cable, and much labor. Yet lights and other outlets controlled from many different points are very desirable. The remote-control system of wiring makes it possible to turn a light on or off from two, three, six, or even a dozen points at a very reasonable cost.

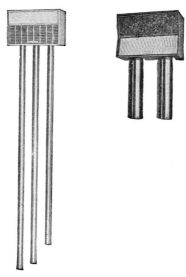

FIG. 20-29. Chimes with musical notes have almost completely displaced doorbells. (*Nutone, Inc.*)

In this system the 115-volt wires are brought only to the outlets which are to be controlled by switches, but they are not run to the switches. An electrically operated switch called a "relay" is mounted *in the outlet box* for each fixture or receptacle to be controlled. Special switches, which are really only push buttons, are used. The power for operating the relays comes from a transformer installed in basement, attic, or other convenient location; it steps the 115-volt alternating current down to 24-volt alternating current. The transformer is the type described earlier in this chapter; even if short-circuited, it delivers so little power that there is no danger of fire. For that reason and because the voltage is so low, inexpensive wires may be used between switches and relays, installed as in the case of doorbell wiring, all of which leads to saving in cost of both material and labor.

FIG. 20-30. The remote-control relay is an electrically operated switch. It is installed in the box on which the fixture is mounted. (*General Electric Co.*)

The relay is shown in Fig. 20-30, the switch in Fig. 20-31, the transformer in Fig. 20-32. Several types of wire commonly used for wiring between transformer, switches, and relays are shown in Fig. 20-33; any wire No. 19 or heavier is suitable.

The operation of the relay is shown in Figs. 20-34 and 20-35, which, however, do not pretend to show the exact mechanical arrangement inside the relay but rather only the principle. Inside the relay are two coils or electromagnets, A and B, connected for the moment to some dry cells for power, and two push buttons, A and B. When push button A is momentarily closed as in Fig. 20-34, current flows through coil A, thus making a magnet out of

FIG. 20-31. The switch used in a remote-control system is equivalent to two push buttons. (*General Electric Co.*)

it while the current flows. This attracts the upper end of the armature inside the relay, closing the 115-volt circuit as shown. The circuit stays closed even if coil A is no longer energized; a momentary flow of current while the push button is closed is sufficient. If later push button B is momentarily closed as in Fig. 20-35, current flows through coil B, thus making a magnet out of

it while the current flows. This attracts the lower end of the
armature in the relay, opening the 115-volt circuit as shown.
Thus the switch operates like any other on-off
switch, except that it is controlled from a
distance.

The relay is so made that the round shank
fits into a ½-in. knockout. Push the relay
through a knockout from the inside of the box.
The 115-volt leads are then inside the box;
the low-voltage leads on the outside of the
box. Instead of using dry cells to operate
the relays, use the transformer already described. See Fig. 20-36, which shows a complete installation of one outlet controlled by
four switches. Use as many as you wish and

Fig. 20-32. One
transformer is used
for an entire in-
stallation of re-
mote-control wir-
ing. (*General Elec-
tric Co.*)

in any location you wish. Merely connect the No. 1 terminals of
all switches together, all the No. 2 terminals, all the No. 3 terminals. If you wish to control two or more outlets at the same
time from the same switch, merely wire the several outlets together just as if ordinary switches were to be used, and place the
relay in the most convenient box.

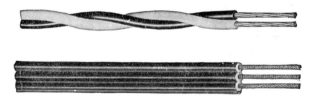

Fig. 20-33. Wire used to connect switches does not need much insulation
because of the low voltage. (*General Electric Co.*)

Many diagrams could be furnished here for wiring many different combinations, but that should not be necessary. If you
study the principle carefully, you will be able to make your own
diagrams.

In actual installation, outlet boxes are used only where 115-
volt wires enter the boxes. The switches shown in Fig. 20-31
are designed for surface mounting; similar ones are available for
flush mounting. They are mounted on special straps, up to three

per strap, occupying the same space as one ordinary switch; special wall plates are used. Since no box is used, much time is saved, and switches may be located where there would be no space for a switch box in ordinary wiring. The low-voltage wire 's merely stapled to the surface over which it runs. In old work,

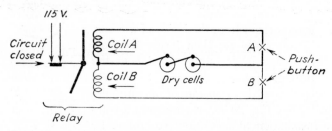

Fig. 20-34. This shows the principle of operation of the remote-control system. Coil A in the relay is momentarily energized, which turns the switch on.

it is fished through walls, concealed behind baseboards, or run exposed.

In new work, two methods of installation are possible. In the first method, all the work is done before the lathing and plastering are done. The relays are installed in the boxes, and the low-

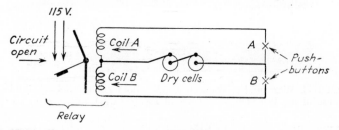

Fig. 20-35. The same circuit shown in Fig. 20-34, but now coil B is momentarily energized. This turns the switch off.

voltage wires are connected to the relay. In that case be sure to leave at least 6 in. of slack in the low-voltage wires at the relay so that if a relay at some future time proves defective, it can be removed from the inside of the box; unless you have provided the extra 6 in. of wire on the low-voltage side, it would be impossible to remove the relay.   The alternate method is to install the relays after the plastering has been done.   Install the low-voltage wires and let them project about 6 in. into the outlet box through the knockout in which the relay will later be mounted.   Then, later, connect the low-voltage wires to the proper terminals on the relay, push them out through the knockout, and install the relay in the knockout.

Use of this remote-control system will make the electrical system of any home many times as flexible as when ordinary switches

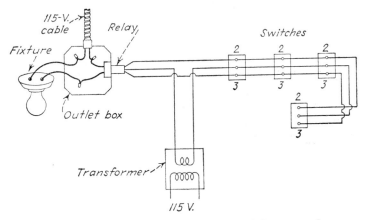

FIG. 20-36. One outlet connected with four different switches.

are used.   A switch can be installed in an additional location at a very nominal cost, even if the switch is an afterthought.   Use it to approach the ideal—enter a house by any door, go to any place in the house, but never be in darkness, yet be able to turn off lights behind you without retracing your steps.

Using 3- and 4-way switches for basement or garage lights, you never know whether or not the light is on unless you can see the light; with the remote-control system, simply push the off button, and if the light was on, it is now off.   Use it on the farm for yard lights, thus avoiding long runs of expensive 115-volt wiring. If you wish, install a master switch in the bedroom and thus be able upon retiring to make sure all lights are off without ever leaving the bedroom.

Three-wire Circuits.   Assuming that the building has a 3-wire
115/230-volt service, 3-wire circuits can be used to good advantage as a method of reducing voltage drop.   Let us analyze what
a 3-wire circuit is.

See Fig. 20-37, which shows an ordinary 2-wire circuit; assume

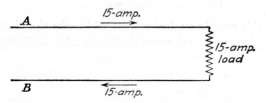

Fig. 20-37. One 2-wire circuit, carrying 15 amp.

that it is wired with No. 14 wire, that it is 50 ft long, which
means that the current flows through 100 ft of wire.   Assume the
load is 15 amp, the maximum carrying capacity of the wire.   The
voltage drop then is approximately 3.86 volts, or about 3.3%.

Now see Fig. 20-38, which shows two such circuits, one on each

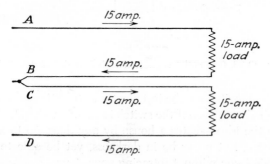

Fig. 20-38. Two 2-wire circuits, each carrying 15 amp and fed by opposite
legs of a 3-wire service.

leg of the 3-wire service.   The voltage drop on each circuit will
still be 3.86 volts.   Note, however, that the two neutrals are
connected to each other at the service and that they run parallel
to each other.   That being the case, why use two wires?   Why
not use just one wire, as in Fig. 20-39?   You could easily jump to
the conclusion that that might be all right, except that the one

neutral wire serving two circuits would have to be twice as big
as before to carry 2 × 15, or 30 amp.   That is a wrong conclusion.
In Fig. 20-38, each of the two neutral wires B and C does carry
15 amp, but note the direction of the arrows in the picture.   The

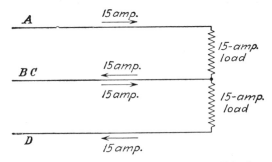

FIG. 20-39. If the two circuits of Fig. 20-38 run parallel, do not run two
neutrals.   Use one and make one 3-wire circuit.   Here each half of the
3-wire circuit carries 15 amp.

flow of current in B at any given instant is in a direction opposite
to that in C.   So also in Fig. 20-39: at any given instant the single
wire BC can be said to carry 15 amp in one direction, also 15 amp
in the opposite direction, and the two cancel each other.   In

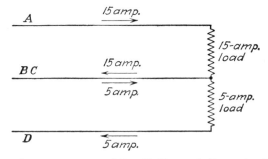

FIG. 20-40. The 3-wire circuit of Fig. 20-39, one half carrying 15 amp, the
other half carrying 5 amp.

other words, wire BC now carries no current at all; the circuit
will operate just as well with wire BC missing.   Note carefully
that this statement is correct only when the amperage in the one
circuit is exactly equal to that in the other.

But what about the voltage drop? In circuits of Figs. 20-37 and 20-38, the voltage drop is 3.86 volts, based on 15 amp flowing through 50 ft of wire A, plus 50 ft of wire B, or a total of 100 ft. In Fig. 20-39, however, 15 amp flows only through 50 ft of wire A, for wire BC carries no current. Therefore the voltage drop is only half as great as in the case of Figs. 20-37 and 20-38. In the entire 3-wire circuit there are only 150 ft of wire as compared with 200 ft in two 2-wire circuits. Therefore by using one 3-wire circuit instead of two 2-wire circuits, we save 25% of the copper and still reduce voltage drop by 50%.

If the two halves of the 3-wire circuit are not equally loaded, as, for example, in Fig. 20-40, there is still an advantage. Sup-

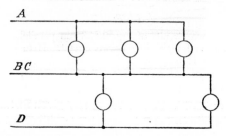

FIG. 20-41. Three-wire circuits need not carry a single large load. Install load where required.

pose, as shown in that picture, one half of the circuit carries 15 amp, the other half 5 amp, then the neutral carries the difference, or 10 amp. The voltage drop will not be reduced by 50%, as in the case of equally loaded halves, but the total losses in the 3-wire circuit will be less than in two separate 2-wire circuits. If one of the two halves carries no current at all, then the other half functions exactly like any 2-wire circuit. This is also what happens if a fuse blows in one of the two hot wires; what is left is an ordinary 2-wire circuit.

While Figs. 20-39 and 20-40 show 3-wire circuits with a single load at the far end of each line, 3-wire circuits are not limited to such applications. See Fig. 20-41, which shows a 3-wire circuit with loads connected at various points. No matter how these loads are spaced, the total losses in such a 3-wire circuit are always lower than in two separate 2-wire circuits.

Application of 3-wire Circuits. If in ordinary wiring (whether in house, barn, or other building) two separate 115-volt circuits would ordinarily be installed more or less parallel to each other, each circuit using two wires, install one 3-wire circuit. When using cable, remember that 3-wire cable has one white wire; it is the neutral of the 3-wire circuit.

When a 3-wire circuit is installed using cable, the cable will have the usual white neutral wire and one black, one red. When

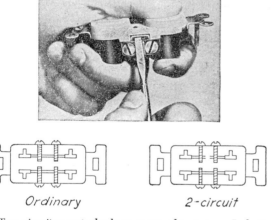

Ordinary   2-circuit

Fig. 20-42. Two-circuit receptacles have many advantages. In better quality receptacles, an ordinary receptacle can be converted into the two-circuit type. (*General Electric Co.*)

using conduit, choose these same colors. Having one hot wire black and the other red makes it easy to know which "leg," or half of the circuit, you are working on. Be sure that the white wire runs to every outlet, for if you were to connect an outlet between the red and the black wire, it would then operate at 230 instead of 115 volts. Be sure to distribute the receptacles on the circuit more or less evenly between the two legs. If two receptacles are located close to each other, so that it is likely both will be used at the same time, be sure that they are on opposite legs of the circuit.

Two-circuit Receptacles. A nicety is to use special duplex receptacles which look like the ordinary type but are wired differently inside and are known as "2-circuit duplex receptacles." The ordinary receptacle has one (or a pair of) terminal screw common to both halves of the receptacle, another screw (or a pair of them) also common to both of the halves of the receptacle. The 2-circuit receptacle has one (or a pair of) terminal screw common to both halves of the receptacle but two separate screws *not* common to both halves. Each of the screws serves only one of the two halves of the receptacle. Ordinary duplex receptacles of better quality are so constructed that they can be converted from the ordinary type into the 2-circuit type. All this is shown in Fig. 20-42.

Such 2-circuit receptacles find their widest use in living rooms and other parts of the house, when you wish to leave half of each receptacle permanently connected for clocks, but want to switch the other half on and off with a wall switch, so that floor lamps, radio, and similar devices can all be turned off at one time. The circuit for this was discussed in Chap. 18, Fig. 18-17.

Another common application for this 2-circuit receptacle is on the two special appliance circuits in the kitchen. If these two circuits are merged into a single 3-wire circuit, run the neutral to the common terminal, the red and black wires to the other two terminals. Then when two different appliances are plugged into the same duplex receptacle, they will automatically be on opposite legs of the 3-wire circuit.

Chapter 21

WIRING OF HEAVY APPLIANCES

The Code classifies all appliances into two groups: portable and "fixed" (permanently installed). It is sometimes difficult to decide whether a given appliance is portable or fixed. Common sense must rule. An appliance which is intended to be plugged into a receptacle is portable. An oil-burner motor once installed will never be moved from one location to another and is therefore fixed. The Code, however, classifies electric ranges and clothes dryers as portable, presumably because, in moving, you can take them from one house to another.

Larger Receptacles. In the wiring of heavy appliances, you will often need receptacles larger than the ordinary household variety. In Fig. 21-1 are shown several varieties with their approximate dimensions. Note that the arrangement and size of the openings are such that a plug that fits one receptacle will not fit the other.

At *A* is shown the ordinary household receptacle (almost always used in the "duplex" form) rated at 15 amp 125 volts. At *B* is shown the same receptacle with a third opening for the grounding prong; this is the "grounding receptacle" described in Chap. 20. It also is rated at 15 amp 125 volts. At *C* and *D* are shown similar receptacles also rated at 15 amp but with tandem instead of parallel slots, and then rated at 250 volts.

At *E* is shown a receptacle rated at 20 amp 250 volts, and at *F* one rated at 30 amp 250 volts.

All those mentioned are for use on 2-wire circuits, with *B* and *D* having provision for a third grounding wire. Heavy-duty 3-wire receptacles are shown at *G* and *H*, and they may be used on 3-wire 115/230-volt circuits or on 230-volt circuits using the

347

third contact for grounding purposes.   The one at *G* is rated at
30 amp 250 volts, and the one at *H* is rated at 50 amp 250 volts.
The two are of the same size, but the one rated at 30 amp has one
L-shaped opening and the 50-amp has a straight opening, so that
one plug will not fit both.

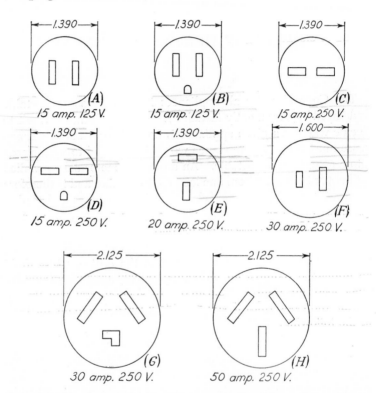

Fig. 21-1. The shape and size of receptacles depends on their rating in
amperes and volts.

Do not imagine that these are the only available receptacles.
There are literally dozens of others, in 2-, 3-, 4-, and even 5-wire
types.   Besides the ordinary varieties there are others so designed
that the plug cannot be inserted or removed without first twisting
it to lock or unlock it.   Other brands are of totally different construction, so that only a plug and receptacle of the same brand

will fit each other. However, the types illustrated are the more common varieties.

Receptacles come in a variety of mounting methods to fit various boxes and plates, flush and surface types. The 50-amp receptacle is shown in both the surface-mounting type and flush-mounting type in Fig. 21-2, which also shows a typical plug with "pigtail" cord attached, to fit. These are used mostly in the wiring of electric ranges. The similar 30-amp receptacle is used mostly for clothes dryers.

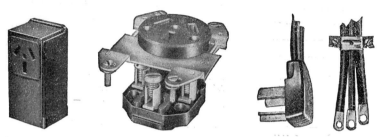

Fig. 21-2. Typical 50-amp receptacles, surface and flush type, and a "pigtail" cord connector. (*General Electric Co.*)

Individual Circuits for Appliances. The Code rules as to when an appliance requires an individual branch circuit, serving no other load, are quite complicated. In general, you will be following the Code rules if you provide a separate circuit for each of the following:

1. Range.
2. Water heater.
3. Clothes dryer.
4. Any 115-volt "fixed" (permanently installed) appliance rated at 12 amp (1,380 watts) or more. This includes motors.
5. Any "fixed" (permanently installed) 230-volt appliance.
6. Any automatically started motor such as on an oil burner, furnace fan, pump, and so on.

Disconnecting Means and Overcurrent Protection. Every appliance must be provided with some means of disconnecting it completely from the circuit, and also with overcurrent protection. The requirements depend on a number of factors:

1. Portable or "fixed."
2. The wattage rating of the appliance.
3. In the case of motors, whether automatically started or not.

Portable Appliances, Disconnecting Means. A plug-and-receptacle arrangement is all that is required. Of course, the plug and receptacle must have a rating in amperes and volts at least as great as that of the appliance.

Small Fixed Appliances. If the appliance is rated at 300 watts or less (⅛ hp or less), no special action need be taken. The branch-circuit overcurrent protection is sufficient. No special disconnecting means is required.

Larger Fixed Appliances (Nonmotor). If the appliance is connected to a circuit also serving other loads, and if the circuit is protected by a circuit breaker (not fuses), no special action need be taken. The branch-circuit circuit breaker is sufficient. But if the branch circuit is protected by fuses, you must install a separate switch of the general type shown in Fig. 15-2 for each appliance. The switch need not be fused, but since unfused switches are hard to locate, it is customary to use the fused kind, with one fuse for 115-volt appliances and two fuses for 230-volt appliances. The fuses in the switch may have a rating not greater than that of those protecting the branch circuit.

If the appliance is connected to its own circuit, the provisions are as described in the previous paragraph, except that the rating of the overcurrent device protecting the branch circuit may not exceed 150% of the ampere rating of the appliance (unless the appliance is rated at less than 10 amp).

Larger Appliances, Motor-driven. See Chap. 15.

Wiring 230-volt Appliances with Cable. You have already learned that white wire may be used only for the grounded neutral wire. But the grounded wire does not run to any load operating at 230 volts. Therefore the wires running to a 230-volt load may be any color except white. Now when you use 2-wire cable to connect a 230-volt load, the cable, of course, contains one black wire, one white wire, but the white wire may not be used. What to do? Follow Sec. 200-6(b) of the Code: Paint each end of the white wire black, and the cable will be considered as having two black wires.

Bear in mind that an electric range does not operate at strictly 230 volts. When any burner or the oven is turned to "high heat," it operates at 230 volts; when turned to "low heat," it operates at 115 volts. In other words it is a combination 115/230-volt appliance; therefore all three wires including the neutral must be run to the range.

Wiring Methods for Heavy Appliances. The Code does not restrict the methods to be used. Use conduit or cable, as you choose. However, the Code does make one important exception. For ranges (including wall-mounted ovens and separate counter-mounted cooking units) and clothes dryers, you may use service-entrance cable with a bare neutral, which otherwise may be used only in the service entrance.

If the appliance is portable,[1] run your cable up to the receptacle, which may be either flush-mounted or surface-mounted.

Wiring of Ranges. Because of the particular way in which the individual burners and the oven are connected within the range, the neutral wire to the range cannot be made to carry as many amperes as the two hot wires. For that reason, the wires to the range usually include a neutral one size smaller than the hot wires. For most ranges, two No. 6 plus a No. 8 neutral are used; for smaller ranges, two No. 8 with a No. 10 neutral are occasionally used.

Run your circuit up to the range receptacle which will be rated at 50-amp 115/230 volts, shown in Fig. 21-2. The range is connected to the receptacle by means of a pigtail cord shown in the same illustration.

The Code requires that the frame of the range be grounded but does not require a separate grounding wire. The range is so constructed that it is automatically grounded through the neutral conductor when you use one of the usual pigtail cords and range receptacles just described.

Sectional Ranges. The trend is away from complete self-contained ranges consisting of oven plus burners, toward indi-

[1] A self-contained range is considered portable, but if the oven and the cooking units are separately installed, each is considered a fixed appliance.

vidual units.   The oven is a separate unit, installed in the wall
where wanted.   Groups of burners in a single section are installed
in the kitchen counter where convenient.   All this, of course,
makes for a very flexible arrangement and permits you to use
much imagination in laying out a modern, custom-designed
kitchen.

The Code calls such separate ovens "wall-mounted ovens" and
the burners "counter-mounted cooking units."   Here they will be
referred to merely as ovens and cooking units.   The proper
method of wiring such ovens and cooking units was not outlined
in previous Codes but was first defined in the 1959 edition, which
should eliminate the widely assorted methods of wiring that pre-
vailed before that time.

Self-contained ranges are considered portable appliances by
the Code (Art. 100), but ovens and cooking units are considered
fixed appliances [Sec. 422-13(a)].

Two basic methods may be used in the wiring of ovens and
cooking units.   The more economical method is probably to supply a separate circuit for the oven, another for the cooking unit.
The alternate method is to install one 50-amp circuit for the two
combined.   Any type of wiring method may be used, and by
special Code exception [Sec. 338-3(b)] service-entrance cable
with a bare neutral may also be used.   Regardless of the wiring
method used, the frame of the oven or cooking unit must be
grounded.   For ranges, ovens, and cooking units only, the Code
permits the frame to be grounded to the neutral wire serving the
unit, provided only that the wire is No. 10 or larger.   If the particular oven or cooking unit you are installing does not have its
frame connected to its neutral terminal, be sure to ground it yourself.

Assuming that a separate circuit is installed for the oven, proceed as outlined earlier in this chapter for fixed appliances.   Use
wire of the amperage required for the load.   The oven will probably be rated about 4,600 watts, which at 230 volts is equivalent
to 20 amp, so No. 12 wire would appear suitable, but the minimum is No. 10 because of the grounding requirement.   At the
oven the circuit wires may run directly to the oven, but for convenience you will probably install a 30-amp receptacle of the
type shown in Fig. 21-1 or the type shown in Fig. 21-2, with a pig-

tail cord, also shown in Fig. 21-2.   This method, using receptacle
and pigtail, will make the installation much easier, but do note
that the receptacle will *not* serve the purpose of the disconnecting
means as it does when a self-contained range is installed (because a range is defined as a portable appliance and the oven as a
fixed appliance).   Therefore, unless your branch circuit is protected by a circuit breaker, you will have to install a separate
disconnecting switch as outlined earlier in this chapter.

As far as the cooking units are concerned, proceed exactly as
for the oven, again using a minimum of No. 10 wire and prefer-

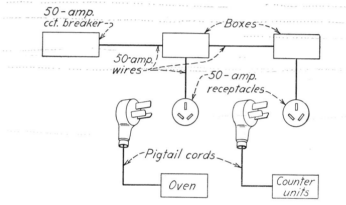

Fig. 21-3. It is best to provide separate circuits for oven and counter units,
but both *may* be connected to one 50-amp circuit.

ably a receptacle and pigtail cord.   Number 10 wire with a carrying capacity of 30 amp will provide a maximum of 6,900 watts,
which will take care of most cooking units.

If you install a single circuit for oven and cooking units combined, it must be a 3-wire 50-amp circuit.   Any wiring method
may be used, including service-entrance cable with bare neutral.
The receptacles may be only the 50-amp type, and may be flush
receptacles installed in outlet boxes, or the surface type shown in
Fig. 21-2.   The circuit will be as shown in Fig. 21-3, which should
be self-explanatory except for the wires from the junction boxes
to the receptacles.   If these are the same size as the circuit wires
no further comment is necessary.   But the Code in Sec. 210-19(c)
does permit a reduction in wire size at this point if the wires are

heavy enough for the load, are No. 10 or heavier, and are not over 10 ft long. This exception is specifically for ranges, ovens, and counter units. Also note that the receptacles shown are not required but will be found convenient in installation; the oven or counter unit may be wired directly to the junction boxes shown on the branch circuit.

Clothes Dryers. Dryers are basically 230-volt devices, although some have 115-volt motors in them. The Code requires that the frame of the dryer be grounded but permits it to be grounded by means of the neutral conductor in the wiring (provided it is No. 10 or heavier wire), so 3-wire cable must be used even if the entire dryer operates at 230 volts. The Code considers dryers to be portable appliances.

Wire the dryer as you would the range. Use a 30-amp receptacle of the type shown in Fig. 21-1 or 21-2 and a pigtail cord similar to the one used with a range, only with smaller wires. Number 10 wires are generally used. The Code permits you to use service-entrance cable with a bare neutral if you wish, provided it is No. 10 or heavier.

If your branch circuit is protected by fuses, you must install a separate switch, as discussed earlier in this chapter. If the branch circuit is protected by a circuit breaker, no further action is needed.

Automatic Washers. The Code considers the automatic laundry to be a permanently installed stationary appliance, which is certainly logical, since the permanently connected plumbing prevents moving the washer from one place to another. Accordingly, install it in a fashion already described earlier in this chapter, not overlooking the disconnecting switch.

Water Heaters. The power consumed by a water heater ranges from 1,500 to 5,000 watts, always at 230 volts. The wiring is simple. Merely run two wires from your service equipment to a disconnecting switch, then to the heater. Number 12 wire is suitable for any heater consuming up to 4,600 watts.

If the service equipment consists of circuit breakers, provide a 2-pole 20-amp breaker. If it is of the fused type of the general style that was shown in Fig. 13-5 or 13-6, you will usually find a couple of special terminal lugs provided for the heater and usually not protected by fuses in most brands. In that case run wires from those terminals to the fused disconnecting switch for the heater.

In most localities power used for heating water is sold at a greatly reduced rate, usually in the area of 1 cent per kilowatt-hour. However, there is a "catch" inasmuch as the heater is connected to the circuit through a special electrically operated switch furnished by the power company which connects the heater to the power line only during "off-peak" hours. In other words, the heater is *disconnected from* the power line during the time of day when the power company's load is at its peak, when there would not be enough generating capacity if thousands of water heaters were also connected. As a result, water cannot be heated for several periods of several hours each on any one day. If your installation is of this type, do the wiring as already described, except that the wires should start from the power company's time switch instead of from your service equipment, as outlined in Chap. 17.

Chapter 22

OLD WORK

In old work, or the wiring of buildings completed *before* the wiring is started, there are few *electrical* problems that have not already been covered. Most difficulties can be resolved into problems of carpentry, in other words, how to get wires and cables from one point to another with the least effort and minimum tearing up of the structure of the building.

In new work it is a simple matter to run wires and cables from one point to another in the shortest way possible; in old work considerably more material is used because often it is necessary to lead the cable the long way around through channels that are available, rather than to tear up walls, ceilings, or floors in order to run it the shortest distance.

No book can give all the answers as to how to proceed in old work; here the common problems will be covered, but considerable ingenuity must be exercised in solving actual problems in the field. A study of buildings while they are under construction will help in understanding what is behind the plaster in a finished building.

Wiring Methods in Old Work. It is impossible to use rigid or thin-wall conduit in old work without practically wrecking the building. It would be used only when a major rebuilding operation is in process, and installation then would be as in new work. The usual method is to use nonmetallic-sheathed cable or armored cable. The material is easily fished through empty wall spaces. It is sufficiently flexible so that it will go around corners without much difficulty. In some localities flexible conduit (greenfield) is generally used. Install it as you would cable, except that the empty conduit is first installed, the wire pulled into place later.

Cutting Openings. To cut good openings for outlet and switch boxes in walls requires a certain amount of skill and a generous measure of common sense. The openings must not be oversize and must be neatly made. Start by marking the approximate location of the box, and, if possible, allow a little leeway so that the opening can be moved a trifle in any direction from the original mark. First make sure there is not a stud or a joist in the way; usually thumping on the wall or ceiling will disclose the presence of timbers. Then dig through the plaster at the approximate location and probe until the space between two laths is found; then go through completely. It would be well to reach through this opening and, with a stiff wire or similar instrument, probe to right and left to confirm that there is no stud or similar obstruction. Assuming that everything is clear, mark the size of the final opening and proceed with the actual cutting, which is done with a hacksaw blade, with the teeth pointing backward, the opposite of the usual fashion. The cutting is done as the blade is pulled, not when pushing the blade away as in usual sawing. If an attempt is made to saw in the usual way so that the work is done while pushing the blade into the wall, there is great danger that the lath will be pulled away from the plaster on either side of the opening, with the result that there may then be a considerable area of plaster unsupported by lath inside. While sawing, hold the hand against the plaster so that it is rigid; otherwise there is a tendency for the plaster to be pulled off the wall.

Temporary Openings. The openings discussed in the preceding paragraph are openings into which a box will later be fitted. In old work it is often necessary to cut temporary openings in odd places to make it possible to pull cable, for example, from the ceiling around the corner into a wall. The cable does not go through the opening; the opening is merely used to get at the cable during the pulling process to help it along, or to get around obstructions in the wall. Such openings must, of course, be repaired when the job is finished.

If the room is papered, the paper must be carefully removed in one place and then reinstalled so that the paper will look like the original installation. This is easily done. With a razor blade cut the two sides and the bottom of a square, but not the top.   Apply moisture with a rag or sponge, soak the cut portion, and after the paste has softened, lift the cut portion, using the uncut top as a hinge.   Fold it upward, and fasten to the wall with a thumbtack.   These steps are shown in Fig. 22-1.

When the opening in the plaster is no longer needed, it is easily patched, using plaster of paris or a ready-mixed plaster, which need only be mixed with water, and set.   The same mixture is

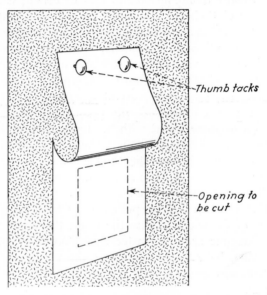

Fig. 22-1. Sections of wallpaper are easily removed temporarily.   Using the top of the cut section as a hinge makes it easy to restore the wallpaper to its original condition, after the installation.

used to fill the openings around switch and outlet boxes, for the Code does not permit open spaces; the plaster must come up to the box.   The section of wallpaper is replaced by applying fresh paste and letting down the hinged section which was loosened and pinned up while the opening was being made.

Mounting Outlet Boxes.   For new work the Code requires outlet boxes with a minimum depth of 1½ in.; for old work this requirement is waived when use of deeper boxes leads to injury of the building.   Boxes ½ in. deep are therefore commonly used. Two of these are shown in Fig. 22-2.   If the outlet box is located so that it can be attached to a joist or similar substantial timber, install as shown in Fig. 22-3. In similar fashion a box may be

FIG. 22-2. In old work, shallow boxes are permitted where the use of standard boxes 1½ in. deep would result in injury to the structure of the building. (*All-Steel Equipment Co.*)

mounted directly on lath even if it is not backed up by a joist, as shown in Fig. 22-4. However, this method is to be discouraged

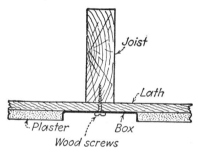

FIG. 22-3. In mounting boxes directly on the ceiling, mount them on a substantial timber where possible.

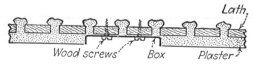

FIG. 22-4. If it is necessary to mount boxes directly on lath, attach them to two laths, not to one only. This distributes the weight of the fixture.

because, if a fixture of any substantial weight is attached to the box, damage to the ceiling may follow.

By far the simplest method is to use one of the old-work hangers shown in Fig. 22-5. The method of its use is shown in

steps in Fig. 22-6.   First make a hole in the ceiling at the proper
place.   Then slip the hanger into the hole; note that the hanger
has a length of wire attached to the stud so that it is not easily
lost inside the ceiling or wall.   Then pull back by this wire and

allow the stud only to project
from the opening in the ceiling.
Turn the bar crosswise so that it
lies at right angles to the lath;
this will later distribute the
weight of the fixture over a number of laths instead of throwing

FIG. 22-5. An old-work hanger
is very handy in mounting a box
on the ceiling.

it all on one or two as is the case when the box is mounted directly on lath.   Remove the locknut from the stud, slip the stud
through the center knockout of the box, tighten the locknut on
the stud inside the box, and the job is finished.

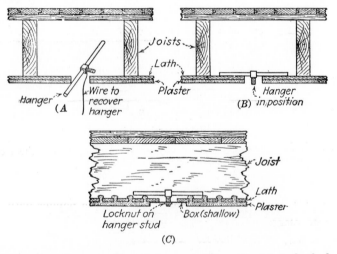

FIG. 22-6. Installing an old-work hanger. When the job is finished, the
hanger should lie at right angles to the lath.

Regardless of the method of mounting, the cable must be at
least partially attached before the box is mounted in place.   This,
in the case of ceiling outlets and in similar cases where the cable
comes in through the bottom, is no problem.   Be sure that the

cable connector is rigidly anchored to the cable and that the lock-nut on the connector is securely driven home before the box is finally mounted.

Often the flooring above the ceiling in which the box is to be installed can be lifted temporarily (as will be explained later). This makes possible a simple installation using a straight bar hanger, used as was shown in Fig. 10-11. Cut an opening in

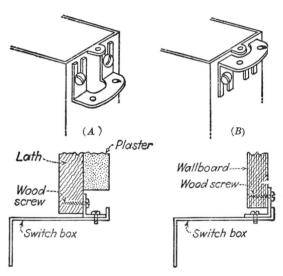

Fig. 22-7. The mounting ears on switch boxes are reversible. In the position at *A* they are used in mounting boxes on lath under the plaster. Reverse them as shown at *B* for mounting on wallboard or similar material.

the ceiling for the box; install the box on the hanger, the ends of which have been bent upward; and nail the hanger with the box into place.

Mounting Switch Boxes. The mounting ears on the ends of switch boxes are adjustable to compensate for various thicknesses of plaster. They are also completely reversible, as Fig. 22-7 shows. In the position in which they come on boxes and as shown at *A*, they are used for mounting such boxes on plastered walls. The ears are fastened to the lath and are of such proportions as to bring the front edge of the box flush with the plaster surface.

In cutting the opening for the switch box, take into consideration the dimensions of the box compared with the width of lath. The ordinary switch box is 3 in. long, while two laths plus three spaces between laths measure more than 3 in.   If two full laths are cut away, it will be difficult to anchor the switch box by its ears on the next two laths, for the mounting holes on the ears will then come very close to the edges of the laths, which will split when the screws are driven in.   Cut one lath completely and

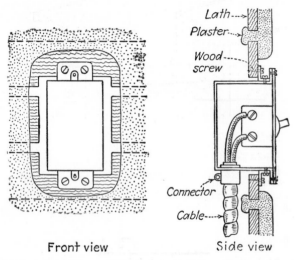

Front view   Side view

Fɪɢ. 22-8. In cutting the opening for a switch box, do not cut away two complete laths.   Cut away one and a portion of each of two others.

remove part of the width of each of the two adjoining laths; this should be clear from Fig. 22-8.

If the box is to be mounted on wallboard, or similar material over which there is no plaster, then the mounting ears are reversed, as was shown in *B* of Fig. 22-7, thus bringing the front edge flush with the plaster.   Mounting a box on such a wall presents a problem because the wall is usually too flimsy to let mounting screws be used for rigid support.   One method of solving this problem is to use the special hanger shown in Fig. 22-9.   It consists of two metal straps.   Place one on each side of the wall opening, with the two ears projecting into the room.

Slip the switch box into place between these two hangers, then bend the ears of the hanger down inside the box, as shown in the illustration. Be sure that the ears lie snug against the inside surface of the box; if they are allowed to bend away from the

Fig. 22-9. A hanger for mounting a switch box on wallboard. (*Appleton Electric Co.*)

inside surface, they can easily cause grounds from the box to the terminals of receptacles or switches.

A different kind of box makes the installation even simpler. As shown in Fig. 22-10, there are two metal strips parallel with

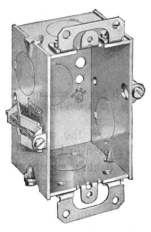

Fig. 22-10. This box is very easy to install on wallboard or similar material. (*All-Steel Equipment Co.*)

the sides of the box. After the box is pushed into its opening, tightening a couple of screws collapses the metal strips so that they bulge against the inside of the wall, effectively anchoring the box in the wall.

Installing Box in Wall. If the cable runs into the bottom of the box, there is no problem involved in cutting the right size of

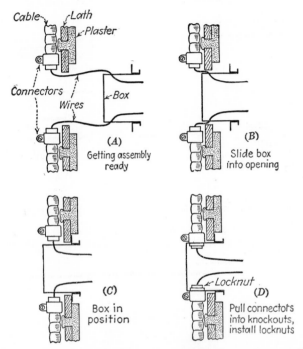

Fig. 22-11. Installing switch box in opening. The cable is anchored by means of locknuts after the box is slid into the opening.

opening. Usually, however, the cable runs into knockouts in the end of the box, as shown in Fig. 22-11; the installation then is not so simple. If the cable is rigidly attached to the box with a connector before the box is mounted, then it will no longer be possible to get the box into the opening—the cable is in the way. If the opening is made big enough so that a box which has been preassembled with cable and connector will slip through easily, there will be a very sloppy fit that no self-respecting work-

man will tolerate. To do a good job, follow the procedure outlined in Fig. 22-11. Cut the opening only big enough for the
box, plus about ⅛ in., or the thickness of the wire inside the
cable. Leave a generous length of wire sticking out of the cable.
Attach the connector to the cable, remove the locknut from the
connector. When ready to install the box, let the wires stick out
of the opening in the wall, with the connectors inside the wall.
Push the wires through the knockout into the box and grasp
them inside the box. Push the box into the wall; there will be
room at the ends of the opening for the wires to slide through

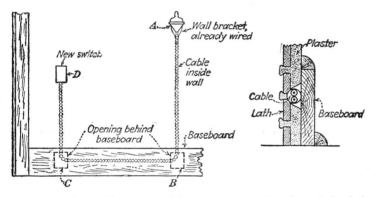

FIG. 22-12. Often cable is concealed in a groove in the plaster behind the
baseboard.

into the wall. When the box is in its opening, pull on the wires,
pulling the connector into the knockout; then slip the locknut
over the connector and tighten.

Cable behind Baseboard. Assume that there is a wall bracket
in the middle of a wall, already wired and controlled by a
switch on the fixture, but that now it is to be controlled by a wall
switch several feet to the left but on the same wall. This is a
relatively simple job (see Fig. 22-12). First cut the opening
for the switch box at D. Then remove the baseboard running
along the wall at the floor, and cut two holes, B and C, behind
the baseboard. Then from B to C, cut a groove or trough in the
plaster between two laths; if the plaster is not very thick, it may
be necessary to slice away part of the laths. In any event, the

trough must be big enough to receive the cable, as shown in the cross-sectional view of the same picture.

When this has been done, prepare a piece of cable long enough to extend from A to B to C to D, with a connector at each end; remove the locknuts. Remove the fixture at point A; remove a knockout from the bottom of the outlet box on which the fixture is installed. Then push a fish wire with a hook bent on the end through the knockout in box A down toward B. Reach into opening B with another piece of fish wire again with a hook on the end. It will not be difficult to hook the two pieces together so that by pulling at B the first piece is pulled in a continuous length from A to B. Attach the cable to the fish wire, and pull it into the wall through opening B until the end appears at A. Pull it into place so that the connector slides into the knockout in A, tighten the locknut, and the job is finished at A except for connecting the wires. Next drop the fish wire in opening D until it appears at C, and fish the cable up inside the wall until it emerges at D, in the meantime laying the cable securely into the trough from B to C to take up slack. Anchor it at D so that it cannot be lost inside the wall; replace the baseboard. Use extreme care that nails are not driven through the cable. All that remains to be done is properly to attach the cable to the box at D, mount the box, and install the switch.

Cable through Attic. In single-story houses or when working on the second floor of two-story houses, it is generally entirely practical to run cable through the attic. It is a simple matter to lift a few boards of the usual rough attic flooring and lead the cable around, in that way avoiding the need for openings in the walls of the living quarters except the openings for boxes. No baseboards need then be lifted. It may require a few feet more of cable, but the saving in labor more than offsets this. Always explore this possibility before proceeding with a more difficult method. For example, in Fig. 22-12 the cable is run from outlet A to attic, under the attic floor over to a point directly above outlet D, and there dropped down to D.

Cable through Basement. In wiring the outlet of Fig. 22-12, often you can run the cable through the basement, going straight down below point B into the basement, then over toward the left, then upward again at point C. More usually there will be obstructions in the walls not making this possible in such simple fashion.

If the point where the cable is to run down into the basement is on the outer wall, the construction is apt to be something on the order of that shown in Fig. 22-13. In that case bore a hole with a long-shank electrician's bit, of the type shown in Fig. 22-14, either upward as indicated by arrow *A* or downward from a point behind the baseboard, as indicated by arrow *B*, after removing the baseboard. If the cable is to enter the basement from an interior wall, it is usually possible simply to bore directly upward from the basement, as shown in Fig. 22-15.

Cable around Corner Where Wall Meets Ceiling. Figure 22-16 shows this problem: how to lead cable from outlet *A* in the ceiling to outlet *B* on the wall around the corner at *C*. At first glance this may seem difficult, but it is relatively simple. In houses that are

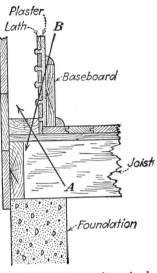

Fig. 22-13. Boring through obstructions. The actual construction found will vary a great deal. Most problems in old-work wiring are problems of carpentry.

not very well built, there may be a clear space at the corner *C*. In that case push a length of fish wire with a hook on the end into the ceiling at *A* until the hook is somewhere

Fig. 22-14. Electrician's bit and extension. (*Greenlee Tool Co.*)

around *C*. Then push another length of fish wire upward from *B* until the hook touches the floor above. With one man at *A* and another at *B*, it becomes simply a problem of fishing, jiggling, pulling, and twisting the two lengths of fish wire until the hook on one catches the other. Then pull at *B* until there is a continuous length of fish wire from *A* to *B*, attach the cable to the fish wire at *A*, and pull it into position. It will not come too easily around the corner at *C*, but with help at *A*, it can be pulled through. Much patience is the greatest asset in this work.

If the house is well built, there will be an obstruction at point *C*. Any one of a dozen different types of construction may be

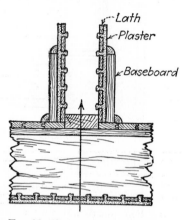

Fig. 22-15. Sometimes obstructions can be cleared by boring upward from the basement.

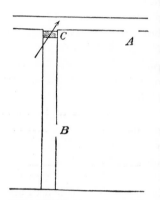

Fig. 22-16. To get cable from *A* to *B* an opening must often be made through obstruction at *C*.

used; that shown in Fig. 22-17, which is simply an enlarged view of point *C*, is typical. The usual procedure is to make a temporary opening in the wall at point *C*, but on the opposite side of the wall, away from opening *B*. Bore upward with a long-shank electrician's bit, as shown by arrow 1. Push a length of fish wire into this hole until the end emerges at *A*. If the opening at *C* is large enough, push the other end of the wire downward to *B*, and pull the loop that is formed at *C* into the wall by pulling at either *A* or *B*; there will then be a continuous fish wire from *A* to *B* with which to pull in the cable. More usually the hole at *C* will be small; hence use two lengths of fish wire. Push one through from *C* to *A*, leaving a small hook at *C* just outside the opening. Push another length from C to B, again leaving the the hook just outside the opening at C. Hook the two hooks together, pull at B, and it is a simple matter then to pull the longer wire from A through C to B and, with this, to pull in the cable.

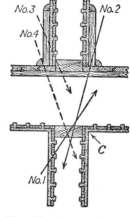

If there happens to be another wall directly above point C, it may be better to bore down from above at a point behind the baseboard, as indicated by arrow 2. In that case fish wire is pushed down from above through the bored hole to B; another length from A toward C; when the hooks at the end engage, pull down at B until a continuous piece of fish wire extends from A through C to B.

Fig. 22-17. An enlarged view of point C of Fig. 22-16.

If there is a molding around the room at the ceiling, it is usually better to remove the molding and to chisel a hole in the corner, probably chiseling away a portion of the obstruction, to provide a channel

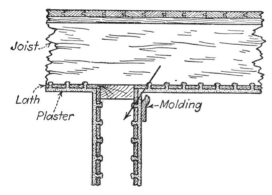

Fig. 22-18. Sometimes temporary openings can best be made behind a molding.

for the cable, as indicated by the arrow in Fig. 22-18. When the molding is replaced, the cable, if it projects a bit, is concealed.

Cable from Second Floor to First. If the first-floor partition is directly below the second-floor partition, it is usually simple to bring the cable through by boring, as indicated by arrows 2 and 3 (or 3 and 4) in Fig. 22-17. Use good judgment so that the holes will lie so far as possible in approximately the same plane, thus simplifying the fishing problem. An opening behind the baseboard is usually necessary.

If the first-floor partition is not directly below the second-

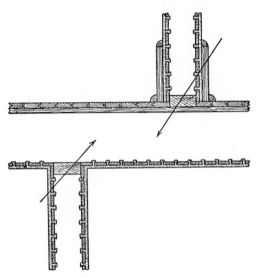

FIG. 22-19. Problem in bringing cable from a second-floor partition into a first-floor partition.

floor partition, handling as indicated in Fig. 22-19 will usually solve the problem. Bore holes as indicated by the two arrows

Lifting Floor Boards. In many cases the outlet and switch boxes may be so located with regard to wall and ceiling obstructions that it is necessary to lift hardwood floor boards in the floor above. This should be avoided if possible, but where necessary use extreme care in lifting the boards so that when replaced there will be no visible damage to the floor. Attic flooring is simply lifted, but the usual hardwood floor with the tongue-and-groove construction presents more of a problem.

It is necessary first to chisel off the tongue on one of the boards. The thinner the chisel used for the purpose, the less the damage that will be done to the flooring. A putty knife with the blade cut off short and sharpened to a chisel edge makes an excellent chisel for the purpose, and a thinner one is not obtainable. Drive it down between two boards and cut off the tongue (see Fig. 22-20). This should be done to the

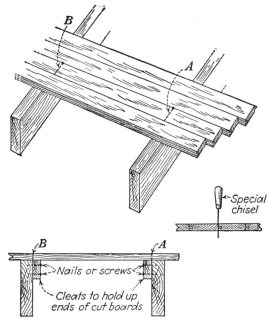

FIG. 22-20. Steps in lifting and replacing floor boards.

entire length between three joists, although the picture shows only two joists. Having the cut section extend over a longer space gives the advantage of a better footing when the board is reinstalled. In cutting off this tongue, the exact location of the floor joists can be determined and in this way points A and B in the picture located. Bore a small hole at these two points next to the joists, and with a keyhole saw cut across the boards as shown.

The board can then be lifted, the electrical work done, and

later the board replaced. It will be necessary to attach cleats
to the joists for the floor board to rest on, at the cut ends.
Anchor these cleats securely so as to give the cut board a really
solid footing. The bored holes are later filled with wooden
plugs.

Extension Rings. In old work it is often desirable to be
able to extend a circuit beyond an existing outlet. If the wiring
is entirely flush, it might entail considerable carpentry if the
new outlet were also to be made flush, and at least in certain
types of work (such as basements) it will be entirely acceptable
to have the new outlet of the surface type. In that case an

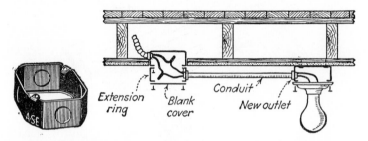

Extension
ring

Blank
cover

Conduit

New outlet

Fig. 22-21. Extension rings are handy in adding new outlets to existing
outlets. (*All-Steel Equipment Co.*)

extension ring of the type shown in Fig. 22-21 is used. Extension
rings are, to all intents and purposes, outlet boxes without bottoms, and they are available to fit all kinds of outlet boxes.

Their use should be made clear by the same picture. Simply
mount the extension ring on top of the existing outlet box and
from there proceed as in any exposed wiring. The extension
ring is covered with a blank cover or with the fixture or other
device that may have been installed on the original outlet box.

Boxes on Brick Walls. When a house is of brick construction, a considerable amount of labor is involved in the mounting of the boxes, for the boxes must come flush with the plaster
when it is applied. A space must be chiseled into the brick
to receive the box. Usually 4-in. square boxes are used, together
with covers of the type that were shown in Fig. 10-12. These are
available in various depths so that, if the ordinary ½-in. type

does not bring the cover flush with the plaster, one of a greater depth, say ¾ in., will be found suitable.

The box cannot be secured to the brick directly with screws;

FIG. 22-22. With a star drill it is not difficult to drill holes in brick or similar material. (*Paine Co.*)

consequently it is necessary to use one of the many types of plugs or anchors available for the purpose. In any case it will be necessary to drill holes into the brick or masonry, using

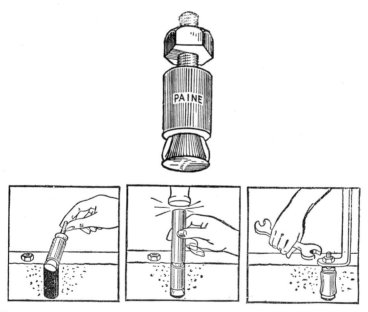

FIG. 22-23. The lead expansion anchor shown at top is dropped into the hole as shown below, and forms a secure mounting for whatever is supported by it. (*Paine Co.*)

for the purpose a star drill of the general type shown in Fig. 22-22. This drill is used by simply pounding on its head with a hammer, rotating the drill a bit after each blow.

A very common mounting method is that using the well-known lead plugs or anchors which are merely inserted into the hole in the masonry, ordinary wood screws then being used. The Code prohibits wooden plugs.

The use of lead expansion anchors of the type shown in Fig. 22-23 provides a mounting which is considerably more secure than that using ordinary lead plugs. There use is clearly shown in steps in the same picture.

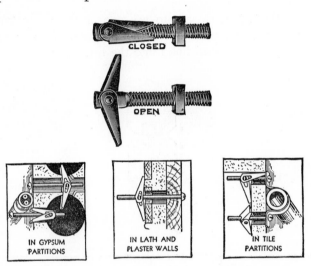

Fig. 22-24. Toggle bolts are used in mounting devices over hollow walls or other hollow spaces. (*Paine Co.*)

If the mounting must be over hollow areas, use toggle bolts. Typical bolts are shown in Fig. 22-24, and this picture also shows their use. Merely slip the collapsible wings through the opening in the wall or other surface; a spring opens the wings, which then provide anchorage for the bolt.

Use Common Sense and Patience. No book can outline all the problems in carpentry that will be encountered in old work. The method of construction of houses varies with the age of the house, the general sturdiness of the building, the skill and integrity of the builder, and many other factors. Plenty of patience, coupled with a generous measure of "horse sense," is the greatest asset in old-work wiring.

Surface Wiring. There are available materials which make it quite simple to start from an existing receptacle outlet and add additional outlets, for example in a living room or kitchen. The same materials are equally suitable for more complicated original wiring in areas such as basements, attics, garages, and farm buildings where the wiring is to be permanently exposed.

The basic materials for this type of wiring are combinations consisting of a receptacle, switch, or other device, each combined with a nonmetallic outlet box. Figure 22-25 shows a representative assortment of them; others are available. They are made for use with 2-conductor No. 14 or No. 12 nonmetallic-

Fig. 22-25. These surface-mounting devices are easy to install. They have no terminal screws. (*General Electric Co.*)

sheathed cable. They have no terminal screws. Just strip the ends of the cable and push the bare wires into the devices for a good permanent connection; each device has a "strip gauge" molded into it showing how far to strip the cable (this method of connecting without terminal screws was shown in Chap. 8, Fig. 8-5).

The devices are available in either brown or ivory color; the cable likewise is available in both colors. For use in living areas of homes, the cable is available with prepunched nail holes in the cable; it may be nailed to the wall, using the special nails that come with it. The cable is about $\frac{3}{16}$ by $\frac{1}{2}$ in. in size and can be bent across either the short dimension or the long dimension without buckling, as shown in Fig. 22-26.

Start from an existing receptacle outlet. Use the special attachment plug shown in Fig. 22-27, and connect it to one end of a length of cable, as shown in Fig. 22-28, by merely pushing the stripped end of the cable into the plug.   The plug has a swivel

FIG. 22-26. A special cable bends easily in either direction. (*General Electric Co.*)

FIG. 22-27. Start from an existing receptacle, using this special plug. It has a built-in swivel. (*General Electric Co.*)

in it so that you can run the cable downward from the starting point or sideways.

Next run the cable to the point where you want the next outlet; install the next outlet and proceed to the one after that.   All this is shown in several steps in Fig. 22-28.

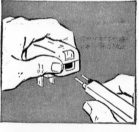

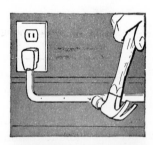

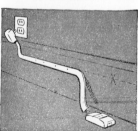

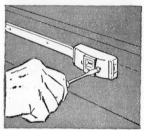

FIG. 22-28. Install the material as shown in the steps above. (*General Electric Co.*)

Instead of starting from a receptacle outlet, the cable may be run into any existing outlet box containing a grounded wire and

FIG. 22-29. Devices similar to those shown in Fig. 22-25 except with terminal screws. (*General Electric Co.*)

a permanently hot wire. Naturally you must use a connector on the cable at such starting point, as in other cable wiring.

The cable described is a special variety of Code Type NMC nonmetallic-sheathed cable, made with particular attention to neat appearance in living areas of homes. In other areas where appearance is not so important, any kind of nonmetallic Type NM or NMC cable may be used, making the system quite suitable for use in basements, attics, garages, farm buildings, and so on.

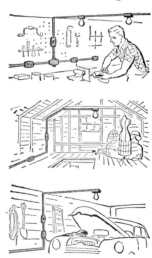

FIG. 22-30. Typical installations using the devices shown in Fig. 22-25 and Fig. 22-29. (*General Electric Co.*)

The devices described up to this point may be used only with 2-wire cable, and only a single length of cable can enter each end. Similar fittings which have screw terminals instead of push-in connections for wires are shown in Fig. 22-29. They can be used with either 2- or 3-wire cable, and two lengths of cable can enter each end. This series includes several devices, including 3-way switches, that are not available in the other kind.

All this makes this series a bit more versatile, especially in the wiring of farm buildings where 3-way switches are necessary. However, the two series may be used intermixed on the same job. Three completed installations are shown in Fig. 22-30.

In using this material in farm buildings and similar locations, you can, with good planning, run a *continuous* length of cable from one point to another without installing outlets as you go along. At points where an outlet is to be installed, leave a slight bulge away from the surface in the cable. Later cut the cable at that point, and install the receptacle or other device.

In installing these fittings, use the same precaution given later in Chap. 24 concerning nonmetallic outlet boxes. If the fittings are mounted on timbers that may swell with moisture, don't pull the mounting screws too tight, to avoid possible future damage.

Chapter 23

MODERNIZING AN INSTALLATION

The wiring installed in a house many years ago (and in very many cases even if installed only 10 years ago) just is not adequate for the job it is called upon to do today. A complete rewiring job is in order—or is it? Do not jump to the conclusion that every outlet must be torn out, every receptacle replaced. Many times a less expensive job will serve the purpose. Analyze the problem.

Is the wiring inadequate because you are using too many lights? Too many floor lamps? Too many radios and TV? That is seldom the case. The wiring is inadequate because of too many electrical appliances that were not allowed for at the time of the original wiring job, probably including some that were not even on the market at that time. The installation does not provide enough circuits to operate a wide assortment of ordinary kitchen appliances, plus range, water heater, clothes dryer, room air conditioners. Some of these appliances operate on 230-volt circuits, which may not be available; others operate on 115 volts but, when plugged into existing circuits, overload those circuits.

Moreover, the service-entrance equipment is just too small for the load, just as two-lane highways built years ago are too small for the number of cars they are called upon to accommodate.

To analyze the problem of your particular house, ask whether *if you disconnect all the appliances* (including motors on oil burner or similar locations), you will have all the *lighting* circuits that you need. The answer might well be "yes," in which case your rewiring problem is simplified. You will still have to rewire the house but not so completely as at first may have appeared necessary. In all likelihood, a large part of the need for wiring will be the fact that the present service entrance is too small. Installing a larger service entrance alone might go a long way toward solving the problem, but that would result in a "patchwork" job and might cost almost as much as doing the job the right way.

Plan the Job. Proceed more or less as if you were starting with a house that had never been wired, but leave the existing *lighting* circuits intact. These lighting circuits will, of course, include many receptacles for small loads like vacuum cleaner, radio, TV, and clock. If the present installation has *individual* circuits to 115-volt motors on the furnace or similar 115-volt loads, leave those circuits also intact. But if such large loads are connected to general lighting circuits, disconnect them from the existing circuits. If the present installation has individual circuits to water heater, range, or similar 230-volt loads, leave those circuits intact.

Your rewiring job will consist of installing a new service of at least 100-amp capacity as outlined in other chapters, some new circuit breakers (or fuses), and new circuits for appliances. You will have to connect the old circuits into the new circuit-breaker equipment; two different ways of doing this will be described.

Install New Service and Appliance Circuits. First, install a new service of at least 100-amp capacity. Install a circuit-breaker cabinet with 100-amp main breaker, enough branch-circuit breakers for all the new circuits you are going to install (plus a few spares), and one additional 2-pole breaker. This additional breaker may be rated at 30 amp if the circuits that you are going to leave untouched serve only lighting outlets, but should be rated at 50 amp if they also serve water heater, range, or similar 230-volt loads. That 30- or 50-amp breaker will become the SOURCE for all the old circuits that remain intact.

Install the two special 20-amp kitchen-appliance circuits as discussed in Chap. 12, or preferably one 3-wire 20-amp circuit described in Chap. 20. Install an individual circuit for each heavy appliance such as range, water heater, clothes dryer, also for each motor on gas or oil burner and so on, all as discussed in other chapters (unless these are already served by individual circuits that you are leaving intact). Connect all the *new* circuits to the *new* circuit breakers.

When you have done all this, you will have no power on your new circuits but will still have power on your old circuits. Call your power company, have them disconnect the power on the outside of the house, and get along for a day or two without electric power while you connect your existing circuits into your new circuit-breaker equipment.

Reconnecting Old Circuits: Method A. You have a choice of two methods in connecting your old circuits into your new equipment. The simplest will be described first: let's call it Method A. Cut off the present incoming wires where they enter the switch box. Remove the short pieces of wire that remain; observe carefully the terminals to which they were connected. If the original service was 3-wire 30-amp, run a length of 3-conductor No. 10 cable from the extra 2-pole 30-amp breaker in the new circuit-breaker cabinet, to the old service equipment, connecting the ends there to the terminals to which the original incoming wires were connected. The white wire of the cable, of course, runs from the neutral strap of the new equipment to the neutral strap of the old equipment. If the original equipment was 3-wire 60-amp, use No. 6 cable instead of No. 10; the breaker in the new equipment then must be the larger 50-amp type.

If the incoming service was of the 2-wire type, not 3-wire, use Method B instead of the Method A just described.

If the present equipment includes a fused main switch, leave it in place. Neither the switch nor the fuses are required, but there is no reason why they can't be left in place.

Reconnecting Old Circuits: Method B. Most likely your present circuits terminate in a fuse box with four or more fuses; the fuse box may or may not be in the same cabinet with the main switch and the main fuses. It is not likely that the existing wires will be long enough to reach the new equipment.

Disconnect the wires of one circuit at a time from the existing equipment. If the wiring is cable of some kind, remove the locknut from the connector, pull the cable out of the box, put the locknut back on the connector, and let the cable dangle.

Eventually you will have four to six ends of cable, one for each lighting circuit.

When all the circuits have been disconnected, disconnect the main incoming wires from the equipment and tear out the old equipment. Then at the point where the old equipment was re-moved, install a second circuit-breaker cabinet with as many breakers as there are old circuits, with a few spares for future use. Connect the old circuits to the new breakers. Run 3-wire No. 10 cable from this new circuit-breaker cabinet to the 30-amp breaker in the larger new breaker cabinet, as outlined under Method A. If there are many circuits, you will use No. 6 cable to the 50-amp breaker in the other cabinet. All this is shown in Fig. 23-1.

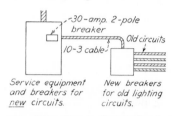

Service equipment and breakers for _new_ circuits.   New breakers for old lighting circuits.

FIG. 23-1. Circuit for moderniz-ing.

If the location of the old equipment was such that you wish to place the circuit breakers for the lighting circuits in a new loca-tion, the original cables of the lighting circuits will certainly be too short to reach the new location. In that case install a junc-tion box at the point where the old equipment was removed and run cables to the proposed loca-tion of the circuit-breaker cabinet, as shown in Fig. 23-2. The junc-tion box can be a 4-in. square box if there are just a few circuits but more likely will be a larger cutout box if there are many circuits. This box will contain only

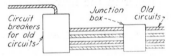

FIG. 23-2. Method of installing junction box.

splices in the cable, it must be located where it will be per-manently accessible, and it must have a metal cover.

Ground. It will be best to install a new ground connection and to disconnect the old ground from the old equipment. Pro-ceed as outlined in Chap. 17; use a ground wire specified for the amperage of the new service.

Call the Power Company. Your job is finished. Call your power company, have them install the new meter, and connect the power to the new service. Then enjoy all the advantages of a house wired in modern, adequate fashion.

Chapter 24

FARM WIRING

In city homes electrical devices and appliances are purchased primarily for the convenience and utility which their use provides. On the farm the same devices are also used, but in addition many others are found which are used in the *business* of farming—devices which are bought, not so much for their mere convenience, but rather as an investment on which the farmer expects dividends. Into this classification fall such things as milk coolers, milking machines, cream separators, hammer mills for chopping fodder, silo fillers, corn shellers, water heaters to provide scalding hot water for the dairy, water heaters which during the winter keep the water for chickens at a temperature which experience has shown will promote egg production, and dozens of others.

The wiring of farms involves all the problems so far discussed as well as a considerable number of new ones. The maximum wattage in use at one time is apt to be considerably larger than in city homes because of the liberal use of motor-driven devices. There is a great deal of outdoor wiring, either overhead or underground, between the various buildings. Substantial distances are involved, which means that wire sizes must be carefully watched, both to avoid voltage drop and for mechanical strength. Relatively poor grounding conditions are usual. These and other factors will be separately considered in this chapter.

Preview. In a typical farm installation, wires from the power line end at a meter pole in the farmyard. From the top of the pole the wires run down to the meter, then back to the top of the pole. Sometimes there is a circuit breaker (or switch with or without fuses) at the bottom of the pole. The wires are always grounded at the pole.

From the top of the pole, a set of wires runs to the house; another set runs to the barn. Often additional sets run to other buildings. Instead of running overhead, underground wires are being used more and more.

At each building, there is a service entrance just as if that building were the only building being wired. This service entrance is installed as was described in Chap. 17, except that the meter is omitted. The Code requires a ground at each building which has more than one circuit and also at each building which houses livestock.

In various buildings, especially barns, there are conditions which require special wiring methods; these will be discussed later in this chapter. Good grounds are difficult to establish, which will also be covered later in this chapter.

Adequacy. In Chap. 12 we studied adequacy of wiring in a house. Everything said there applies to a farm home just as much as to a city home. Indeed, if anything, the farm home deserves more attention and probably needs more circuits, because especially in the case of smaller farms, certain appliances are put into the house, which in the case of larger farms are put into the dairy barn.

In addition to the problems of adequacy in the house, special attention must also be paid to adequacy in and between other buildings and also on the meter pole.

Few farmers whose farms are being wired for the first time can foresee all the different electrical appliances and machines they will use in a few years. Almost always the number of circuits originally provided turns out to be too few; wires between buildings turn out to be too small; wires on the pole should be larger. Always provide more capacity than is needed at the time of installation; doing so will increase the labor hardly at all, the cost of material only a little, but it will do away with the later expensive alterations.

Overhead or Underground? A farm wired with overhead conductors will have a large number of wires running all over the place. This gives the farm a very untidy appearance and also invites troubles of various kinds. Wires to low buildings can be damaged by moving vehicles. Many overhead wires on an isolated farm invite trouble from lightning. In northern climates where sleet storms are common, wires can break from the weight of the accumulated ice; a broken wire on the ground is dangerous. Underground wires cost little more than overhead wires and do away with these problems.

If you are going to use overhead wiring, watch wire size carefully. Make sure the wire size selected is big enough to carry its load in amperes. Make sure it is strong enough for the length of the span, which means that sometimes you must use wire larger than would otherwise be necessary for the amperage involved. All this has already been discussed in Chap. 7.

If you are going to use underground wiring, use the materials and follow the methods already discussed in Chap. 17 concerning the service entrance.

If several sets of underground cable are to enter the bottom of the meter socket on the pole, you will have trouble because the threaded hub in the bottom of the socket is too small. In that case provide a junction box immediately below the meter, inside which quite a number of runs can be terminated, with only a single set of wires from the box into the meter socket. A typical junction box for such purposes is shown in Fig. 24-1. A telescopic metal channel to protect a group of underground wires running up the side of the pole is shown in

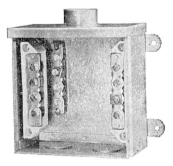

FIG. 24-1. A junction box of this type makes it easy to combine a number of runs of underground cable. (*Hoffman Engineering Corp.*)

Fig. 24-2, installed in connection with one of the junction boxes shown in Fig. 24-1.

Made Electrodes. In cities the underground water system provides an excellent ground. On farms you must provide a substitute; how this is done was discussed in Chap. 17. It will probably be well for you to review the subject at this time.

Grounds on Farms. In Chap. 9 we studied the subject of grounds in general. We learned that, for safety, the neutral wire must be connected to the earth through a water pipe or ground rod. A good ground offers protection not only against accidents in the electrical wiring system but also against lightning.

Now, on a farm there is considerably more danger from lightning than in a city. A good ground is many times as hard to obtain on a farm as in a city. All that makes the subject of farm grounds a hundred times more important and difficult than the subject of grounds in a city. It is a most important subject, and too little attention is given to it. Study it well and apply the principles outlined below.

In a city, run a grounding wire to the nearest cold-water pipe, and automatically you have a good ground, ninety-nine times out of a hundred. The underground city water system provides a good, permanent, low-resistance ground. How good a ground is, is determined by the resistance in ohms between the ground rod and the surrounding earth. The Code in Sec. 250-84 says that the maximum permissible resistance is 25 ohms. A 25-ohm ground is passable; it is not a good ground. A good ground should have a resistance considerably under 25 ohms; city grounds are usually under 10 ohms.

Fig. 24-2. The trough protects underground cables at the pole. (*Hoffman Engineering Corp.*)

A study of over 200 farms was made in Minnesota in 1949, a rather dry year. Only 9 out of 215 (1 in 20) farm grounds had a resistance of 25 ohms or less—and remember that a 25-ohm ground is not a good ground. The other 19 out of every 20 grounds had resistance of more than 25 ohms, some well over 100 ohms.

Perhaps one in a hundred farms had a ground that would be considered a good ground in a city. The others had "grounds" in that they consisted of wires leading to earth, but they did not fully serve the true purpose of grounds—safety. They were probably better than no grounds at all, or were they? Perhaps such a ground is like a spare tire in an automobile, which turns

out to be without air when needed: it looks like a spare but
serves no useful purpose because it is "flat"; the ground looks like
a ground but does not really serve the purpose of safety, which
is the only basic purpose of a ground.

How does one tell a good ground from a poor ground? We
have already discussed the fact that the lower the resistance
of a ground, the better the ground is. So quite properly, after
the ground is installed, we must measure its actual resistance. If
it measures 25 ohms or less, it is a ground that meets Code requirements; it just barely passes. If it measures 10 ohms, it (for

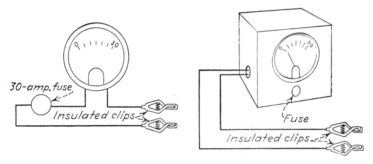

FIG. 24-3. An ordinary alternating-current ammeter lets you determine the
approximate resistance of a ground.

the conditions usually prevailing on farms) is better than the
average. If it measures under 5 ohms, it is an excellent ground.
How are you going to measure that resistance? Unfortunately
it is not simple to measure it accurately.

The only instrument on the market for measuring ground
resistance simply, accurately, and directly in ohms sells at over
$100, so few people will be able to afford one of them. So we
must use a method which may not give an exact answer but
which will nevertheless give an approximate answer, which will
be more accurate than a guess.

To test a ground, you will need an alternating-current ammeter
reading to at least 25 or 30 amp. Mount this in a convenient
box with a fuse of a size that will burn out when the capacity
of the meter is exceeded. Provide two test leads. All this is
shown in Fig. 24-3.

See Fig. 24-4, which shows the basic installation of a ground. The only hitch is that we do not know whether or not the ground is a good one.   Then see Fig. 24-5 which shows the same installation, except that the ground wire has been disconnected from the neutral wire.   You would never do this except for the purpose of the test.

<table>
<tr><td>

Fused hot wire

115 V.

Ground wire connected to neutral - - - - - - - →

Earth

</td><td>

Fused hot wire

115 V.

Ground wire temporarily disconnected - - - - - - →

Earth

</td></tr>
</table>

Fig. 24-4. The neutral is grounded in a normal installation.

Fig. 24-5. In testing for ground resistance, temporarily disconnect the ground from the neutral.

Now see Fig. 24-6, which shows the circuit used in measuring the approximate resistance of the ground.   It boils down to grounding the "hot" wire through the ammeter and fuse.   (Be sure all other grounds are connected and that all fuses are in place.)   From the ammeter reading, the approximate resistance of the ground can be determined, using Ohm's law, volts/amperes

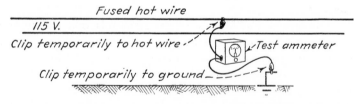

Fig. 24-6. In determining ground resistance using an ammeter, temporarily ground the *hot* wire.

= ohms.   Assuming that the line voltage is 120 volts, it follows that if 15 amp flows, the resistance is 120/15, or 8 ohms.   Other values are as shown on the next page.

In inspecting an 0–30 alternating-current ammeter, you will notice that it has a nonlinear scale.   The scale is very crowded near 0, and it is almost impossible to tell the difference between 2 and 5 amp.   That, however, is not serious, for if the amperage

Amperes flowing	Approximate resistance	Amperes flowing	Approximate resistance
1	120	10	12
2	60	15	8
3	40	20	6
4	30	30	4
5	24		

on test is below 5, you will know that your ground has a resistance above 24 ohms and that it is not a very good ground.

After the resistance of any ground has been determined, remove the tester, reconnect the ground wire to the neutral, and proceed to the next ground.

It should be noted that this test will not work if there is only a single ground on a wiring system, for the approximate resistance determined by this system is not really the resistance of the particular ground under test, but rather the resistance of that ground, plus the resistance of all the other grounds on the wiring system in parallel. Since on a farm there are usually from two to six other grounds and since all these are in parallel while the one particular ground is being tested, the total resistance determined by this ammeter method will be higher than the actual resistance. The percentage of error should range from 10 to 25%. The greater the number of grounds connected to the system, the less the percentage of error.

Remember that the resistance of a specific ground connection varies from time to time. The drier the earth, the higher the ground resistance. Therefore it is good practice to try for a ground of, say, 6 ohms or less resistance, one which will pass at least 20 amp when tested as described. But how are you going to make a ground better than it is? There are several methods.

First of all, when possible, install the ground rod where rain off the roof will tend to keep the earth wet. Wet earth makes for low-resistance grounds.

Second, if one rod driven to an 8-ft depth does not provide a ground of sufficiently low resistance, install two or three rods, all connected together. Do make sure that the rods are at least 10 ft apart, for experiment shows that, if they are closer together, extra rods do not greatly reduce the resistance.

Third, salt the ground, pouring salt water around the rod and letting it soak into the ground. This is common practice among the power companies but little used on farms, although it is so simple. Experiments have shown that, if the water in the earth immediately around the rod contains as little as 1% of salt, the resistance of the ground connection may drop as much as 90%; in other words, the 25-ohm ground becomes a 2½-ohm ground. The salting should take place at least once a year, although cases have been found where a single salting was to a degree still effective after two years. Salt the ground when it is first installed; salt it at intervals thereafter.

Meter Pole. On practically all farms today, the power company's wires end on a pole in the farmyard. On the pole are found the meter and usually a switch to disconnect the entire installation. The wires are grounded at the pole. From the top of the pole, sets of wires run to the house, to the barn, and to the other buildings to be served. At each building there is a service entrance as already described in Chap. 17, except without the meter—more about that later in this chapter.

There is a right and a wrong location for the meter pole. Why is there a pole in the first place? Why not run the wires to the house and from there to the other buildings, as was done when farms were first being wired? That would lead to very large wires to carry the total load involved; a very large main switch in the house; expensive wiring to avoid voltage drop, which is wasted power; a cluttered farmyard; and many other complications.

Locate the pole as close as is possible to the buildings where the greatest amount of power will be used per year; on modern farms, the house rarely consumes the greatest total. That also means locating the pole so that the largest wires will be the shortest wires. In that way you will find it relatively simple to solve voltage-drop problems without using wires larger than would otherwise be necessary for the number of amperes to be carried. The large expensive wires to the building with the big loads will be relatively short, and the smaller less expensive wires to the buildings with the smaller loads will be relatively long. This keeps the total cost down.

Basic Construction at Pole. The three wires from the power line end at the top of the pole. *The neutral wire is always the top wire.* Note that the neutral from the power line is spliced at the top of the pole to the neutral running on to the various buildings, so that in effect the neutral is a continuous wire from the power line direct to every building. The neutral wire is grounded at the pole, as will be explained later. The neutral is also continued down to the meter socket, where it ends.

The two hot wires from the power line run down to the meter socket, then back to the top of the pole. This makes a total of five wires from the top of the pole to the meter socket. The usual construction is to run all five of them inside a single conduit to the meter socket, as shown in Fig. 24-7. In some localities, three wires are run to the socket in one conduit and two run back to the top of the pole in another conduit, as shown in the same illustration. Use whichever method seems to be standard in your locality; consult your local inspector. Regardless of the details of the installation, leave at least one-third of the circumference of the pole clear, so that linemen and repairmen can climb the pole without difficulty.

Installing the Meter Socket. The meter socket is sometimes furnished by the power company but installed by the contractor. In other localities the contractor furnishes the socket. Mount it securely about 5 ft from the bottom of the pole. If a switch or circuit breaker is also used, mount it about 5 ft from the bottom, the meter socket just above it.

Insulators on Poles. Near the top of the pole install insulator racks of the general type that were shown in Fig. 17-5. Provide one rack for the incoming power wires, one for each set of wires running from the pole to various buildings. Remember that the pull on the wires in a heavy wind or under ice conditions in northern climates is terrific. Anchor the racks with heavy lag screws. Better yet, use at least one through-bolt, all the way through the pole, for each rack.

Installing the Stack. Whether you use a single-stack construction (all wires in one conduit) or the double-stack, the general procedure is the same. In the past the conduit has often ended at a point below the insulators, which then required great care

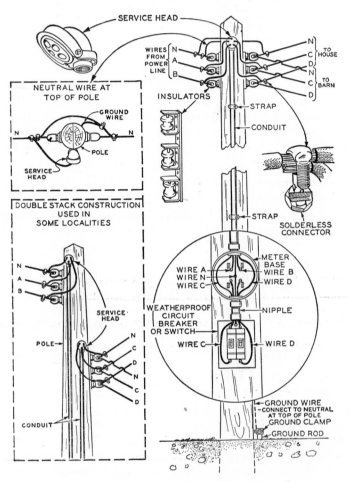

Fig. 24-7. Typical meter-pole installation on a farm.

in the installation of the wires to make sure that a drip loop was provided in order to prevent water from following the wires into the service head. The Code requirement today is to bring the top of the conduit to a point *above* the topmost insulator, as shown in Fig. 24-7, thus automatically solving the water problem.

At the top end of the conduit use a service head of the general type shown in Fig. 17-6, with the right number of holes in the insulator. Run wires through the conduit, white for neutral, black or other color for the hot wires.

In practice, the switch, meter socket, the conduit with wires inside, and insulators are usually preassembled on the pole before it is erected. When the pole goes up, it is ready for wires to be installed on the insulators.

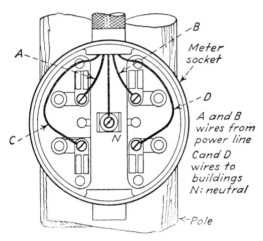

FIG. 24-8. Connections in meter on pole, without switch.

Wire Size on Pole. The 1965 Code was the first to establish requirements for farms; see Secs. 220-4(1) and 220-4(m). First you must establish the minimum ampacity for each feeder (set of wires) starting at the pole; after this has been done, you can then establish the minimum size for the main service conductors on the pole.

Start with the set of feeders from the pole to the building or buildings that will constitute the heaviest load. It is assumed that this will be a 3-wire 115/230-volt feeder. List all the loads to be operated off that feeder that are likely to be in operation at one time. Determine the amperage at 230 volts, including all motors. If the total amperage so determined is less than 125% of the ampere-rating of the largest motor, ignore the total you have just determined, and use 125% of the motor rating instead.

But if the total reached either way is less than 60 amp, ignore the previous totals and use 60 amp instead, for that is the minimum.

If the total reached is over 60 amp but under 120 amp, count only half the difference. For example, if the total is 100 amp (40 amp more than 60 amp), count only 50% of the difference, or 20 amp. The new total to meet Code requirements then is 60 + 20 or 80 amp. If the actual total (before applying the 50% factor) is over 120 amp, count only 25% of the excess over 120 amp. Assuming a total of 160 amp, your calculation is as follows:

First 60 amp	100%	60 amp
Next 60 amp	50%	30 amp
Next 40 amp	25%	10 amp
Total		100 amp

Your feeder must have an ampacity of 100 amp.

In like fashion, determine minimum capacity for each of the other feeders. One of them will serve the farmhouse. Determine its minimum capacity as outlined in other chapters, for non-farm residential work.

Having determined the minimum size of each feeder, you must determine the minimum size of the service conductors on the pole. This is simple. Add the amperage of the largest feeder, plus 75% of the next largest, plus 65% of the third largest, and 50% of all the others. Assume five feeders having minimum requirements of 100, 80, 70, 60 and 60 amp. The service conductors then must have a minimum capacity as follows:

100 amp	100%	100 amp
80 amp	75%	60 amp
70 amp	65%	45 amp
60 amp	50%	30 amp
60 amp	50%	30 amp
Total		265 amp

All this has to do with minimum requirements. Good judgment suggests that you look forward to future years when additional equipment will be added, by using wire larger than the minimum required.

Connections at Top of Pole. Be sure that the neutral is the topmost of the wires. The wires on the pole will be of large size and even on the ground would be difficult to solder. Use solderless connectors of the types that were shown in Figs. 8-22 and 8-23. These connectors being made of metal should be taped after installation.

Connections at Meter. If there is to be neither switch nor fuse (nor circuit breaker) at the pole, the connections are very simple, as shown in Fig. 24-8. The service wires always run to the top terminals of the meter socket; the wires running back up to the top of the pole (and from there to the various buildings) are connected to the bottom terminals of the socket.

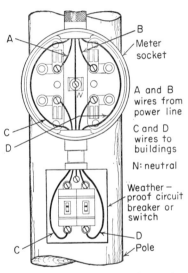

Fig. 24-9. Connections in meter on pole, with switch or circuit breaker.

If there is to be a circuit breaker or a switch, the connections change only a little, as Fig. 24-9 will show. Naturally any switch or circuit breaker installed must be the weatherproof type.

If the wires from pole to the various buildings are to be underground, the wires from the bottom terminals of the meter socket will then (instead of running back to the top of the pole) be connected to the various underground wires.

Ground at Meter Pole. The neutral wire always runs from the top of the pole, through the conduit, to the center terminal of the meter socket. Formerly it was standard practice to run the ground wire from the meter socket (out of the bottom hub) to ground, but experience has shown that better protection against lightning is obtained if the ground wire is run outside the conduit. Run it from the neutral at the top of the pole, directly to the ground rod at the bottom of the pole. It is usually run tucked in alongside the conduit as far as it goes, then to ground. In some localities it is stapled to the pole on the side opposite the conduit.

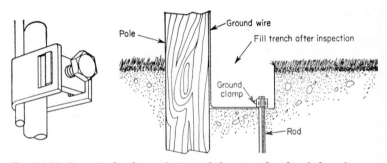

Fig. 24-10. In some localities, the top of the ground rod is below the surface of the ground. Fill the trench after inspection. If the ground rod is copper, use only a copper clamp as shown at left.

In some areas the custom is to let the top of the ground rod project a few inches from the ground. The ground clamp is permanently exposed. In other localities the ground rod is driven about 2 ft from the pole (or building) after a trench has first been dug about a foot deep from rod to pole. The top of the rod is a few inches above the bottom of the trench. The ground wire runs down the side of the pole (or building) to the bottom of the trench, then to the ground clamp on the rod. After inspection the trench is filled in and the rod, the clamp, and the bottom end of the ground wire remain buried (see Fig. 24-10). Use the method favored in your locality.

Grounds in buildings housing livestock should be installed so that seepage from animal manure does not saturate the ground around the rod. Chemical action in time eats the wire, the clamp, and sometimes even the rod, so that what was formerly a good ground turns out to be no ground at all.

Ground at Buildings. The Code requires a ground at any building with two or more circuits and also at every building that houses livestock, regardless of the number of circuits.

Entrance at Individual Buildings. The entrance at any one building served directly from the meter pole is made as already outlined in Chap. 17, except that the meter is omitted. Instead of running the ground wire from the neutral strap of the service equipment, run it from the neutral wire, at the point where it reaches the building, to the ground rod. Run it along the service cable or service conduit, just as on the pole, for maximum protection against lightning. If, however, underground wires have been used, ground them in the usual way.

In the house, provide circuit breakers (or fused service switch plus branch-circuit fuses) just as if the house were the only building being wired. In other buildings you have a considerable choice of equipment, with one restriction: You must be able to disconnect *all* the wiring with one or more switches. In a very small building with only one or two lights and maybe a receptacle, the switch might be an ordinary toggle switch such as you use to control lights in the house, but it must disconnect the receptacle at the same time.

In the category of buildings with more outlets, there might be at one extreme a building with one circuit, at the other extreme a dairy barn with 20 circuits, and the equipment must be selected according to the load and the number of circuits. For the smaller of the buildings mentioned you might use a small fused switch of the general type that was shown in Fig. 13-3 and in the larger building one of the 100-amp type shown in Fig. 13-5, or even larger. In-between buildings will require in-between switches in proportion to the load and the number of circuits. Circuit breakers are being used more and more in place of fused equipment.

Buildings Fed through Another Building. On farms it often happens that one building is fed by wires from another building. At any such building proceed as if the wires came directly from the pole, except that the switch (or circuit breakers) that controls the wiring may be located either at the building *from* which the wires run or at the building *to* which they run.

Whether this disconnect switch needs to be fused or not depends entirely on the size wires used and the size fuses ahead of the starting point (see Fig. 24-11, which shows several buildings served through the main barn). The wires are No. 14 inside

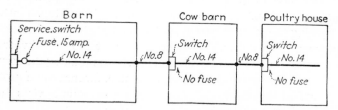

FIG. 24-11. Whether disconnect switches in outbuildings need to be fused or not depends on the size of the fuse at the starting point.

the buildings, but, for mechanical strength, No. 8 is used between buildings. Since the fuse in the barn is the 15-amp size, it protects the smallest wire in the entire circuit; therefore the switches in cow barn and poultry house need not be fused.

In Fig. 24-12, No. 8 wires run through the barn, between the barn and cow barn, and through the cow barn, serving a motor

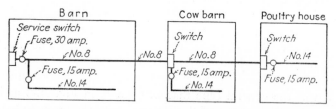

FIG. 24-12. In this case, fuses are required because the 30-amp fuse in the barn does not protect the No. 14 wires.

there which requires up to 30 amp for starting. Therefore a 30-amp fuse is used in the barn, and since the No. 8 wire continues straight through to the poultry house, this wire must be fused at not over 15 amp at the point where the change is made to No. 14 wire in the poultry house. Likewise at the point where No. 14 wire is connected to the No. 8 in the cow barn, a fuse block must be used with 15-amp fuses to protect No. 14 wire.

Farmhouses. The wiring in farmhouses is no different from that in city houses, and the procedure is therefore the same as already covered in other chapters. Usually any wiring system may be used in the house, even if the inspector insists on a special kind of cable for barns and other buildings.

Use Nonmetal System. The Code in Sec. 300-1(c) recommends a nonmetal system, in other words nonmetallic-sheathed cable,

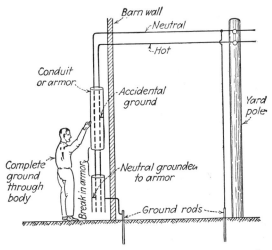

Fig. 24-13. If there were no break in the armor, the accidental ground shown would blow a fuse. Since the armor has a break, a dangerous condition exists.

for locations where a good permanent ground is not found. Certainly farms fall into that classification; hence conduit and armored cable are seldom used for farm work. The reasons for this are not hard to understand. In barns considerable moisture is always present, and in addition there are other corrosive vapors such as, for example, ammonia from the excreta of animals. This quickly attacks the conduit or metal armor, so that the life of the metal is relatively short. As the metal raceway rusts out, it may open the continuous ground that otherwise exists from outlet to outlet in the usual metal system. If an accidental ground occurs in such a system at a point beyond the break and if a person or an animal touches a part of the metal raceway above the break, the circuit is completed through the body with at least an unpleasant, if not a dangerous, shock. Figure 24-13 should make this clear; the ground through the body is equivalent to touching both wires and may be equally dangerous. Many dairy animals have been killed every year through just such occurrences—metallic systems apparently but not actually grounded. For these reasons the nonmetal systems are recommended for such locations.

The objection can be raised that, even if nonmetallic cable

FIG. 24-14. Boxes made of bakelite or other insulating material are very desirable in farm installations. (*Union Insulating Co., Inc.*)

is used, dangerous conditions can and will still arise when an accidental ground happens to occur inside one of the usual metal outlet boxes; anyone touching the outlet box is then still subject to the same shocks encountered with a metal system in which the metal raceway is eaten through as outlined in the previous paragraph. To this objection there is no good answer, with the result that nonmetallic outlet and switch boxes have been developed to make the entire system nonmetallic. Such boxes are made of bakelite or porcelain. Figure 24-14 shows representative boxes and covers.

Such boxes are used like other boxes except that, per Code Sec. 370-7(c), connectors are not required provided the cable is supported within 8 in. of the box. In spite of this exception, many such boxes are provided with clamps.

In the installation of nonmetallic boxes, one precaution is in order. When they are installed in barns or other locations where the humidity is high, wood timbers shrink and swell with the variations in humidity. Steel boxes, if rigidly nailed or screwed to supporting timbers, do not present a mechanical problem as the timbers swell with moisture, for the steel boxes "give" a bit if required. Nonmetallic boxes on the other hand, if screwed down tightly on dry timbers, have been known to break out their bottoms as the timbers swelled with increasing humidity. When mounting such boxes, leave just a little bit

Fig. 24-15. These handy devices replace outlet box, cover, and wiring device. (*General Electric Co.*)

of slack and don't drive the mounting screws down completely tight.

Also very popular for barns and similar locations are the combination surface devices shown in Fig. 24-15. Their use and method of installation have already been fully covered in Chap. 22 and will not be repeated here.

Cable for Barn Wiring. In the early period of farm wiring the only kind of nonmetallic-sheathed cable then made (now known as Code Type NM) was used in wiring barns and other farm buildings. It gradually became clear that the usual high humidity in such buildings caused rotting of the cable, leading to danger of shock and fire. It became necessary to rewire many farm buildings because of the short life of the cable.

This led to the development of several types of "barn cable" which have now been standardized into two basic types: Code Types NMC and UF. Some brands of cable qualify for both types and are then marked "Type NMC-UF." This was discussed in Chaps. 11 and 17.

In the wiring of barns and other buildings housing livestock, use only one of these two types. There is no good reason why they should not be used throughout all the buildings on a farm.

Barn Wiring. The physical make-up of the circuits, that is, the combinations of cable and boxes and switches and receptacles, is not different from that already discussed and therefore needs no further amplification. The chief points to observe are points of practicability and common sense. Locate switches and receptacle outlets so that they cannot be bumped by animals in passing. Locate switches at convenient height so that they can be operated by the elbow; farmers' hands are often both full. A great convenience is to have 3-way switches to control at least one light from either end of the barn. Never use brass-shell sockets; use only porcelain or bakelite, for the same reasons that nonmetallic boxes are used.

Plenty of light outlets should be provided; a minimum is considered one light for every two stalls. It is best to locate the outlets for lamps between joists, so that the lamp does not project too far down into the aisle between stalls, where it might easily

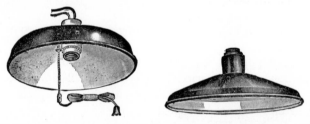

Fig. 24-16. A 60-watt lamp with a reflector is often as effective as a 100-watt without a reflector. Reflectors become an investment rather than an expense. (*Steber Mfg. Co.*)

be damaged. Since most barn ceilings are dark and dusty, they reflect practically no light. About half the light from an exposed lamp falls on the ceiling and is lost. Provide a reflector for every socket; the area underneath will be lighted almost twice as well as without a reflector. Several types of suitable reflectors are available at reasonable prices; two are shown in Fig. 24-16. Their use is a good investment.

Provide a light to illuminate the steps to the haymow. In haymows inspectors frequently require vaporproof receptacles of the type shown in Fig. 24-17. A vaporproof receptacle is simply a socket with a tight-fitting glass globe that encloses the lamp. The dust that arises in haymows is inflammable or even explosive, and if an unprotected lamp is accidentally broken, although the lamp burns out instantly, during that instant there is a flash while the filament melts. This flash may set off an explosion; hence the requirement for the vaporproof receptacles.

Fig. 24-17. A typical vaporproof receptacle, often used in haymows. (*Killark Electric Mfg. Co.*)

Cable should always be installed in a location where it cannot possibly be damaged accidentally. In haymows, cover it with strips of board at all points where it might be damaged by pitchforks. Where it passes through a floor, the Code requires that it be protected by conduit or pipe for at least 6 in.; many inspectors sensibly require this protection for about 6 ft, especially where there is danger of hayforks damaging the cable. Note, however, that this length of pipe or conduit does not then make the system a conduit system; the pipe is there purely for protection against accidental mechanical damage to a length of approved cable.

Cable in barns and other farm buildings should not be run along or across the bottoms of joists or similar timbers, because this exposes the cable to mechanical injury. The cable will receive good protection if it is run along the side of a joist or beam. More cable will be required to run the cable from the side of an aisle out to the middle for an outlet, then back to the side of the aisle, but consider the extra cost as insurance against damage. Figure 24-18 will show the details of recommended practice.

In barns or other buildings which house livestock, cable should not be run on the outer walls, for since these walls are colder than other areas, they will have condensed moisture on them. Run cable where it will stay reasonably dry.

Poultry Houses. One point that should be particularly noted is that special wiring is frequently required for lighting designed to promote egg production. It is well known that hens produce more eggs during winter months if light is provided during part of the time that would otherwise be dark. It is best to provide

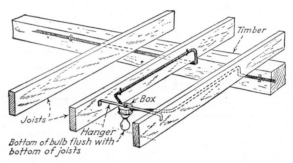

FIG. 24-18. Keep exposed cables away from the center of aisles. The bottom of the lamp should be very little below the bottom of the joists. Reflectors should be used, extending very little below the bottoms of joists.

artificial light both in the morning and in the evening. If the transition from light to dark is abrupt, the hens will not go to roost but will stay where they are when the lights are turned off. In the morning better results are obtained if the light does not come on to full brilliancy suddenly. If a special time switch of the type shown in Fig. 24-19 is used, in the morning it turns on first the dim lights, then bright lights, then when full daylight arrives turns all off. In the evening the procedure is reversed; as darkness sets in, the lights are turned on full. At the time set, the bright lights go out and the dim lights go on; during this interval the hens go to roost. Shortly thereafter all lights are automatically turned off. The wiring for such clocks is simple, and diagrams are furnished with such clocks.

FIG. 24-19. This poultry - house switch properly controls lights, dim and bright, for forcing egg production. (*Paragon Electric Co.*)

Be sure that the light falls upon the roosts, for if the roosts remain in darkness when the lights come on, the hens will probably not leave their roosts. Neither will they be able to find the roosts in the evening if they are in darkness while the lights illuminate the rest of the pens. One 40- or 60-

watt lamp for every 200 sq ft of floor area is usually considered sufficient.

Manually controlled circuits can easily be provided so that one switch controls bright lights, another dim lights.

Water Pump. Every farm will have a water pump. It not only will serve to provide water for all usual purposes but, in addition, will be a tremendous help in case of fire. But in case of fire, quite often power lines between buildings fail and fuses blow, so that the pump cannot run just when it is needed most. That can be avoided by simply considering the pump as a fire pump. The Code in Sec. 230-2 permits a fire pump to be connected through an independent service. In practice this simply means that wires are run to the pump house directly from the meter pole, ahead of the main fuses or circuit breaker. Then, even if the main fuses blow, the pump will still run. Simply run two wires from the meter, ahead of circuit breaker or main fuses, to the pump. There must be a fused disconnect switch (or a circuit breaker) for the pump only, and if this is mounted on the pole, it must naturally be of the weatherproof type. Underground wires provide additional insurance against failure.

Other Buildings. No particular problems are involved in other buildings. Use only nonmetallic sockets; provide switch control instead of pull chains. Every building, no matter how small, should have a receptacle outlet, if for no other reason than to provide a connection for a trouble light of the type that was shown in Fig. 20-6.

Motors. Stationary motors should be wired as discussed in Chaps. 15 and 31. For a portable motor of considerable size it will be necessary to provide a heavy-duty receptacle with a rating in amperes and volts at least equal to the rating of the motor. One of the types shown in Figs. 21-1 and 21-2 will be found suitable. If the receptacle must be outdoors, of course a weatherproof type must be used. Except in the smallest sizes, these are very expensive; one is shown in Fig. 24-20, together with a plug to fit. If a weatherproof receptacle is to be mounted on the outside wall of a barn or other farm building, consider installing one of the ordinary nonweatherproof type inside the building, with a door over it that can be opened to make the indoor receptacle accessible from the outside.

Yard Lights. Every farm will have at least one yard light of the general type shown in Fig. 24-21, usually located at the meter pole. In most cases the light is controlled by two 3-way switches, located at house and barn. A 4-way switch in a weatherproof housing is often located at the pole.

The wiring of a yard light is often haphazard. It is not un-

Fig. 24-20. This weatherproof heavy-duty outlet and plug should be employed where large portable motors are used outdoors. (*Crouse-Hinds Co.*)

common to see it wired by tapping one of the two wires from the light directly to the neutral wire at the pole, running the other to a switch at any convenient location and then on to the nearest "hot" wire. The scheme works but is contrary to Code, for the neutral wire at the pole is a feeder and not a branch circuit; it is not permissible to tap a feeder except to form a branch circuit.

Fig. 24-21. Yard lights should be liberally used in lighting the farmyard. (*Steber Mfg. Co.*)

Today most inspectors will insist on a carefully planned installation. To operate a yard light from one switch, it is necessary to run two wires to it from the nearest fused circuit, and to operate it from two points, it is necessary to run three wires. Figure 24-22 shows a method that makes a weatherproof and mechanically sturdy job out of the installation; it also shows the wiring diagram.

An alternate scheme that is becoming more popular every day is the remote-control yard light. The basic principles involved have been discussed in Chap. 20. Figure 24-23 shows a typical unit which houses the transformer and the relay or remote-

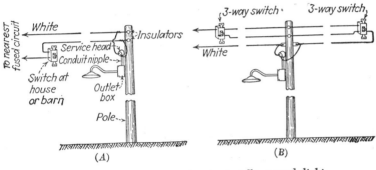

Fig. 24-22. Good construction in installing yard light.

controlled switch. Only low-voltage wires are run from this yard-light unit to the various locations where the switches are to be installed, so inexpensive twisted 3-wire cable can be used. The wiring is in accordance with Fig. 20-36.

Fig. 24-23. A remote-control yard light. A gooseneck fixture of the type shown in Fig. 24-21 may be used instead of the reflector-style lamp. (*Steber Mfg. Co.*)

The particular unit in Fig. 24-23 shows an exposed lamp of the reflector type. The reflector is a silver coating inside the bulb, which therefore remains bright during the life of the lamp. Such lamps are available in spotlights and floodlights, depending on whether a small or a large area is to be lighted. They are also available in two types of glass: ordinary for indoor use and "hard glass" for outdoor use. Ordinary glass bulbs will break when cold rain hits a lighted lamp; the hard-glass type will not be damaged.

Wires Entering Buildings. Use any of the methods described in Chap. 20 in connection with garage wiring.

Tapping Service Wires at Building. Often two buildings are quite close to each other and can then be served by a single set of wires from the pole, which should run to that building with the greater load. Naturally the wires must be heavy enough

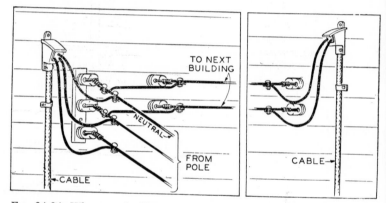

FIG. 24-24. When two buildings are near each other, tap the service wires from pole where they are anchored on the first building. Run them to the second building.

for the combined load of both buildings. At the service insulators of the first building, make a tap and run the wires on to the second building, all as shown in Fig. 24-24. At the second building, proceed just as if the wires came directly from the pole.

If the second building is very small and requires only 115 volts, tap off only two wires including the neutral, as shown in the picture. If the second building has a considerable load so that 115/230 volts is desirable, tap off all three wires. Remember the requirement for a separate service switch and ground at the second building, as discussed in other paragraphs.

Outdoor Receptacles and Switches. On farms it will frequently be found convenient to install a switch or receptacle outdoors. The simplest method of handling an outdoor switch is to use a cast housing of the type shown in Fig. 24-25. Inside install any kind of switch whether single-pole or 3- or 4-way. The receptacle housing of Fig. 24-26 will accommodate any kind of single receptacle of the ordinary 15-amp variety.

Wiring the Very Small Farm. On a very few farms only a little power is used outside the house. If you are absolutely

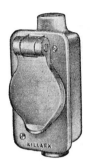

FIG. 24-25. Install any kind of switch inside this housing, for outdoor use. (*Killark Electric Mfg. Co.*)

FIG. 24-26. Install any single receptacle in this housing, for outdoor use. (*Killark Electric Mfg. Co.*)

sure this will always be so, the buildings other than the house can be treated like the garage in city wiring. Bring the main entrance into the house. Leave one circuit for the wiring beyond the house. Run ordinary service-entrance cable from the fuse cabinet or circuit breaker to the outside of the house, up the side of the house (making a sort of "backward" service entrance), from the outside of the house onward; follow the principles outlined for garage wiring in Chap. 20.

Chapter 25

ISOLATED AND STANDBY POWER PLANTS

An isolated power plant may be defined as any installation by which the owner makes his own electric power. Such installations are used where electric power is not available from commercial power lines. The same generating plants (if they develop 60-cycle AC power) are also commonly used for standby service to provide emergency power when commercial power lines fail.

Battery-type Plants. The most ordinary type charges a 32-volt battery, thus constituting what has long been known as a "32-volt farm light plant." Others charge 6-, 12-, and 110-volt batteries. Battery-type plants are comparatively little used today.

Alternating-current Plants. By far the most common type of isolated generating plant today is the type which generates 60-cycle alternating current. Capacities are available from 400 to 100,000 watts and more. Several are shown in Fig. 25-1. Among the many advantages of this type of plant are these: Ordinary appliances (motors and so on) are used, costing far less than special low-voltage devices and far more readily obtainable. Since their voltage is 115 (or 115/230), the wiring is the same as for ordinary electrical work. Combining these two advantages means that if such a plant is installed in an isolated location and commercial power later becomes available, the wiring and all the appliances can be used without change. There are no problems of excessive voltage drop as in the case of low-voltage battery plants. Plants are available in any required wattages, so that there is no limit to the number or size of appliances that can be used.

Since such generators are engine-driven, means must be provided for starting the engine. The simplest is the hand-starting method, using a rope or crank. The usual method uses two 6-volt automobile-type batteries which crank the engine; in smaller engines this is done by a special winding in the alternating-current generator, in larger engines by starting systems similar to those used on automobiles. Electrically cranked engines are further divided into those which start by pushing the start button on the engine, and remote-control types which can be started by pushing start buttons placed at a distance up to several hundred feet, and connected by inexpensive control wire. The next step is the "full-

FIG. 25-1. Typical engine-driven generating plants developing 5,000 and 25,000 watts of 60-cycle 115/230-volt power. (*D. W. Onan & Sons, Inc.*)

automatic" type which starts automatically when a light or appliance is turned on, stops when everything is turned off. The special type which starts automatically when commercial power fails will be discussed separately.

In selecting the capacity of the generator needed, naturally you must choose one which has as many watts output as the maximum number of watts to be consumed by all the different loads turned on *at the same time.* Manufacturers of these plants provide helpful literature for that purpose.

Standby Plants. Plants which generate 60-cycle power are very commonly used to provide power during periods when commercial power has failed. In a city house an interruption of a few hours may not be important. It is important in a hospital operating room, in a broadcasting station, and on a railway signal system. It is important in a modern windowless office, in a store open during periods of darkness, in a theater, where complete darkness might lead to panic. It is important in a chicken hatchery, where a few hours' interruption may ruin a large load of eggs; in a greenhouse with an electrically operated oil burner, where a few hours' interruption might let the temperature drop to a dangerous point; on a farm, where interruptions are often measured in days rather than in hours—without power, milking machines are out of operation, pumps do not operate, hot water is no longer available in required volume, oil burners do not work. Continuous power is important in many hundreds of different circumstances, and the only guarantee against an interruption is a standby generating plant.

Type of Control for Standby Plants. The user has a choice of two methods for controlling a standby plant. The first and simplest consists merely of a hand-operated double-throw switch. When the power fails, start the plant, then throw the switch. The second is the automatic line-transfer control which, when the power fails, disconnects the load from the commercial line, starts the plant, then transfers the load to the plant. When commercial power is restored, it transfers the load back to the commercial line and stops the plant.

The important part of either control is the double-throw switch, which in one position leaves the load connected to the commercial power line, in the other position it completely disconnects the power line from all wiring and connects the load to the generating plant. (In the case of an automatic control, this double-throw switch is electrically operated.) Do not under any circumstances try to install a standby plant without using such a double-throw switch, for doing so is apt to result in having a dead commercial line connected to the wiring of your establishment at the same time that the standby generator is feeding the power into that wiring system. The standby generator is then *feeding power back* into an otherwise dead line, which can be-. come quite dangerous to linemen working on the supposedly "dead" line. Several deaths on REA lines have been traced to linemen working on a supposedly dead line which was actually energized by a generating plant connected in haphazard fashion without using a double-throw switch. Remember that the same transformer which reduces high-line voltage from 2,300 to 115 volts for use on the farm also steps 115-volt power from a standby plant back to 2,300 volts, if the line is not disconnected while the standby plant is in use.

In selecting such a double-throw switch (whether hand or electrically operated) do not make the mistake of using one which is large enough to carry only the amperage developed by the standby plant. For example, a 5,000-watt 115/230-volt plant will produce about 22 amp, so a 30-amp switch would appear to be large enough. However, the switch is usually connected in the main line, so it will have to carry up to the full

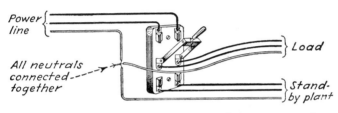

FIG. 25-2. In installing an emergency or standby generating plant, for safety's sake *always* install a double-throw switch. If the controls are automatic, the switch will be electrically operated. Naturally the switch must be completely enclosed, not open as in the picture above.

capacity of that line, usually 60 amp or more, during normal operation, that is, during periods when the commercial line has *not* failed. The amperage rating of the switch is determined by the maximum number of amperes it must carry during normal periods.

Normally, select a switch with as many poles as are found in the service switch, *not* counting the neutral. Thus for a 3-wire 115/230-volt service you would use a 2-pole switch. Some REA lines, however, require that *all* poles, including the neutral, must be switched, this then requiring a 3-pole switch.

The installation of such double-throw switches is very simple. as Fig. 25-2 will show. Trace the circuit as shown, and you will see that, when such a switch is properly installed, there is no possible way in which a standby plant can feed back through the transformer into an otherwise dead line.

Advantages of Manual Control. With the use of a hand-operated switch, part of the load can be turned off by hand

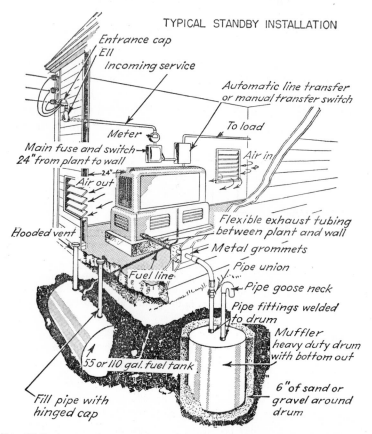

TYPICAL STANDBY INSTALLATION

Entrance cap
Ell
Incoming service
Automatic line transfer or manual transfer switch
Meter
To load
Main fuse and switch 24" from plant to wall
Air in
24"
Air out
Flexible exhaust tubing between plant and wall
Hooded vent
Metal grommets
Pipe union
Fuel line
Pipe goose neck
Pipe fittings welded to drum
Muffler heavy duty drum with bottom out
55 or 110 gal. fuel tank
6" of sand or gravel around drum
Fill pipe with hinged cap

Fɪɢ. 25-3. A typical emergency or standby installation. (*D. W. Onan & Sons, Inc.*)

before starting the standby generator. Then a smaller generator can be used. For example, on a small farm the range and the water heater can be disconnected, making a 3,500- or a 5,000-watt plant big enough. If this were not done, a 10,000-watt plant might be needed. In a factory, certain large motors or heating devices might be disconnected if their use is not essential, leaving everything else in operation and thus making practical a much smaller plant than would otherwise be required. In this way a considerable saving can be made in the original cost.

Advantages of Automatic Control. For some applications, there is no choice. If the lights were to go out in a hospital operating room during an operation, a delay might be serious. If a store is open in the evening and if the lights go out, a delay might lead to panic and injuries. If installed to provide power for oil burners, the automatic control provides protection even at night and over week ends, when perhaps no one is on the premises. Automatic installations are frequently made in isolated locations, as, for example, in microwave transmitting stations, where no caretaker is seen for a week at a time.

In addition to the basic advantage of being automatic, such controls usually also provide other conveniences, such as automatic charging of the cranking battery; test switches for checking the operation without taking over the load; "exercisers," if wanted, to run the plant once a day or once a week; and many optional features.

Installation Hints. Manufacturers' literature provides complete installation instructions, but some general hints will be in order. The plant must naturally be installed where the engine will cool properly. A small room is not considered a good location unless means are provided for adequate circulation of air to carry away the heat created by the engine. The fuel-supply system must be considered. If gasoline is used, an underground tank outside the building provides the best installation. If you have natural or other gas in your building, use it for fuel, thus doing away with gasoline entirely. The output of the plant, however, may be reduced somewhat, depending on the richness of the gas in your particular area. Figure 25-3 shows a properly installed plant.

Chapter 26

WIRING APARTMENT HOUSES

If an apartment is considered merely as that space within a building which is occupied by one family, no new wiring problems of any consequence are encountered. If the apartment house is considered in its entirety as a multifamily dwelling, many new problems arise.

Planning an Individual Apartment. To determine the minimum number of circuits required by Code for any single apartment, proceed as outlined for a single-family dwelling in Chap. 13. For lighting, allow 3 watts per sq ft. For example, a small apartment of 800 sq ft will require 800 × 3, or 2,400 watts, which means two circuits. To this must be added two separate No. 12 circuits for appliances, just as in the case of the single-family house, thus making four circuits the minimum. Naturally, too, an additional circuit must be provided for each appliance consuming more than 1,650 watts, for example, an electric range.

Service-entrance Problems. In practically all cases there is but a single service drop for the entire building. In most cases each tenant pays for the power he consumes, so there is a separate meter for each tenant, plus usually another meter to carry hall lights, oil-burner motors, and similar loads. The service drop therefore must feed a number of separate meters and disconnecting means. The Code in Sec. 230-75 requires that each occupant must have access to his disconnecting means.

Apartment buildings fall into what the Code calls "multiple-occupancy" buildings. Service-entrance problems are discussed in Code Sec. 230-75, which reads as follows:

230-75. Multiple Occupancy. In a multiple-occupancy building, each occupant shall have access to his disconnecting means. A multiple-occupancy building having individual occupancy above the second floor shall have service equipment grouped in a common accessible place, the disconnecting means consisting of not more than six switches or six circuit breakers. Multiple-occupancy buildings that do not have individual occupancy above the second floor may have service conductors run to each occupancy in accordance with Sec. 230-2, Exception No. 3, and each such service may have not more than six switches or circuit breakers.

The section just cited first appeared in the 1951 Code and has plagued the public ever since. It has led to many gray hairs and probably has induced much profanity. In part, the difficulty stems from the fact that there is no definition of just what is meant by "individual occupancy above the second floor." A building has individual occupancy above the second floor if on the third or a higher floor there is one (or more than one) occupant who does *not* occupy space *below* the third floor.

Do note the distinction in the quoted paragraph between the two types of structures: "A multiple-occupancy building having individual occupancy above the second floor *shall* have . . . ," but "multiple-occupancy buildings that do not have individual occupancy above the second floor *may* have. . . ." In the first case, there is no choice; in the second case, there is a choice.

Service Equipment. The Code defines the service equipment as "the necessary equipment, usually consisting of a circuit breaker or switch and fuses, and their accessories, located near the point of entrance of supply conductors to a building and intended to constitute the main control and means of cutoff for the supply to that building."

Note that the supply conductors themselves are not included in the definition, nor is the service drop which ends where the power company's wires are attached to the building. Neither are the branch-circuit fuses or circuit breakers included, only the switch or circuit breaker that controls the entire flow of current.

Classes of Buildings. While the Code does not spell it out, multiple-occupancy buildings can be grouped into three classes as far as the service equipment is concerned:

1. One- and two-story buildings.

2. Three-story or higher buildings, *not* having individual occupancy above the second floor.

3. Three-story or higher buildings that *do have* individual occupancy above the second floor.

In the diagrams that follow, fuses are shown. It must be understood that circuit breakers may be used instead.

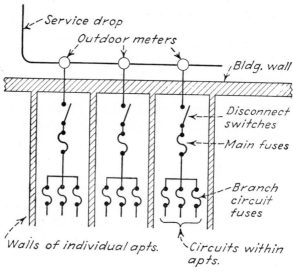

FIG. 26-1. If the apartment building is one- or two-story, a separate outdoor meter for each apartment may be installed.

One- and Two-story Buildings. Per the Code, the service equipment *may* be in a common space at all times accessible to all the occupants, but it is not required.

Perhaps the simplest installation is that shown in Fig. 26-1, in which a separate outdoor meter is used for each apartment, regardless of the number of apartments. From the meter, the wiring to the inside of each individual apartment is exactly the same as if each apartment were a separate house. There is no limit to the number of separate apartments that may be handled in this way.

If preferred, the service wires may be brought into a common space which must at all times be accessible to all occupants, and wires may be run from there to each apartment, as shown in Fig. 26-2. (If there are not over six individual switches, the main switch may be omitted.) Note that in this scheme all the equipment, including the branch-circuit fuses, is in the common space. Each set of equipment for one apartment consists of dis-

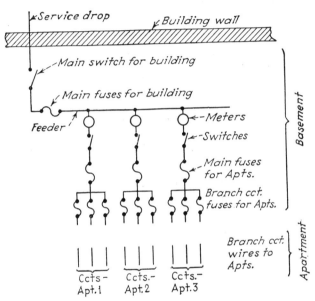

Fig. 26-2. Here all the service equipment is located in a common, accessible space. This scheme *may* be used in any apartment building and *must* be used in most of them.

connecting means, main fuses, and branch circuit fuses; all this may be telescoped for each apartment into a single circuit-breaker cabinet of the type shown in Fig. 13-8 or into a common "range switch" of the type shown in Fig. 13-4 or 13-5.

That scheme may be changed to the one shown in Fig. 26-3, where the branch-circuit fuses for each apartment are found in that apartment. In that case, the wires from the common space to each apartment become feeders and must be individually protected where they begin, that is, in the common space. As a matter of fact, in larger buildings when a common space is used, this is the only logical scheme to avoid waste of materials.

Three-story and Higher Buildings. The procedure for larger buildings is the same as for one- and two-story buildings, except that the scheme of Fig. 26-1 may not be used *if there is individual occupancy above the second floor.* In that case you must use the

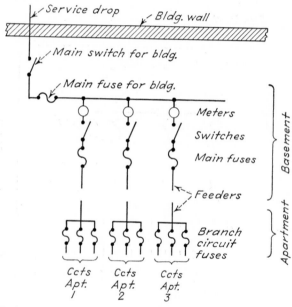

FIG. 26-3. A variation of the scheme of Fig. 26-2. The branch-circuit fuses have been moved to the individual apartments.

scheme of Fig. 26-2 or 26-3 and put all the service equipment into a common space which is accessible to all occupants.

A very large apartment may need a service of, say, 750 amp. Since each apartment must have its own disconnecting means (which means many more than six individual switches), you could reach the conclusion that an 800-amp main switch would be required. That need can be avoided by breaking up the total load into not more than six subsections, for example, two fused switches of 200 amp and four of 100 amp. With six such switches installed, no main disconnecting means is required ahead of them all. Each of the six switches then feeds a group of smaller switches, just as a 100-amp switch in a smaller apartment would serve as a disconnecting means for a considerable number of switches each controlling an individual apartment. See Fig. 26-4.

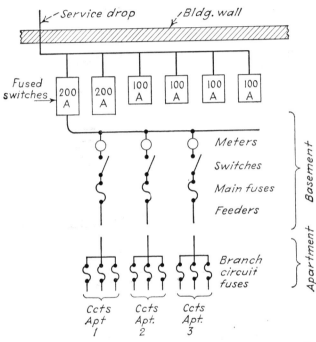

FIG. 26-4. If there are not over six separate disconnecting means, the main switch may be omitted.

Determining Feeder to Individual Apartment. The feeder from the disconnecting means to the overcurrent devices in the individual apartment corresponds to the service-entrance wires in the single-family house (but in the apartment the wires are not service-entrance wires but are feeders). Wire size is determined in general in the same way that was described in Chap. 13. Just as in the case of the single-family house, the first 3,000 watts are counted at their full value; in other words, the demand factor is 100%. For that portion of the load above 3,000 watts the demand factor is 35%. The range load is added separately, after applying the demand factor to the lighting load.

For an apartment of 500 sq ft, figure 3 watts per sq ft, or 1,500 watts for lighting; add 3,000 watts for the two special-appliance circuits, for a total of 4,500 watts. Count the first 3,000 watts at 100% demand factor. Count the remaining 1,500 watts at 35% demand factor, or 525 watts. Add the two, making a total of 3,525 watts. At 115 volts this is equivalent to 3,525/115, or 31 amp.

According to Table 310-12 of the Code, No. 8 wire is the smallest that may be used. (Incidentally, the Code in Sec. 215-2 specifies No. 10 as a minimum when a feeder serves two or more 2-wire circuits.)

If the apartment were larger, having, say, 1,200 sq ft, the calculation would be 1,200 × 3, or 3,600 watts for lighting, plus 3,000 watts for small appliances, or 6,600 watts altogether. Counting the first 3,000 watts at their full value and adding 35% of the remainder of 3,600 watts, or a net of 1,260 watts, make a total of 4,260 watts. At 115 volts this is the equivalent of 4,260/115, or 37 amp, for which No. 8 is the smallest wire permissible. More likely you would consider the load a 115/230-volt load and would run a 3-wire feeder capable of carrying 4,260/230, or 18.2 amp. According to Table 310-12 of the Code, No. 12 wire may be used, but Sec. 215-2 of the Code again requires No. 10 as the minimum.

In this connection do not overlook the requirement of Code Sec. 215-3; the wire used for the feeder must be of sufficient size so that the voltage drop will not exceed 1%. See tables on pages 107 and 108; these tables are for 2% drop, so divide all distances shown by 2 to arrive at the maximum distance any given size of wire will carry a specific load with 1% voltage drop.

Assume now that a range is to be added to the smaller apartment just calculated. Follow the recommendations of Code 220-5, and allow 8,000 watts, which assumes that the range is rated at not over 12,000 watts. (If the range is larger, allow more, per Note 4 of Table 220-5. See Appendix.) This 8,000-watt allowance is to be added to the net watts for lighting and small appliances *after* application of the demand factor.

In the case of the smaller of the two apartments under discussion, adding 8,000 watts to the 3,525 watts brings a total of 11,525 watts. Since a range operates at 115/230 volts, naturally a 3-wire feeder must be provided. At 230 volts the amperage is 11,525/230, or 50 amp, for which No. 6 wire is suitable as a minimum.

However, the neutral wire serving a range can never be made to carry as many amperes as the "hot" wires sometimes carry, as has already been discussed. Therefore the Code in Sec. 220-4(d) permits for the *neutral* of the feeder a wire smaller than for the "hot" wires. Consider only 70% of the allowance for the range as far as the neutral is concerned. In the example above, the carrying capacity of the *neutral only* would be calculated as follows: For the range consider 70% of 8,000 watts, or 5,600 watts. For lighting and small appliances we have already reached an answer of 3,525 watts. The two make a total of 9,125 watts, which at 230 volts is equivalent to 39.7 amp, and thus No. 8 wire is adequate unless a larger size is required to avoid voltage drop.

Determining Service Entrance. The minimum size of the service-drop wires for the building as a whole is determined by the maximum probable load *in the entire building* at any given moment. The method of arriving at this probable maximum is very similar to that used for single-family houses: The lighting, the small appliances, and range loads are considered separately.

The greater the number of apartments in a building, the less the likelihood that all tenants will at the same time be consuming current at the maximum rate available to the individual apartment. Therefore the Code in Sec. 220-4(a) permits a demand factor to be applied. This demand factor is applied on the gross computed total watts figured on the basis of 3 watts per sq ft of total area for all apartments, plus the minimum of 3,000 watts for small appliances for each apartment, applied as follows:

First 3,000 watts	100%
Next 117,000 watts	35%
All above 120,000 watts	25%

For ranges there is no likelihood whatever that all will ever be used at their maximum capacity at the same moment; the Code in Table 220-5 (see Appendix) permits a demand factor that varies from 75% in the case of two small ranges consuming less than 3,500 watts each, to as little as 16% in the case of 61 or more ranges each consuming 3,500 watts or more.

However, the Code contains a simplification in column A of Table 220-5, which shows a figure in watts that can be used as the maximum demand for any given number of ranges consuming not over 12,000 watts each. This is far simpler than taking each range separately, determining its maximum capacity, multiplying by the number of ranges involved, and multiplying in turn by the proper demand factor for that number of ranges to arrive at the total watts that must be allowed for the total range load.

Since the use of electric clothes dryers has become common, the number to be installed in an apartment building must be considered. See Table 220-6 in your copy of the Code for the demand factor that is applicable. These demand factors were first established in the 1959 Code.

Planning Three-apartment Installation. Assume a building containing three apartments of 800 sq ft each or 2,400 sq ft in total, plus the usual basement. Each apartment will have four circuits, as determined earlier in this chapter. Each circuit will probably run direct to the overcurrent device for that circuit in the basement. The service entrance will probably be in accordance with Fig. 26-1 or 26-2. There is little to calculate except the service entrance.

Service Entrance for Three-apartment Building. The maximum probable load is very simply calculated in accordance with preceding paragraphs, as shown in the following table:

	Gross computed watts	Demand factor, per cent	Net computed watts
Lighting, 2,400 sq ft at 3 watts......	7,200		
Small appliances, 3 apartments at 3,000 watts..................	9,000		
Total gross computed watts.......	16,200		
First 3,000 watts...............	......	100	3,000
Remaining 13,200 watts..........	......	35	4,620
Total net computed watts......	......		7,620

The total of 7,620 watts covers only the three apartments proper. It does not make allowance for the basement, and it is well to allow 1,500 watts for basement lighting, the outlets for the tenants' washing machines, and similar devices. This makes a total of 9,120 watts, which at 230 volts is equivalent to 39.4 amp. Theoretically, then, No. 8 wire, which has a capacity of 40 amp could be used.

However, the Code in Sec. 230-41 requires wire with a mini-mum of 100-amp carrying capacity, even for a single-family house. Certainly, then, nothing smaller should be considered for this building with three apartments.

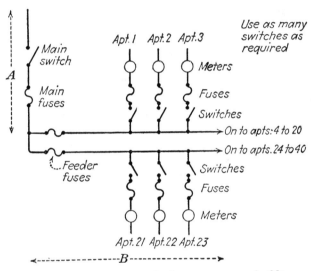

FIG. 26-5. Feeder diagram for larger apartment building.

If an electric range consuming not over 12,000 watts is added to each of the three apartments, column A of Table 220-5 (see Appendix), shows that 14,000 watts in total must be added for that purpose in calculating feeder capacity. Adding this to the 9,120 watts already determined for lighting and small appliances produces a total of 23,120 watts, which at 230 volts is equivalent to about 101 amp. Now that is just 1 amp above the Code mini-mum, and most people would feel that if they installed the 100-amp minimum required, they would be meeting the intent of the Code. They would, however, be overlooking the fact that the Code concerns itself with *safety* only, not with convenience or practicability. Meeting that Code minimum would not make the occupants of the building permanently happy. Install a service of at least 140- and preferably 200-amp capacity.

Instead of using column A of Table 220-5, column B or C may be used, depending on the capacity of each range. Assuming that the ranges have a capacity of 8,000 watts each, the total would be 24,000 watts; column C shows the demand factor to be

Fig. 26-6. A typical group metering panel for use in apartments and similar installations. (*General Electric Co.*)

55%, which applied to 24,000 watts leads to an allowance of 13,200 watts, substantially the same as the 14,000 watts shown in column A. It will usually be found to be quicker and more convenient to use the ready-made answers of column A than to calculate the answers from column B or C.

Planning a 40-apartment Installation. Assume that a larger building containing 40 apartments is to be wired. Assume that each apartment has 800 sq ft of area and that half of the apartments will have electric ranges. Since all apartments are of the same size, all will be wired in the same fashion, and the calculations for the individual apartments will be as just discussed in preceding paragraphs.

Since 40 meters and 40 disconnecting means are to be installed, it is likely that they will be arranged in several banks: two banks of 20 or four banks of 10. Since more than six disconnecting

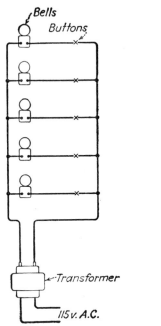 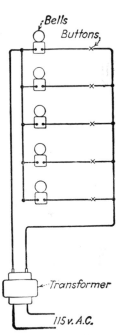

FIG. 26-7. Using this wiring diagram, the more distant bells ring too faintly, the nearby ones too loudly.

FIG. 26-8. Using this wiring diagram, all bells ring with equal volume. This wiring diagram requires only a little more material than the other diagram.

means are involved, a main disconnecting means will be required ahead of all. The hookup will probably be similar to that shown in Fig. 26-5, which shows two banks of 20.

The final installation will resemble that shown in Fig. 26-6 which shows equipment for 16 meters; similar equipment is available for any number of meters. (The illustration shows only the meter sockets; the meters are plugged into the sockets.) The main circuit breaker is at the left. Above each vertical row of

four meters there are four circuit breakers, one for each of four
apartments.   Run a feeder from each of these circuit breakers
to the individual apartments.   In each apart-
ment install a small circuit breaker cabinet or
fuse cabinet, as you would in an individual
residence.

Similar equipment using fuses instead of circuit breakers is available for those who prefer
fused equipment.

The calculation of the various feeders and
subfeeders is covered by the Code in Example

Fig. 26-9. A typi-
cal door opener.
(*Edwards & Co.,
Inc.*)

No. 4, which will be found in the Appendix of
this book and need not be repeated here.

Low-voltage Wiring. The usual doorbell
and buzzer system will be installed in accordance with the principles already outlined in other chapters.
However, it is necessary to take into consideration the problem

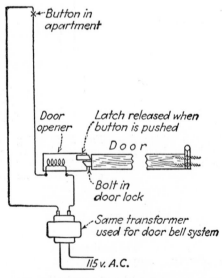

Fig. 26-10. Installation of door opener.

created by the longer lengths of wire involved in buildings of
considerable size.

In the wiring of fairly large apartments, it is not uncommon for the doorbell and buzzer system to be installed in accordance with the diagram of Fig. 26-7. Theoretically this diagram is correct, but if ordinary No. 18 wire is used, as in residential work, it will be found that the more distant bells ring rather faintly because of the substantial voltage drop in the long run of the small wire. A drop of 2 volts in a 115-volt circuit is not so serious, but when the starting voltage is only 10 volts or thereabouts, a 2-volt drop is of the order of 20%. If the transformer voltage is stepped up sufficiently so that the more distant bells ring properly, the nearby bells ring too loudly. A larger size of wire helps, but the distant bells still ring less loudly than the ones nearer the transformer.

The solution is to use the circuit of Fig. 26-8. A little more wire is involved, but if this circuit is analyzed, it will be found that the number of feet of wire involved for any one bell is exactly the same as for any other bell. Accordingly all will ring with equal volume; a transformer voltage that is correct for one is correct for all the others.

Door Openers. Many apartments have the door leading into the inside hall equipped with a door opener so that intruders cannot enter. Pushing a button in any apartment releases a latch which permits the door to be opened. A typical door opener is shown in Fig. 26-9. It consists simply of an electromagnet, similar to that found in a doorbell, which releases a latch when the button is pushed, permitting the door to be swung open. The opener is mortised into the door frame opposite the lock in the door. The diagram is most simple, as Fig. 26-10 shows.

Part 3

ACTUAL WIRING: NONRESIDENTIAL PROJECTS

Part 3 of this book covers the same subject matter as Part 2 but applies to nonresidential structures, such as factories, stores, schools, and similar projects.

Buildings of this type involve greater amounts of power, higher amperages, heavier wires, different kinds of wire, and other problems not met in residential work. Nevertheless the method of installation is in most respects greatly similar to that employed for residential work, and accordingly only *new* problems will be here explained.

Only the smaller projects are included. The very large projects, such as skyscrapers and steel mills, have been deliberately avoided as being beyond the scope of this book. This is also the case with all wiring at voltages in excess of 600, transformer vaults, and similar subjects which are encountered only in the larger projects.

Chapter 27

ADDITIONAL INFORMATION ABOUT WIRE

Chapter 6 described the kinds of wires used in the wiring of residential and farm buildings. In this chapter additional kinds of wire used mostly in nonresidential and nonfarm wiring will be discussed. In addition, some of the fundamental facts concerning insulations, constructions, ampacities, and installation restrictions will be discussed in more detail than in Chap. 6.

What Determines Ampacity of Wire. Before entering into a discussion of the Code and its provisions concerning wire, it will be well to analyze the reasons why the ampacity of any given size of wire varies with the kind of insulation on the wire and the method of installation.

Copper is not harmed by heat; insulation is harmed by heat. If insulation is overheated, it is harmed in various ways, dependent on the degree of overheating and the kind of insulation. Some kinds melt, some harden, some burn. In any event insulation loses its usefulness if overheated, leading to breakdowns and fires.

The ampacities specified in various tables for any particular kind and size of wire is the amperage that it can carry *without increasing the temperature of its insulation beyond the danger point.* The insulation on Types T and R stands the least heat; consequently these types have the lowest ampacity of all the different kinds. Asbestos will stand the most heat; consequently asbestos-insulated wire has the highest ampacity. The temperature of the asbestos-insulated wire when carrying its rated amperage will be higher than the temperature of the rubber-insulated wire carrying its rated amperage, but its insulation,

433

being designed for it, will not be harmed by the higher temperature.

The rated ampacity of each kind and each size of wire is based on the assumption that the wire is installed where the temperature is 30°C or 86°F. The Code in Table 310-2(a) (see Appendix) shows the maximum temperature that the insulation of each kind of wire is permitted to reach. That temperature will be reached if the wire is carrying its rated amperage in a room where the temperature is 30°C or 86°F.

It will be worth repeating: When a wire is approved for 140°F, it does not mean that the wire may be used in room temperatures up to 140°F. It means that the maximum operating temperature of the wire itself may not exceed 140°F. If the room temperature is above the assumed standard of 86°F and the wire is carrying its rated capacity, its operating temperature will exceed 140°F. Therefore, if *any* kind of wire is installed in hot locations, its ampacity is reduced from that shown in Code tables. How to apply the proper correction factors will be explained later.

The actual ampacities of various kinds and sizes of wire are shown in Code Tables 310-12 and 310-13 (see Appendix). The footnotes following the tables are important. Note that these tables apply only to copper wires. For aluminum wire, see Tables 310-14 and 310-15 in your copy of the Code.

Types -W. The letter "W" in a Code Type designation means "wet." Ordinary wires such as the Types T and R discussed in Chap. 6 may be installed only in permanently dry locations. But similar wires are made with insulation that is quite moisture-resistant. These then become Code Types TW and RW, which may be used in either dry or wet locations. Their ampacities are the same as the ordinary types, per column 2 of Table 310-12 (see Appendix).

Types -H. The letter "H" in a Code Type designation means "heat." Ordinary wires such as Type T and Type R, discussed in Chap. 6, have ampacities in accordance with column 2 of Table 310-12, with a maximum allowable operating temperature of 60°C or 140°F while carrying their maximum rated capacity. But similar Type R wire is made with a much higher quality of insulation, which will stand a higher temperature without deteriorating, and such wire is approved for a maximum operating temperature of 75°C or 167°F. It is called Type RH and, in sizes heavier than No. 10, has an ampacity from 10 to 20% higher than ordinary Type R (column 3 of Table 310-12). For that reason a smaller size Type RH may be used to carry a given amperage than would be required if Type R were used. (NOTE: There is no Code Type TH.)

The more expensive Type RH then often becomes less expensive for a particular amperage than the cheaper Type R. This is especially true when the use of a smaller size of Type RH also permits a smaller size of conduit to be used. For example, to carry a 200-amp 3-phase load in conduit, if Type R wire is used, three 250,000-circular-mil cables will be required, which in turn means that 2½-in. conduit must be used. If Type RH wire is used, No. 3/0 is sufficient, requiring only 2-in. conduit.

One word of caution may be in order: While the use of Type RH permits a smaller size conductor, that smaller conductor leads to greater voltage drop. If the runs are long enough for voltage drop to become a factor, the advantage of the Type RH may disappear.

It should be worth noting that some manufacturers produce the larger sizes of wire only with Type RH insulation.

Types -HW. These two letters in the Code Type designation mean "heat-resisting, wet." Thus Code Types T and R become Types THW and RHW and accordingly may be used in either dry or wet locations, like Types TW and RW, and have higher ampacities like Type RH (column 3 of Table 310-12). Note that while there is no Code Type TH, there is a Type THW, first recognized in the 1959 Code.

Type RHH. This type is quite similar to Type RH, except that its insulation is still more heat-resistant; Type RHH is permitted to operate at a temperature of 90°C or 194°F, as compared with 75°C or 167°F for the Type RH. Accordingly, in sizes No. 8 and heavier it has an ampacity slightly higher than that of Type RH. Use column 4 of Table 310-12.

Type RH-RW. This type combines the advantages of Types RH and RW, but to a lesser degree than Type RHW. When used in wet locations, it has the ampacity of Types RW wire (column 2 of Table 310-12); when used in dry locations, it has the ampacity of Type RH wire (column 3 of Table 310-12).

Type RR. Although you see "Type RR" mentioned in magazine articles and in advertising and see wire that is so marked on its cartons, no such type is recognized by the Code or by the Underwriters. It is a wire with the usual rubber insulation of varying grades, but instead of having a final *fabric* cover, it has a second layer of varying grades of rubber or neoprene. That in a general way also describes Type USE service-entrance cable (described in Chap. 20). But if a wire is labeled only "Type RR," it is not a listed wire. If it is labeled "Type USE," some manufacturers may add their own private designation "Type RR."

Type THWN. This wire first became acceptable under the Code by a 1963 amendment to the 1962 Code. Its insulation consists basically of a moisture- and heat-resistant thermoplastic material, plus a final extruded coat of nylon which is exceptionally tough mechanically, besides having excellent insulating properties. It may be used in dry or wet locations. In sizes No. 8 and heavier, it has more ampacity than ordinary wires. It is an expensive wire.

Its construction leads to an overall diameter, and cross-sectional area, much smaller than that of ordinary wires, especially in the smaller sizes. This is no great advantage in new work, for the Code requires conduit just as large for any given combination of Type THWN wires, as for the same combination of other wires. But if you are replacing wires in an *existing* conduit, the Code in Sec. 346-6(b) permits a greater "fill" than is permitted in new work. In other words, when installing new wires in an existing conduit, any size conduit may hold more wires, or the same number of larger wires, than is permissible in new work. Then the use of the more expensive wire is fully justified (see last paragraph of this chapter).

Asbestos and Varnished-cambric Insulations. Although rubber and plastic insulations are continuously being improved, the best now on the market, Type RHH, is approved only for an operating temperature not to exceed 90°C or 194°F; it will reach that temperature when carrying its rated ampacity in a room where the normal temperature is 30°C or 86°F. But there are many locations where the normal temperature is higher: boiler rooms, foundries, crowded switchboards, and similar locations.

A wire is needed with insulation that will not deteriorate at temperatures higher than 90°C or 194°F.   Such wires are available, with insulations of asbestos, varnished cable, or a combination of the two.

Varnished cambric is a fine cloth impregnated with certain insulating varnishes, and it has been found that this will withstand very high temperatures without deteriorating.   It will also withstand more voltage per mil of thickness than will rubber or plastic insulation.

Asbestos is not affected by temperature but used by itself is somewhat flimsy, and a rather thick layer is needed for a given voltage.

There are many Code types of wire insulated with varnished cambric, asbestos, or a combination of these two materials.   Of

Fig. 27-1. Varnished-cambric insulation wire.   This type withstands heat better than wire with more ordinary insulation.   (*General Electric Co.*)

all these types, Type V is probably the most common.   It is shown in Fig. 27-1 and consists of the conductor, a layer of varnished cambric, plus an outer fabric layer, usually of cotton saturated with flame-retardant compounds.   Similar types may have a layer of asbestos over the cambric; some have asbestos in the outer braid.   Note that such wires, size for size, usually have a larger over-all diameter than Type T or Type R wires.

All these types may be used only in permanently dry locations unless covered with an outer lead sheath.

Type MI.   The letters "MI" stand for "mineral insulated." This is a comparatively new kind of wire and consists basically of a bare copper wire, one or more conductors properly spaced, with a continuous seamless copper tube around the outside.   The wires are separated from each other and from the outer copper tube by tightly packed mineral insulation (magnesium oxide), which is both a good insulator and also unaffected by heat.   See Fig. 27-2, which shows both the material and the special connectors used with it.   It is available in sizes up to No. 4/0.

It is installed like cable, requires no protection such as conduit, and being of relatively small diameter can be easily installed even in crowded quarters. The outer copper tube, of course, is waterproof so the material may be installed in any location. It is not an inexpensive material, yet because no conduit is required, it can become an economical type of wire as far as total installed cost is concerned.

Other Types of Wire. The types discussed here are the more common varieties. There are many other kinds that cannot be described here. A listing of all types together with their maximum operating temperatures and limitations of use can be found

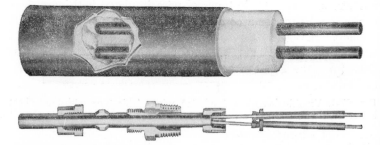

Fig. 27-2. Code Type MI cable and the special fittings used with it. (*General Cable Co.*)

in Table 310-2(a) (see Appendix). Further details of construction can be found by referring to Sec. 310-2(b) in your copy of the Code. Their ampacities can be found in Table 310-12 of the Code (see Appendix).

Using Code Table 310-12. At first glance this table may seem very complicated, but for installations within the scope of this book it is quite simple. Remember that the ampacities shown for different sizes apply only if the following conditions are *all* met:

1. The wires are used inside a raceway (conduit) or in the form of cable or buried directly in the ground. If the wires are suspended in free air, use the allowable ampacities shown in Table 310-13.

2. Not more than three wires are used in the same conduit or

cable. The neutral wire is not counted except in the case of a 3-wire circuit consisting of two phase wires and the neutral of a 4-wire 3-phase system (Note 10, Tables 310-12 and 310-13). If 4 to 6 wires are used, reduce the ampacities to 80%; if 7 to 24 wires are used, reduce to 70% of the values shown.

3. The room temperature is not over 30°C or 86°F. If higher room temperatures are encountered, apply the correction factors shown below the table. For example, if No. 8 Type RH wire with a normal ampacity of 45 amp is to be used in a room temperature of 40°C or 104°F, the corrected ampacity is 45 × 0.88, or 39.6 amp.

4. The wire is copper. If it is aluminum, use Tables 310-14 and 310-15.

Using Code Table 310-13. When wires are installed in raceways such as conduit or in the form of cables, the heat that develops in the wires does not dissipate very fast. The ampacity of wires under those conditions is established in Table 310-12. But if individual wires are installed in free air, the heat is dissipated much faster, and any given size of wire can carry a larger amperage without overheating. For wires installed in free air, use Table 310-13 (see Appendix).

Replacing Wires in Existing Conduits. If you are replacing the wires in an existing conduit, the Code in Sec. 346-6(b) permits a greater "fill" than in the original installation. The answers are found in Code Tables 1, 1A, and 1B, all appearing in the Appendix of this book. Careful study is necessary to determine the right answer.

Table 1 must be used for all *new* work, regardless of the type of wire used.

Table 1A is used only when replacing wires in an existing conduit, and only when wire of Types TF, T, THW, TW, RUH, or RUW are used.

Table 1B is used only when replacing wires in an existing conduit, and only if Types FEP, FEPB, THWN, or THHN are used.

Assume you have an existing run of 1½-in. conduit, containing three No. 1 wires of some ordinary type such as T or R, which have an ampacity of 110 amp. Table 1A permits you to replace these with three No. 1/0 provided you use one of the types listed above.   If you use T or TW, these have an ampacity of 125 amp; type THW has an ampacity of 150 amp.

Table 1B permits three No. 3/0, provided you use Type THWN or THHN.   These have an ampacity of 200 amp.

Thus, by pulling out the original No. 1 wires and replacing them with the larger sizes permitted by Tables 1A and 1B, you can increase the ampacity of the circuit from 110 amp to as much as 200 amp, without the expense of tearing out the original conduit and installing a larger size.

Chapter 28

PLANNING NONRESIDENTIAL
INSTALLATIONS

The wiring of nonresidential projects follows the same basic principles covered in Parts 1 and 2 of this book, but many new problems arise. Much larger amperages must be handled than is customary in ordinary residential work. Sometimes the voltages are higher. Usually polyphase power is involved in addition to the usual single-phase power. Devices and materials are used which are not common in residential work. Some points, which in residential work are left to the discretion of the contractor, are covered specifically by the Code for nonresidential work.

Heavy-duty Lampholders. A "lampholder," which term is seldom met outside the Code, is simply a socket or other device by means of which current is carried to the lamp. A "heavy-duty" lampholder as defined in Code Sec. 210-8 is one *rated* at not less than 750 watts. Accordingly it includes (but is not limited to) all the so-called mogul sockets for incandescent lamps rated over 300 watts.

Branch Circuits. The general provisions regarding branch circuits outlined in Parts 1 and 2 apply not only to houses but also to "apartments, guest rooms of hotels and clubs and in other occupancies used for dwelling purposes." For nonresidential occupancies the requirements are totally different.

In nonresidential occupanies each outlet is assumed to carry a specific load, which automatically limits the number of outlets per circuit. If the outlet serves a specific appliance or other load, the amperage consumed by the load must be allowed for that

441

outlet. If the outlet is to serve a heavy-duty lampholder, an arbitrary minimum load of 5 amp is assumed for that outlet. Every other outlet[1] is assigned an arbitrary minimum load of 1½ amp. These are minimum specifications, and if, for example, 750-watt lamps are definitely specified, consuming roughly 7 amp each, obviously allowance must be made for that amperage instead of the Code minimum of 5 amp.

From this starting point it is a simple matter to determine how many outlets may be served by any particular branch circuit. In this calculation it is necessary to bear in mind the requirement of Sec. 220-2 of the Code, which specifies that, if a circuit supplies a continuous load (for example, store lighting), the load shall not exceed 80% of the capacity of the circuit. If some of the outlets on the circuit are controllable by individual switches, the presumption is that the load is not continuous.

Fifteen-ampere Branch Circuit. The basic requirements are the same as for residential work. It is wired with No. 14 wire with 15-amp overcurrent protection. Since each outlet is limited to 1½ amp, obviously each circuit may have not over 10 outlets. If any outlet serves a heavy-duty lampholder, the number of outlets is reduced in proportion.

If receptacles are installed on the circuit, they may be only those rated not over 15 amp. No portable appliance on the circuit may be rated at more than 12 amp. The total rating of fixed appliances on the circuit may not exceed 7½ amp if the circuit also serves lighting units or portable appliances.

Twenty-ampere Branch Circuit. Again the basic requirements are as for residential work. In nonresidential work it is quite commonly used for lighting purposes and is wired with No. 12 wire and, of course, 20-amp overcurrent protection. Either ordinary or heavy-duty lampholders may be used on the circuit; receptacles may be either the 15- or the 20-amp type. The number of outlets is determined by allowing 1½ amp for each stand-

---

[1] Where multioutlet assemblies of the type shown in Fig. 20-4 are used, the Code specifies in Sec. 220-2(c) that "in other than dwellings and guest rooms of hotels, each 5 ft or fraction thereof of each separate and continuous length shall be considered as one outlet of not less than 1½-amp capacity, except in locations where a number of appliances are likely to be used simultaneously when each 1 ft or fraction thereof shall be considered an outlet of not less than 1½ amp."

ard outlet, 5 amp for each heavy-duty lampholder, and the amperages of other specific loads. Don't overlook the 80% rule if the circuit is likely to be continuously loaded.

No portable appliance on the circuit may be rated at more than 16 amp. The total rating of all fixed appliances on the circuit may not be more than 10 amp if the circuit also serves lighting units or portable appliances.

A 20-amp circuit has a capacity of 115 × 20, or 2,300 watts. If the common four-lamp 40-watt (160-watt total) fluorescent unit is used for lighting, the error may be made of dividing 2,300 by 160 and arriving at an answer of 14 such units per circuit. However, as pointed out in another chapter, the 40-watt rating of a fluorescent lamp is that of the lamp itself; its ballast requires additional power; the lamp does not have 100% power factor. The over-all wattage of a four-lamp 40-watt unit is more nearly 200 watts, and considering power factor, each unit consumes about 2 amp. The maximum capacity then is 10 units per circuit or 8 units if the lighting is continuous. Moreover, since in nonresidential work the runs are often quite long, loading the circuit to its full capacity may easily lead to excessive voltage drop. It is wise to limit carefully the number of units per circuit.

If the circuit serves heavy-duty sockets, the Code requires a minimum of 5 amp per outlet, which means a maximum of four per 20-amp circuit, reduced to three if the entire circuit is controlled by a single switch.

Thirty-, Forty-, and Fifty-ampere Branch Circuits. These are wired with Nos. 10, 8, and 6 wire respectively, with 30-, 40-, and 50-amp overcurrent protection. Fluorescent-lighting fixtures may *not* be used on these circuits; the incandescent type may be used but the sockets must be the heavy-duty type. On the 30-amp circuit only 30-amp receptacles may be used; on the 40-amp circuit they may be either the 40- or 50-amp type; on the 50-amp circuit use only 50-amp receptacles.

Appliances connected to the 30-amp circuit may be of any type but if portable must not exceed 24 amp. On the 40-amp circuit, only fixed or stationary cooking appliances, or fixed water heaters or clothes dryers may be used. On the 50-amp circuit only fixed cooking appliances may be used.

Which Circuit to Use. Many factors will influence the choice among 15-, 20-, 30-, 40-, and 50-amp circuits. If each fixture is on a separate circuit controlled by a switch on the panelboard, then naturally the lightest wire permissible would be used, considering the amperage involved and not overlooking voltage drop.

If a number of outlets are to be on one circuit and controlled simultaneously by one switch on the panelboard, then the heavier circuits will automatically be required. If a number of outlets are to be placed on one circuit, but individually controlled by pull chains or other local switches, the heavier circuits will probably be found more economical.

Taps. On 20-amp and heavier circuits, taps to individual lampholders or fixtures (or, if not over 18 in. long, those to receptacles) may be smaller than the wire used in the circuit proper. For these purposes No. 14 wire may be used except on the 50-amp circuit, where No. 12 is the minimum. This is subject to the restriction that the specific load served by the tap in question must not exceed 15 amp in the case of the No. 14 wire and 20 amp in the case of No. 12. If the specific load is greater, larger wire must be used. All this is covered by Code Sec. 210-9(c).

277/480-volt Lighting. In general, lighting in offices, stores, factories, and so on has been at 115 volts. The trend has been and still is continuing toward better and better lighting, consuming more and more watts per square foot of area. That in turn requires more and more circuits or larger wires to take care of the increased amperage. Instead of using 115 volts, why not use a higher voltage, thus reducing the amperage? Then any given size of wire would carry a greater wattage. For example, No. 14 wire at its rated capacity of 15 amp will at 115 volts carry 15×115, or 1,725 watts; at 230 volts, 15×230, or 3,450 watts; at 277 volts, 15×277, or 4,155 watts.

The Code, in Sec. 210-6, permits lighting at voltages above 150 volts but not over 300 volts under certain conditions in certain occupancies. Today such installations are common, operating at 277 volts. If 277 seems a peculiar voltage, note that if an establishment is served by a 480-volt 3-phase system, and if the transformers are Y-connected and a neutral added, the voltage from neutral to any one phase conductor is 277 volts. If the over-all voltage of the basic system is 460 volts, the voltage from neutral to the phase conductor becomes 265 volts.

Under the Code, lighting at voltages above 150 but below 300 volts is permitted in Sec. 210-6 under clearly defined conditions. If the lighting is *not* fluorescent, it may be used only in industrial establishments provided the fixtures use only mogul sockets or their equivalent, provided the fixtures are permanently installed at least 8 ft above floor level and are controlled by separate switches and not by switches that are built into the fixtures. If the lighting is *only* by fluorescent fixtures, the scheme may be used in "industrial establishments, office buildings, schools, stores, and public and commercial areas of other buildings such as hotels and transportation terminals" provided the fixtures are permanently mounted and controlled by individual switches, not switches that are part of the fixture.

This 277-volt system will permit the installation of a large load for lighting using smaller wires and usually smaller conduit than would be required for the same load at 115 volts. This in turn leads to a very considerable saving in the installation cost. Install it as you would a 115-volt system, but be sure to use switches and branch-circuit circuit breakers that are approved for use at the higher voltage. Since the voltage is above 150 to ground, fuses, if they are used, must be the cartridge type and not the plug type.

Appliances. The requirements for nonresidential use are the same as for residential use; therefore this subject need not be covered again (see Chap. 13).

Motors. The wiring of electric motors is a sufficiently complex subject to warrant an entirely separate chapter, which will follow later.

Service-entrance Problems. Before going into this subject, it will be well to review a few definitions that were originally covered in Chap. 13. Service conductors are the wires that extend from the power company's distribution system up to the service switch. The service drop is that portion of the service conductors which runs overhead; the service drop ends where the wires are anchored to the building. The service-entrance conductors consist of that portion of the service conductors from the point where the service drop ends up to the service switch. If the service is underground, there is no service drop, and the entire underground run of wire from the power company's wires up to the service switch then makes up the service-entrance conductors.

A building is defined by the Code as "a structure which stands alone or which is cut off from adjoining structures by fire walls with all openings therein protected by approved fire doors."

Several Service Drops per Building. This subject is thoroughly covered by the Code in Sec. 230-2 which reads as follows:

230-2. Number of Services to a Building. In general, a building shall be supplied through only one set of service conductors, except as follows:

Exception No. 1. Fire Pumps. If a separate service is required for fire pumps.

Exception No. 2. Emergency Lighting. If a separate service is required for emergency lighting and power purposes.

Exception No. 3. Multiple-occupancy Buildings.

(a) By special permission, in multiple-occupancy buildings where there is no available space for service equipment accessible to all the occupants.

(b) Buildings of multiple occupancy may have two or more separate sets of service-entrance conductors which are tapped from one service drop, or two or more subsets of service-entrance conductors may be tapped from a single set of main service conductors. See Section 230-75 and Section 230-90 (a) Exception No. 4.

Exception No. 4. Capacity Requirements. If capacity requirements make multiple services desirable.

Exception No. 5. Buildings of Large Area. By special permission, if more than one service drop is necessary due to the area over which a single building extends.

Exception No. 6. Different Characteristics or Classes of Use. Where additional services are required for different voltages, frequency, or phase, or different classes of use. Different classes of use could be because of needs for different characteristics, or because of rate schedule as in the case of controlled water-heater service.

The exceptions noted above should require no great amount of explanation. Obviously it is desirable to have a separate source of power available for fire pumps and for emergency lighting. Likewise, where a large building is occupied by a number of tenants, it would be objectionable to have one service entrance controllable by one tenant, with the other tenants not able to get at the service switch at all.   In that case a number of service drops may be used.   Another choice is one drop, with several sets of service-entrance conductors.

It should be noted that a single-phase distribution system and a polyphase distribution system are considered separate systems, so that it is entirely in order to serve a building with a single-phase drop for lighting and similar purposes and also a polyphase drop for the power requirements.

Several Sets of Service-entrance Conductors per Building. Generally speaking, only one set of service-entrance conductors is permitted per building, but there are a number of exceptions. Obviously, where more than one service drop is permitted, as discussed above, each drop will require its own set of service-entrance wires.

In a multiple-occupancy building it is usually necessary to provide each tenant with a separate meter with its disconnecting means and overcurrent protection.   The several methods that may be used are the same as already covered in connection with apartments in Chap. 26.

Skeleton of Nonresidential Installation.   In a house the service-entrance wires constitute a feeder, which ends at the service switch or main breaker.   There are no feeders between the service and the branch circuits.   The individual branch circuits begin at the service.

In larger installations the distances involved and the number of branch circuits make it totally impractical to lead all branch circuits back to a common starting point.   In that case the service-entrance wires end at the service switch with a feeder to the main switchboard; from the switchboard feeders run to panelboards located where needed and placed so that the individual branch circuits (which begin at a panelboard) will be reasonably short.

The riser diagrams of Fig. 28-1 show several types of buildings. A typical single-story building which might be a factory or office building or a store is shown at A, a three-story building is shown at B, and a larger three-story building at C.

Switchboards and Panelboards. Switchboards and panelboards are nothing but convenient distribution points where one incoming set of wires is broken up into more and more individual runs of wire. All necessary switches, overcurrent devices, instruments, and similar accessories are located at such points. Look at such a system as you would a big oak tree: the trunk is the service-entrance wire, the point where the trunk breaks up into half a dozen large branches is the switchboard, and the points

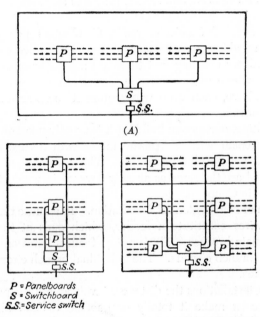

P = Panelboards
S = Switchboard
$S.S.$ = Service switch

Fig. 28-1. Typical distribution systems of switchboard and panelboards.

where the large branches in turn split up into smaller branches are the panelboards.

There is nothing in the Code which requires that an installation must have one switchboard plus a number of panelboards. These devices are installed to suit the convenience of the user. Often the service wires run from the service switch to a main panelboard and from there to other panelboards. As a matter of fact, it is difficult to define when a panelboard ceases to be a panelboard and becomes a switchboard. The Code, however, makes some distinctions and defines the two as follows:

Switchboard: A large single panel, frame, or assembly of panels, on which are mounted, on the face or back or both, switches, overcurrent and other protective devices, buses, and usually instruments. Switchboards are generally accessible from the rear as well as from the front and are not intended to be installed in cabinets.

Panelboard: A single panel, or a group of panel units designed for assembly in the form of a single panel; including buses, and with or without switches and/or automatic overcurrent protective devices for the control of light, heat, or power circuits of small individual as well as aggregate capacity; designed to be placed in a cabinet or cutout box placed in or against a wall or partition and accessible only from the front.

Generally speaking, then, if the device is enclosed in a cabinet with a master door, it is a panelboard; if mounted away from a wall and if accessible from back as well as front, it is a switchboard. There is no precise line of demarcation between the two.

A simple fuse cabinet of the type shown in Fig. 28-2 is a panel-

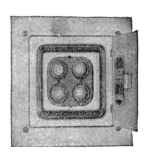

Fig. 28-2. This simple fuse cabinet is also a small panelboard. (*Square D Company.*)

Fig. 28-3. A larger fuse cabinet or panelboard. This particular unit contains toggle switches, each switch controlling one circuit. (*Square D Company.*)

board. A larger panelboard is shown in Fig. 28-3. If the device were not in a cabinet but on a separate stand, it would be a switchboard. In addition to the branch-circuit overcurrent protection there may be a switch for each circuit, so that the entire circuit can be controlled by throwing the proper switch. The fuses may be ordinary plug fuses or the largest type of cartridge fuses, or circuit breakers may be used instead. Not more than 42 overcurrent devices may be installed in a single cabinet.

In addition the panelboard may contain a main switch disconnecting the entire panelboard, and also main overcurrent devices protecting the entire panelboard. The main overcurrent protection is *required* on every panelboard that serves only lighting and appliance circuits if it is fed by a feeder which, in turn, is protected by overcurrent devices rated above 200 amp; the overcurrent device in the panelboard must not be greater than the rating of the panelboard in amperes. For example, a 100-amp panelboard may be fed by a feeder which, in turn, is fused at 150 amp; in that case no main overcurrent protection is required at the panelboard. If, however, it is fed by a feeder fused at 250 amp, then overcurrent devices not over 100 amp, the rating of the panelboard, are required on the panelboard.

Feeders. All the wires in an electrical system are termed "feeders" except the wires beyond the *final* overcurrent device, which are known as "branch-circuit" wires. (Exception: when the overcurrent device is used for motor-*running* protection, this definition is not correct; this will be covered fully in Chap. 31.) The wires from the service switch up to the switchboard constitute a feeder. The wires from the switchboard to each panelboard are feeders. When a panelboard feeds smaller subpanels, the feeders to such subpanels are sometimes known as "subfeeders."

Feeder Sizes. Into the feeder classification fall the service-entrance wires also, as far as method of calculation of the size is concerned. This calculation is not a difficult procedure and is substantially the same as outlined in Chap. 13 in connection with ordinary residential work, except that the heavier loads as well as the varying Code requirements of watts per square foot must be taken into consideration. Total the watts required for lighting, plus appliances, plus motors; then divide by the voltage to arrive at the amperage, which, in turn, establishes the minimum size wire required to meet Code requirements.

Feeders—Lighting Load. The watts per square foot required by the Code for the purpose of such calculations vary considerably with the type of occupancy of the building and are found in Table 220-2(a) of the Code (see Appendix). Reference to this table shows that the requirement varies from ¼ watt per sq ft in storage warehouses to 3 watts per sq ft in schools and stores and some other occupancies, with 5 watts per sq ft in offices. Demand factors, shown in Table 220-4(a) of the Code (see Appendix), reduce this in many cases. Later chapters will cover the different types of occupancies in detail.

Feeders—Appliance. Handle as in residential work.

Feeders—Motor. The Code in Tables 430-147 to 430-150, all of which will be found in your copy of the Code, specifies the full-load current of different types and horsepowers of motors at various voltages. If only a single motor is involved, add 125% of the amperage, which can be found in the proper table for the motor in question, to the amperage determined for lighting and appliances.

If several motors are involved, add to the amperage determined for lighting and appliances 125% of the amperage of the *largest* motor in the installation, and the actual amperage of each of the other motors. If several motors are of the same size, consider one of them the largest and the others as the smaller motors. When a number of motors are involved but not all of them are operated at one time, good judgment must be used in creating a demand factor. Likewise, if the motors do not operate continuously but rather intermittently or in regular cycles, a reasonable reduction from the full amperage that would otherwise apply is in order. The local inspector should be consulted in case of doubt.

Determining Size of Service Entrance. Proceed as in residential wiring. Assume that the total calculated lighting and appliance load, after application of the proper demand factors, amounts to 26,800 watts. The amperage will then be 26,800/230, or 117 amp. Assume the load for motors calculated as outlined is 120 amp; this makes a total of 237 amp. Table 310-12 (see Appendix) shows that, if Type R rubber-covered wire is used, 300,000-circular-mil cable is the *minimum* size permitted; if Type RH is used, 250,000-circular-mil cable is sufficient.

In like fashion the correct size wires for any other amperage can be determined.

Neutrals of Feeders. Most of the time the neutral of a feeder does not carry as much current as the underground wires. This

452 **Actual Wiring: Nonresidential Projects**

is never true in a 2-wire system, but consider what happens in a 3-wire single-phase system. Figure 28-4 shows the usual 115/230-volt circuit, except that two separate neutrals have been run instead of one. The voltage between A and B is 115 volts;

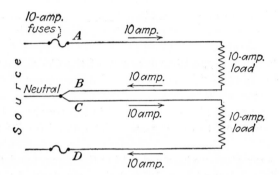

Fig. 28-4. Two 2-wire circuits operating from a 3-wire feeder.

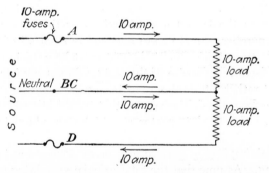

Fig. 28-5. The two 2-wire circuits of Fig. 28-4 here are wired with a common neutral, which saves material and labor, and makes one 3-wire circuit out of the two 2-wire circuits. Here the load on each half is the same.

between C and D it is also 115 volts. Between A and D the voltage is 230 volts.

Assuming a 10-amp load on A and B, also a 10-amp load on C and D, the current flows in each of the four wires in the amounts shown and in the directions shown by the arrows. This should be evident if first A and B are considered separately, then C and D separately.

Since, however, B and C are connected together, why use two separate wires? It is not necessary, and in practice a single wire is used as shown in Fig. 28-5, where there is one wire *BC* in place of two separate wires *B* and *C*.

Consider now the current flowing in *BC*. In one direction 10 amp flows (as in wire *B* of the previous example), and in the opposite direction 10 amp flows (as in wire *C* of the previous example). The two currents in opposite directions cancel out, and the wire *BC* carries no current at all. The circuit will work just as well if wire *BC* is missing entirely; this condition, of course, holds true only if the two loads on the two pairs of wires are absolutely identical.

If, however, one of the two fuses blows, then *BC* will carry 10 amp. As far as the neutral wire *BC* is concerned, there is then said to be a maximum unbalance of 10 amp because no matter which fuse blows, this wire cannot be made to carry over 10 amp (assuming, of course, that the fuses are not increased above 10 amp).

Consider now the circuit shown in Fig. 28-6, which is the same circuit except that instead of having two loads each of 10 amp, there is one of 5 amp and another of 15 amp; the fuses have also increased to 15 amp. The wire *BC* carries 5 amp in one direction, 15 amp in the opposite direction, or a net actual 10 amp. If the fuse in wire *D* blows, *BC* will carry 5 amp, the load on wires *A* and *BC*. If the fuse in wire *A* blows, *BC* will carry 15 amp, the load on wires *BC* and *D*. The maximum unbalance is therefore 15 amp.

Proceed now to Fig. 28-7, which is the same as Fig. 28-6 with the addition of a 20-amp 230-volt load which is connected only to the wires *A* and *D*. The main fuses have been increased to 35 amp, and two additional fuses of 15-amp rating are used; hence neither of the two 115-volt loads can be increased above 15 amp. Wire *A* will then carry the same 5-amp load as before, plus the new 20-amp load, or 25 amp altogether. Wire *BC* is not connected to the new load, hence will carry the same current as before, or 10 amp. Wire *D* will carry the same 15-amp load as before, plus the new 20-amp load, or 35 amp altogether. If the 35-amp fuse in wire *D* blows, the new 20-amp load is disconnected as is the 15-amp load on *BC* and *D*; the wire will then carry only 5 amp. If the 35-amp fuse in wire *A* blows, the new

20-amp load is also disconnected as is the 5-amp load on *A* and *BC*, and wire *BC* will carry only 15 amp. No matter what is done, the maximum unbalance will be only 15 amp.

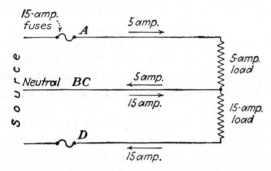

Fig. 28-6. The circuit of Fig. 28-5, but with unbalanced loads.

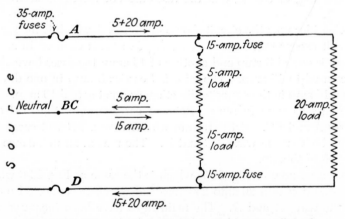

Fig. 28-7. The circuit of Fig. 28-6, plus a 230-volt load.

Since wires *A* and *D* may be called upon to carry 35 amp and are protected by 35-amp fuses, they must have a carrying capacity of 35 amp, and according to Table 310-12 they will be No. 8 wires if Type R rubber-covered is used. However, as far as wire *BC* is concerned, no matter what is done, it cannot be made to carry over 15 amp, the maximum unbalance. Why then should it be No. 8 like *A* and *D*? There is no reason why it should be; it need be big enough only to carry 15 amp, and No. 14 is suitable.

Calculating Size of Neutral in a Feeder. If 50% or more of the load on a feeder consists of fluorescent lighting, the neutral, per Code Sec. 220-4(d), must be as large as the hot wires. In other circuits (with exceptions to be mentioned) the neutral can be smaller; its carrying capacity need be enough for only the "maximum unbalance." In Sec. 220-4(d) the Code defines this: "The maximum unbalanced load shall be the maximum connected load between the neutral and any one ungrounded conductor." It is a simple matter to determine the maximum unbalance.

If the circuit is 115/230-volt single-phase and only a single house is involved, ignore this paragraph and proceed as outlined in Chap. 13. But if an apartment building, for example, is involved, with a number of electric ranges, the maximum unbalance in a feeder serving such ranges shall be considered 70% of the load on the ungrounded conductors as determined considering column A of Table 220-5 (see Appendix).

In case no range is involved and if no other 230-volt loads are involved, there is no unbalance and the neutral must be as big as the hot wires.

If both 115- and 230-volt loads are involved, figure the total load in amperes, as, for example, in the sample calculations of Chap. 13; the answer is the minimum size of the hot wires. Then start over but *ignore* all the loads operating at 230 volts, and determine the wire size; that is the minimum size of the neutral.

An example should be helpful. Assume a 115/230-volt single-phase feeder, with a total load of 34,500 watts and 230-volt loads (not connected to the neutral) of 16,100 watts. The calculation is as follows:

Total load, 34,500 watts. At 230 volts this is ...... 150 amp
230-volt load, 16,100 watts. At 230 volts this is ...... 70 amp
   Difference .... 80 amp

In the case of single-phase feeders, the difference is the maximum unbalance. Accordingly, the neutral need be only big enough for 80 amp but the two hot wires must be big enough for 150 amp.

Now assume a 3-phase 4-wire 120/208-volt feeder, serving both 3-phase loads connected only to the hot wires and also one or more single-phase loads. Any one single-phase load, of course, will be connected to the neutral and one of the hot wires. For the purpose of determining minimum size of the neutral, ignore the 3-phase load. Then consider each of the single-phase loads separately, and determine the amperage for each. Select the amperage of the largest of these loads. That amperage is the maximum unbalance in the circuit, and the minimum size of the neutral is the size that will carry that amperage.

Unbalance over 200 Amp. In any system, if the unbalance is over 200 amp, a 70% demand factor may be applied to the amperage over 200 amp. For example, if the maximum unbalance is determined to be 300 amp, the final figure to use is:

First 200 amp, demand factor 100% . . . . 200 amp
Remaining 100 amp, demand factor 70% . . . . 70 amp
Final maximum unbalance . . . . 270 amp

Common Neutrals. In connection with Figs. 28-5 and 28-6 two separate wires *B* and *C* were combined into a single wire *BC*,

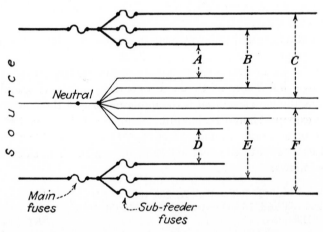

FIG. 28-8. Six 2-wire subfeeders operating off a 3-wire feeder. Note that there are six neutral wires, one for each circuit, but all joined together.

because the two were connected to each other and were therefore more or less a single wire. Now consider Fig. 28-8, which shows an incoming 3-wire feeder with its neutral and two main fuses, also six separate 2-wire subfeeders, *A, B, C, D, E,* and *F,* with six fuses. For each circuit a pair of wires runs back to the feeder, making 12 wires altogether. The six neutral wires are all connected together at the starting point; why run six separate wires? It is not necessary, and the Code in Sec. 215-5 permits one single wire common to a number of feeders, in other words a common neutral, under certain conditions. See the next diagram in Fig. 28-9, which shows the same 3-wire feeder with two main fuses and six fuses, as in Fig. 28-8, but instead of six neutral wires, one to each of six circuits, a single neutral wire was used, making only seven wires altogether.

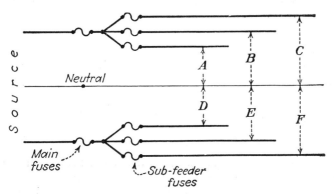

FIG. 28-9. The six subfeeders of Fig. 28-8 now operate with a single or common neutral. This is permitted by the Code under certain conditions.

A common neutral is permitted for *two or three* 3-wire feeders. See Fig. 28-9, which shows the same basic feeders shown in Fig. 28-8 except that the six separate neutrals have now been combined into one. Now since Fig. 28-9 shows *six* circuits A, B, C, D, E, and F and the Code permits a common neutral for not over *three* circuits, is this a Code violation? Not at all. In either Fig. 28-8 or 28-9, circuits A and D may each be considered as 2-wire feeders, but the two combined may equally properly be considered as one 3-wire feeder. The same applies to B and E, C and F, so that in total there are only three 3-wire feeders. Common neutrals are also permitted for two sets of 3-phase 4-wire feeders.

Advantages of Common Neutrals. Common neutrals are practical only if several feeders run in the same direction for some distance. They may be used when practical, for less material is required and there is less voltage drop with a common neutral than with separate neutrals. For example, going back to Fig. 28-4, assume that each of the wires A, B, C, and D is No. 14 and 100 ft long and that there is a 15-amp load on both A and B, and C and D. The voltage drop in wires A and B combined, in any of the ways covered in Chap. 7, is 7½ volts; therefore, instead of 115 volts across the load, there is only 107½ volts. The same applies on the load across C and D. If, however, a common neutral BC is used, as in Fig. 28-5, then BC carries no current whatever as long as the two loads are balanced. Since it carries no current, there can be no voltage drop in that wire. Therefore wire BC can be disregarded entirely in the calculations, and instead only wire A considered. In other words, only 100 ft of wire is involved instead of 200 ft. The voltage drop is then only 3¾ volts instead of 7½ volts, and the voltage on the load is 111¼ volts instead of 107½ volts. This is a considerable advantage; for example, 115-volt lamps burned at 111¼ volts produce about 10% more light than when burned at 107½ volts.

The voltage drop is halved only when the loads on the two circuits are exactly balanced. The advantage decreases as one load becomes smaller than the other; when one load is disconnected entirely, the voltage drop is the same as if a separate neutral were used for each circuit.

Calculating Common Neutral. The Code requires only that the carrying capacity of the common neutral be sufficient for the maximum unbalance. How to calculate the size for a single feeder has already been covered. If a common neutral is to be used for several feeders, merely add together the maximum unbalances for all the feeders. If the total is over 200 amp, apply the 70% demand factor on the portion above 200 amp, if the system is one where this is permitted. For example, if three feeders have maximum unbalances of 125, 75, and 190 amp, respectively, or 390 amp total, calculate the carrying capacity of the neutral as follows:

If the system is 3-wire direct current, or single-phase alternating current, or 4-wire 3-phase alternating current, then the neutral must have a carrying capacity of 200, plus 70% of 190, or 133, a total of 333 amp.

For all other systems the neutral must have a carrying capacity of 390 amp.

Consider the sizes of wire involved in the installation shown in Fig. 28-10; assume that it is single-phase alternating current. At the left is a switchboard which contains the main fuses and six other fuses protecting three 3-wire feeders running to panelboards *A*, *B*, and *C*. The three feeders are to run through a single conduit up to point *X*, so a common neutral may be used

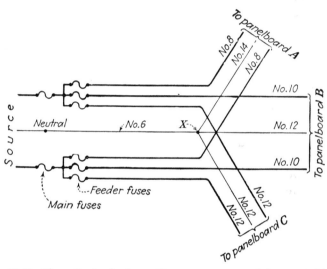

Fig. 28-10. Three 3-wire feeders with a common neutral from switchboard up to the point where the feeders start running in different directions.

up to that point. At *X* the three feeders separate and run in three different directions to the three panelboards. It is a simple matter to calculate each of the three feeders from point *X* up to the respective panelboards.

For feeder *A* assume a total load of 35 amp, of which 25 amp is a 230-volt load which is not connected to the neutral. The maximum unbalance for this feeder is therefore 35 minus 25, or 10 amp. The neutral therefore need be only big enough to carry 10 amp, and accordingly No. 14 wire is suitable from *X* to the panelboard. The ungrounded wires, however, must carry 35 amp and accordingly must be No. 8. Since these wires run directly to the switchboard, the same size is used for the entire length.

For feeder *B* assume a total load of 25 amp, of which 8 amp is a 230-volt load unconnected to the neutral. The maximum unbalance is 25 minus 8, or 17 amp, and the neutral wire from *X* to panelboard *B* must be No. 12. The ungrounded wires must carry 25 amp and, accordingly, must be No. 10.

For feeder *C* assume a total load of 20 amp, of which 3 amp is a 230-volt load unconnected to the neutral. The maximum unbalance is 17 amp, and the neutral from *X* to panelboard *C* must be No. 12. The ungrounded wires must carry 20 amp, and No. 12 is suitable. In this case the neutral is the same size as the ungrounded wires.

The maximum unbalances in the three feeders are 10, 17, and 17 amp, respectively, or a total of 44 amp; consequently the common neutral from the switchboard to point *X* must have a capacity of 44 amp. If all the load on each of the three panelboards *A*, *B*, and *C* consisted of lighting or other load, with no portion of it unconnected to the neutral, then the maximum unbalance would be 80 amp, requiring No. 2 wire for the neutral.

The wire sizes mentioned above are based on the assumption that Type T or Type R rubber-covered wire is used. If other types of insulation are involved, the wire sizes would change therefore in accordance with Table 310-12. The sizes determined in the calculations are the *minimum* sizes permitted by Code, and good practice will in many instances demand heavier sizes to avoid voltage drop.

Calculating Different Occupancies. With the above general discussions it should be possible to calculate almost any type of building, taking into consideration the requirements of Sec. 220-4(a) of the Code (see Appendix). However, different types of buildings will be covered in more detail in future chapters.

Grounding. The Code requirements for grounding may appear at first to be complicated, but for the buildings covered by the scope of this book, they are relatively simple. The theory of grounds and the actual method of grounding of small projects were fully covered in Chap. 17. It will be well for you to review the subject there before proceeding with this chapter. There are two different kinds of grounds: system and equipment.

System Grounds. The system ground is one which grounds one of the wires bringing power into the premises. It is intended to provide protection against faults in the distribution system, against lightning surges, and so on.

Single-phase installations are ordinarily grounded not only at the transformer but also at the individual service. But in the rare instances when the service is 2-wire 230-volt single-phase (not 3-wire 115/230-volt), there would be no ground at the service, although the mid-point of the transformer serving the premises would usually be grounded at the transformer location.

Polyphase service may consist at times of only ungrounded wires, at other times include a grounded wire. If the service is of the 4-wire 3-phase type (120/208- or 277/480-volt), the neutral wire would be grounded. A 3-wire 3-phase delta system normally would be ungrounded, although occasionally one of the three wires is grounded. In some localities the service is basically a 3-wire delta system at 230 volts, with the mid-point of one of the 230-volt legs grounded (thus making a 4-wire service), that leg of the transformer then delivering 115/230-volt single-phase power.

If the polyphase system does include a grounded conductor, it *may* be grounded at the individual service, but the Code does not require it. It is best always to consult the power company to make certain whether any given polyphase service does or does not include a grounded wire.

Equipment Ground. The equipment ground is used to ground all cabinets housing service and overcurrent equipment, the conduit or armor of the wiring system, motors, fixtures, and similar equipment. If a metal-clad wiring system, such as conduit or armored cable, is used, the various runs of such a raceway are automatically tied together into a continuous system through connectors or locknuts and bushings at outlet boxes, and the entire system is grounded through the usual ground at the service switch. Devices such as motors, appliances, etc., are considered sufficiently grounded if the metal raceway of the wiring system is securely fastened to the device in the same way as to the outlet boxes.

If the voltage *to ground* [2] is more than 250 volts, different

[2] For definition of "voltage to ground" see page 131.

methods must be used both at such devices and also in making up joints at boxes. This will be covered in the next chapter.

If nonmetallic cable wiring is used, the problem is more complicated. In the case of nonmetallic cable, special cable is available with an additional uninsulated grounding conductor included in the assembly. It is used to tie together all outlet boxes where the local inspector insists, and also to ground specific devices which the Code may require. This latter classification includes all devices in permanently wet locations and all devices operating at voltages above 150 volts to ground. It also includes certain devices regardless of voltage; among the ones likely to be met in installations of the type discussed here are motor controllers, garage equipment, motion-picture projectors, electric signs, transformers (unless mounted on wooden poles and at least 8 ft above the ground), mercury-vapor lamps if within reach of grounded objects, generator and motor frames in electrically operated organs, lighting fixtures if mounted on metal lath unless the fixtures are insulated from the lath.

If the wiring system is *not* grounded at the premises, it is still necessary to ground the service equipment, including the conduit of the service entrance, or the armor of the entrance cable. For this purpose copper wire may be used, but empty conduit or pipe may also be used. The following listing from Code Sec. 250-94(b) shows the requirements with respect to size.

Size of largest service conductor or equivalent for multiple conductors	Size of grounding conductor		
	Copper wire, AWG No.	Conduit or pipe trade size, inches	Electrical metallic tubing trade size, inches
2 or smaller..........................	8	½	½
1 or 1/0............................	6	½	1
2/0 or 3/0	4	¾	1¼
Over 3/0 to 350,000 c.m............	2	¾	1¼
Over 350,000 to 600,000 c.m.........	1/0	1	2
Over 600,000 to 1,100,000 c.m.......	2/0	1	2
Over 1,100,000 c.m.................	3/0	1	2

Common Grounds. A common grounding conductor may be used in practically 100% of the installations within the scope of this book, serving for both system and equipment ground. The size required is simply covered by the Code in Sec. 250-94(a) and can be determined from the following table:

Size of Largest Service Conductor	Size of Grounding Conductor, Copper, No.
No. 2 or smaller.....................	8
No. 1 or 1/0........................	6
No. 2/0 or 3/0......................	4
Over No. 3/0 to 350,000 c.m..........	2
Over 350,000 to 600,000 c.m..........	1/0
Over 600,000 to 1,100,000 c.m.........	2/0
Over 1,100,000 c.m..................	3/0

Chapter 29

MISCELLANEOUS PROBLEMS IN
NONRESIDENTIAL WIRING

In nonresidential installations the conduit system is used in practically all cases. This automatically provides a really good continuous ground. It provides a certain amount of flexibility in that circuits may be changed, wires added, and breakdowns repaired by merely pulling in new wires, with a fair degree of

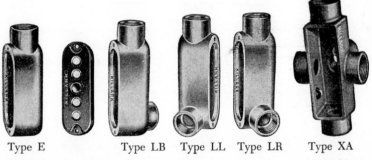

Type E   Type LB   Type LL   Type LR   Type XA

Fig. 29-1. For exposed runs of conduit, conduit fittings of the type shown here are commonly used. There are dozens of different shapes or types. (*Killark Electric Mfg. Co.*)

ease and not too much mechanical change in the actual conduit. Where exposed, the conduit is reasonably neat in appearance and certainly affords ample protection for the wires.

Conduit Fittings. For exposed runs of conduit, it is customary to use, instead of ordinary outlet boxes, cast fittings of the type shown in Fig. 29-1. They are known by various trade names such as Condulets, Unilets, etc. These devices are merely specialized forms of outlet boxes, but instead of being

464

provided with knockouts which can be removed to form openings, they have one or more ready-made openings. Accordingly, with a few basic body shapes, hundreds of different combinations are available. Each basic type is available for each size of conduit. Each opening is threaded to fit the size of conduit for which it is designed. These fittings are also available with threadless openings but with clamping devices for thin-wall conduit.

A few of the more common types are shown in Fig. 29-1. The Type E with the cover shown is frequently used at the

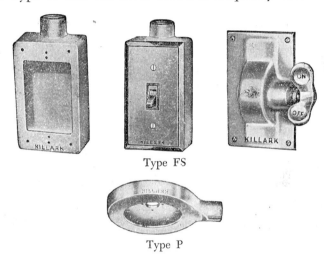

Type FS

Type P

Fig. 29-2. Larger fittings are used to house switches, receptacles, and similar devices.   (*Killark Electric Mfg. Co.*)

end of a run to a motor or similar device. The LB is commonly used at a point where a run of conduit comes along and then must go at right angles through a wall or ceiling; it is equally useful in going around a beam or similar obstruction. Fittings of this kind avoid awkward bends in conduit. The Types LL and LR are handy for 90-deg turns on a straight run. There are all kinds of combinations, some as complicated, for example, as the Type XA, which obviously is not used very frequently.

In a different style of body there are available many types similar to the Type FS shown in Fig. 29-2, which is used mostly for the mounting of switches and similar devices. In the same picture is shown a weatherproof cover which will operate a toggle switch mounted in a Type FS fitting—a handy combination for outdoor switches. On exposed runs of conduit, lighting fixtures are mounted on Type P fittings.

Pull Boxes. Wires of ordinary sizes as used in residential work are sufficiently flexible so that they can be pulled through long lengths of conduit even if there are offsets and bends. The heavier the wire, the more difficult it becomes. In really heavy sizes, such as the circular-mil cables, it becomes more and more necessary to install pull boxes at strategic locations; it is customary in many cases to use them instead of conduit bends. Such a pull box, as the name implies, is nothing but a steel box located where the wires can be helped along as they are pulled into the conduit. Pull boxes may be used only where they will be permanently accessible. A single pull box is often used for a number of runs of conduit, as shown in Fig. 29-3.

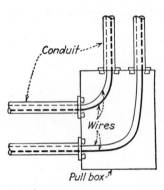

Fig. 29-3. Pull boxes are used with conduit to make it easier to pull wires through long lengths of conduit, and they also serve other purposes.

Concrete Boxes. In nonresidential buildings of all types, walls and ceilings frequently are of reinforced-concrete construction. The conduit and the boxes must be embedded in the concrete if the devices later are to be flush with the surface of the wall. Ordinary outlet boxes may be used, but special concrete boxes are also available. One of these is shown in Fig. 29-4. These boxes have special ears by which they are nailed to the wooden forms for the concrete. Stuff the boxes full of paper before installing; this will prevent concrete from seeping in. The conduit and the boxes must be in position before the concrete is poured. When the forms are removed, the conduit and the boxes are solidly embedded; the interior of the box is clean and ready for use. These boxes come in a variety of depths up to 6 in. Figure 29-5 shows an installed view.

For floor use, special cast boxes are available: these are of the two-piece type so arranged that, even if the box proper is installed crooked in the rough concrete, the top section can be leveled off with respect to the final floor surface. This is accomplished because the two pieces telescope together, as is clearly shown in Fig. 29-6. Receptacles and similar devices cannot in practical fashion be installed flush with the floor, so that it is customary to use nozzles and outlets which raise the final device a few inches above the floor.

Number of Wires in Conduit. For smaller sizes of wire this was discussed in Chap. 11. For heavier sizes see Tables 1 to 7

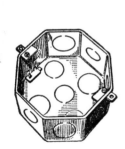

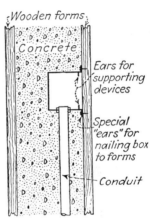

FIG. 29-4. A concrete box designed to be embedded in the concrete as it is poured.

FIG. 29-5. Concrete boxes are nailed to the wooden forms before the concrete is poured.

in your copy of the Code. These tables are clear and need no further explanation here.

Deflection of Wires. Small wires are so flexible that it is not likely that they will be damaged even by sharp bends. In the larger sizes, on the other hand, it is conceivable that, if bent too sharply where they emerge from a run of conduit, the insulation might become damaged to the point where grounds might be caused. The Code in Sec. 373-6(b) requires that ungrounded wires No. 4 and heavier must be further protected "by a substantial bushing providing a smoothly rounded *insulating* surface unless the conductors are separated from the raceway fitting by substantial insulating material securely fastened in place." This is commonly accomplished by inserting sheet insulating fiber securely anchored, or by means of special bushings similar to the usual conduit bushings but made of an insulating material. In that case, two locknuts must be used on the conduit before the

FIG. 29-6. Adjustable floor box for concrete work. Because the two parts telescope, the exposed portion can always be made flush with the final plaster.

insulating bushing is installed: one on the outside of the box and one on the inside.

Moreover, the Code in Sec. 373-6(a) further requires that wires No. 1 and heavier, if running in a vertical position, shall not be deflected at all at the point where they enter or leave a cabinet, unless gutters or empty spaces are provided between the wall of the cabinet and the devices or mechanisms that the cabinet encloses. The width of gutter required varies with the size of the wires in question, as follows:

Feeder Size	Minimum Width of Gutter, Inches
No. 1	3
Nos. 1/0 and 2/0	3½
Nos. 3/0 and 4/0	4
250,000 c.m.	4½
300,000 to 350,000 c.m.	5
400,000 to 500,000 c.m.	6
600,000 to 900,000 c.m.	8
1,000,000 to 1,250,000 c.m.	10
1,500,000 to 2,000,000 c.m.	12

This requirement is of greater concern to manufacturers than to contractors, and panelboards and similar equipment automatically incorporate the proper gutter widths.   Locate cabinets so that the incoming runs of conduit will be so placed as to require a minimum deflection of the wires where they emerge from the conduit, and so that in vertical runs the weight of the wire will not be supported by the bend at the end of the run.   Figure 29-7 shows the wrong and Fig. 29-8 the right method.   Let the bends in the wires be sweeping and gentle rather than abrupt.

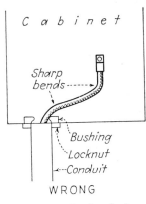 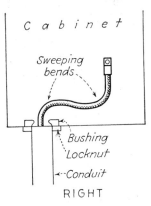

FIG. 29-7. The bends here shown are too abrupt.   The weight of the wire is supported by the bushing where the wire emerges from the conduit.

FIG. 29-8. The bends in wires should be gentle and sweeping.   This avoids grounds where the wires emerge from the conduit.

Supporting Vertical Runs of Wire.   Terminals on panelboards and similar equipment are not designed to support any substantial weight.   When there is a vertical run of wire, the weight of the wire itself is considerable, especially in the larger sizes.   If such runs of wire are connected directly to terminals, damage may result.   The Code in Sec. 300-19(a) therefore requires that in such vertical runs the wire be independently supported at intervals as follows:

Nos. 18 to 1/0 .... At least every 100 ft
Nos. 2/0 to 4/0 .... At least every 80 ft
250,000 to 350,000 c.m. .... At least every 60 ft

350,001 to 500,000 c.m. .... At least every 50 ft
500,001 to 750,000 c.m. .... At least every 40 ft
750,001 c.m. and larger .... At least every 35 ft

There are a number of ways to accomplish the required support. Special clamping devices of the type shown in Fig. 29-9 may be used. Pull boxes may be installed and the wire anchored there in a manner acceptable to the inspector, one approved method being that shown in A of Fig. 29-10 and consisting of running each wire over a couple of offset insulators as shown, while the method shown at B involves split porcelain cleats of appropriate size.

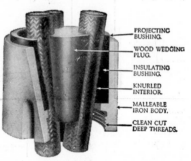

PROJECTING
BUSHING.

WOOD WEDGING
PLUG.

INSULATING
BUSHING.

KNURLED
INTERIOR.

MALLEABLE
IRON BODY.

CLEAN CUT
DEEP THREADS.

Fig. 29-9. This fitting is very handy in supporting vertical runs of wire. (*O. Z. Electrical Mfg. Co.*)

Continuity of Ground. Previous chapters showed how the various runs of conduit or metallic cable tie together outlet boxes and other equipment into one continuously grounded system. If, however, in any such wiring system one or more of the wires have a voltage above 250 volts *to ground,* the usual methods are no longer acceptable. Instead the Code in Sec. 250-75 gives a choice of several other methods.

If conduit fittings of the type illustrated in Figs. 29-1 and 29-2 are used, that is sufficient for either rigid or thin-wall conduit. The same fittings may be used for armored cable or flexible conduit, for the connectors that are used with such raceways fit directly into the tapped openings in the fittings.

If ordinary outlet and similar boxes of drawn sheet steel are used, several methods are open for use. The most common as far as rigid conduit is concerned is the double-locknut system shown in cross section in Fig. 29-11.   This involves simply one locknut on the outside of the box and another one inside, plus the usual bushing.

With thin-wall conduit, armored cable, or flexible conduit, the simplest method is to use on the connector involved, inside the box, a grounding locknut, shown in Fig. 29-12, in place of the usual locknut that is used on such connectors.   It is not necessary to use jumper wires from one such locknut to another

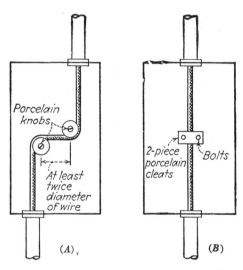

Fig. 29-10. Two other methods of supporting vertical runs of wire.

inside the same box; the screws on the locknuts are designed to bite into the box and will stay in place where vibration or other causes may loosen the ordinary locknut.

In case the run of conduit in question is the service conduit, any of the schemes shown above may be used except the double-locknut method.

Double-pole Switches.   When lamps are operated on two ungrounded wires, only double-pole switches which open both wires may be used.   This is only part of the general rule that switches must always open all ungrounded wires, although there are a few exceptions to this in connection with motors, which will be covered in a separate chapter.

T-rated Switches. In Chap. 4 you learned that newer switches are of the "general-use AC-only" type and that there are two kinds of the older switches: those that are T-rated and those that are not. The discussion below will concern nonresidential installations.

To control ordinary incandescent-(filament) style lamps, you may use either the new general-use AC-only switches or the older switches if T-rated. For fluorescent lighting and noninductive loads such as appliances, any kind of switch may be used.

For inductive loads, such as transformers, small motors, and so on, the switch must have an ampere rating at least twice that of the load controlled, unless the switch is a general-use AC-only switch, in which case it must have an ampere rating at least as great as that of the load controlled.

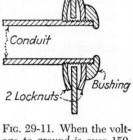

FIG. 29-11. When the voltage *to ground* is over 150, use the double-locknut construction shown here, instead of the ordinary construction that was shown in Fig. 10-6.

Switches are available in 10-, 20-, and 30-amp ratings, some being limited to 125 volts, others to 250 volts, 277 volts, or even higher. Select switches to suit the amperage, the voltage, and the type of load involved.

Surface Metal Raceway. This style or method of wiring is seldom seen in homes but is widely used in industrial work, especially for making additions to existing installations or in original installations where numerous future changes are probable. A number of different brands are available, all operating on the general principle of a two-piece metal channel. In use one piece is securely fastened to the wall, ceiling, or floor; then the other piece is snapped on the first, in cover fashion.

FIG. 29-12. A special type of locknut with bonding screw.

One type, with a number of the fittings used, is shown in Fig. 29-13, and no great amount of explanation should be necessary. The material comes in a number of sizes and types; which size and kind to use depends on the number and sizes of wires involved, as well as the purpose to be served. It may run through walls if a continuous piece is used. It is used not only for the usual wiring but frequently also for signal and telephone

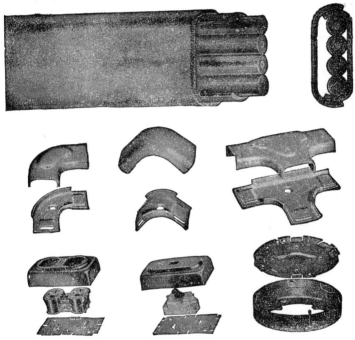

FIG. 29-13. Surface metal raceway and fittings. This material is most convenient where frequent changes must be made or where concealed wiring is not practical. (*National Electric Products Corp.*)

wire and similar purposes. Wires of two separate systems may never be mixed in the same channel.

The Code in Sec. 352-1 limits this material to exposed runs in

FIG. 29-14. This type of surface metal raceway is flat and may be used on the floor. (*National Electric Products Corp.*)

dry locations at voltages not over 300 volts between conductors. It may not be used where exposed to severe mechanical injury, although the type shown in Fig. 29-14 is approved for use on floors, the abuse which it receives from ordinary foot traffic not being considered as causing "severe mechanical injury." The number of wires per channel depends on the size of the channel. Not more than 10 wires may be installed inside a single channel under any circumstances except for signal purposes. No wire heavier than No. 6 may be used.

Chapter 30

NONRESIDENTIAL LIGHTING

Chapter 14 discussed the fundamentals of lighting and the kinds of incandescent and fluorescent lamps used mostly in residential lighting and in smaller nonresidential projects. In this chapter we shall discuss other lamps and lighting equipment used mostly in nonresidential work, and factors involved in designing a good lighting system in such locations.

Reflector and Projector Lamps. In addition to the ordinary incandescent lamps already discussed, one additional kind should be described here. This is the kind with silver reflectors deposited on the bulb as a permanent part of the lamp. The reflectors, being integral with the bulb, are permanently bright and untarnished; being silver they are excellent reflectors. The two factors combined provide lasting efficient lighting that could not be obtained with separate reflectors that get dusty and dirty in time, reducing the efficiency of the lighting.

Three kinds are shown in Fig. 30-1. The type shown at *A* is known as the silvered-bowl type and is an ordinary lamp with the reflector on the outside of the bulb. At *B* and *C* are shown, respectively, the "R" and "PAR" types in which the reflector is on the inside of the bulb, on the neck and body.

The silvered-bowl type is available in sizes from 60 watts upward and is used mostly in indirect lighting, where the light is to be thrown upward and then reflected downward. Expensive and ugly separate reflectors are not needed with this type of lamp. The proper use of such lamps for general lighting and for special effects is much too broad a subject to be fully discussed here.

The Type R, or reflector type, throws a circular beam and is available in sizes from 75 to 1,000 watts, used mostly in the 150- to 300-watt sizes. It is available in two styles: spots with a beam of about 30 deg and floods with a beam of about 60 deg. This type fits ordinary sockets.

The Type PAR, or projector type, throws an oval beam and is available in sizes from 150 to 500 watts. Spots are either narrow or standard; floods are either medium or standard. However, any one size is not necessarily available in each of the four kinds. The 150-watt type fits ordinary sockets; the 200-, 300-, and 500-watt fit three different special sockets. An ordinary lamp will shatter when used outdoors if rain hits the hot glass;

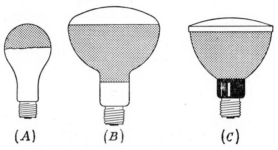

(A)   (B)   (C)

Fig. 30-1. Typical reflector lamps.

the PAR are made using special "hard" glass and are less likely to be damaged in that way.

Both the Types R and PAR concentrate the light into beams of greater intensity than could be obtained with the use of external reflectors of equivalent size. They are widely used for floodlighting and spotlighting. Outdoors they find application in lighting driveways, walks, farmyards, parking areas, and similar locations. Indoors they are useful for high-level lighting of small areas, such as merchandise displays, decorations, and danger areas.

Special-service Lamps. If lamps are located where it is extremely difficult to change them, it may be wise to burn them at less than their rated voltage, which will increase their life but reduce the wattage consumed and also reduce their efficiency; they will produce fewer lumens per watt. This scheme leads to a lot of guesswork as to probable life and wattage. It would be better to use a special type of lamp known as the "special-service" type. Lamps of this type will last about 2,500 hr when burned at their rated voltage, will consume their rated watts, but produce about 15% fewer lumens per watt than ordinary 1,000-hr lamps.

In buildings other than homes, it often becomes a very costly matter from a labor standpoint to replace *one* lamp. If a hundred were replaced at one time, the cost per lamp would be very low. For that reason, often all lamps are replaced at one time, even if not burned out. The extra cost of the new lamps is lower than the total added labor cost of repeatedly replacing one lamp at a time.

Other Incandescent Lamps. Since a large manufacturer of lamps may make over 10,000 kinds, obviously only the most commonly used kinds can be mentioned here. To show the range, you can buy a "grain-of-wheat" lamp used in surgical instruments and consuming a fraction of a watt or a large lamp consuming 75,000 watts. You can buy a lamp for deep-sea diving, not damaged by 300-lb water pressure on the bulb. You can buy "black-light" lamps which produce little visible light, but when their "black light" falls on properly painted surfaces, they glow brightly in spectacular color. You won't find these kinds of lamps on dime-store counters.

More Information about Fluorescent Lamps. Chapter 14 discussed only the bare fundamentals of ordinary fluorescent lamps. This chapter will discuss many other details concerning such lamps: kinds of bases, various starting methods, efficiencies, and other characteristics.

Bases on Fluorescent Lamps. Figure 30-2 shows the various kinds of bases used on fluorescent lamps, depending on their size and the starting method. Later paragraphs will define the particular base used on each kind of lamp. The original variety is the medium bi-pin, shown at *A*; the diameter and spacing of the pins are always the same, but the over-all diameter of the base, of course, depends on the diameter of the lamp. The mogul bi-pin, shown at *B*, has larger pins and larger over-all diameter. The single-pin is shown at *C*; the pin is always the same diameter, but the over-all diameter of the base varies. The recessed-double-contact type is shown at *D*, while *E* shows the 4-pin type used only on Circline (circular) lamps. There are a few other types used only on lamps not described in this book.

Types of Fluorescent Starting. There are three types of starting in common use: preheat, instant-start, and rapid-start. Lamps designed for one type of starting will not, with a few exceptions, fit sockets designed for a different kind. In every case a ballast must be used, and the ballast must be carefully matched to the kind of starting and to the particular lamp under discussion.

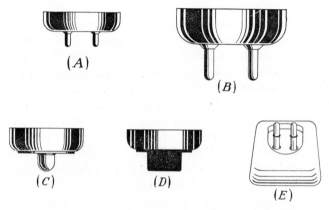

Fig. 30-2. Types of bases used on fluorescent lamps.

The preheat type of starting was the kind used when fluorescent lighting was first introduced, and is still widely used. It was described in Chap. 14. Lamps for preheat starting have a filament or cathode at each end of the tube. When the lamp is first switched on, the current heats these filaments or cathodes. Then the starter opens, current flows as an arc through the tube, limited to proper values by the ballast; this flow of the arc current keeps the cathodes hot as long as the lamp is lighted. Fluorescent lamps designed for preheat starting have bi-pin bases, either medium or mogul.

Lamps of the instant-start type also have a filament or cathode at each end, but each one is short-circuited inside the lamp. Obviously then a current can't be made to flow through the filament of the cathode before the lamp lights. No starter is needed, but the ballast is of a variety such that the open-circuit voltage before the lamp is turned on is about 450 volts; when the lamp is turned on, that voltage is high enough to start the lamp instantly. The amperage consumed by the lamp is such that the ballast under load drops the voltage to a value that is proper for the lamp. After lighting, the cathode is kept hot by the arc current in the tube. Instant-start lamps are mostly of the "Slimline" type using a single-pin base. A few of the earlier type made used a medium or mogul bi-pin.

More recent fluorescent lamps are of the rapid-start type. (The difference in time between the instant-start and rapid-start is very small; the former is truly instant; in the latter there is a lag of a small fraction of a second.) Rapid-start lamps require no starter; the ballast must be of the proper type. The lamp has a filament or cathode at each end, not short-circuited as in the instant-start; the cathode is kept heated (while the lamp is lighted) by special $3\frac{1}{2}$-volt windings in the ballast, plus the heat of the arc current in the tube. Starting is based on much the same principle as in the instant-start: The ballast delivers an open-circuit voltage of about 450 volts at the instant of starting and then controls the voltage to the proper value for normal operation. Rapid-start lamps do not have a uniform kind of base. Most have the recessed-double-contact type; others use the medium or mogul bi-pin.

The first fluorescent lamps made were of the preheat variety; then the trend was to the instant-start as that type was developed. Now the trend is toward the rapid-start in new installations.

A subvariety of the instant-start is the cold-cathode type. In this kind there is no filament in the lamp; instead, at each end there is a cathode which is a metal "thimble" containing electron-emitting materials, as is found on the filaments or cathodes of the usual fluorescent varieties, all of which can be called the hot-cathode type. The construction at the ends is substantially that found in the tubes of neon signs. Starting is based on the same principle as in ordinary instant-start lamps. As the lamp is turned on, the ballast delivers a high open-circuit voltage to start the lamp, but the voltage is very high, in the order of 800 volts. For that reason ordinary building wire, which is limited to usage

at not over 600 volts, cannot be used in wiring such lamps.   Wire
designed for a higher voltage must be used.

Efficiency of Fluorescent Lamps.   The lumens per watt delivered by a fluorescent lamp depend on many factors and particularly on the color of the light produced by the lamp.   From
Chap. 14 you will remember that there are many kinds of "white."
Tables showing the lumens produced are generally based on the
"cool-white" color.

The nominal wattage ratings of fluorescent lamps are based on
the power consumption of the lamp itself, not including the power
consumed by the ballast.   Since the ballast consumes about 15%
of the total power consumed in the circuit, the actual efficiency
of the over-all fluorescent-lighting system is roughly 13% lower
than indicated by the apparent efficiency of the individual lamp.
The light output of brand-new fluorescent lamps drops rapidly
during the first hours of operation, then stabilizes.   Efficiency
tables are based on the output after 100 hr of operation.   After
100 hr of operation, the output drops slowly but continuously so
that as the lamp approaches the end of its life, the output may
be 20 to 30% below the 100-hr figure.   During its life the lamp
delivers an average output of perhaps 85% of its 100-hr rating.

The efficiency of the lamps also varies with the type and size;
in general the larger lamps produce more lumens per watt than
the smaller ones.   The actual efficiency of the lamps varies from
about 45 to 75 lumens per watt.

Lumens per Foot of Length.   Entirely aside from the lumens
per watt, the lumens *per foot of length* of a fluorescent lamp are
another important consideration.   Most of the ordinary "garden
varieties" produce from 550 to 700 lumens per foot.   Thus a
fixture using four of the 40-watt 48-in. lamps will have altogether
16 ft of total lamp length and will produce about 11,000 lumens.
To produce the high footcandle levels of lighting demanded today for efficient work in office and other areas, many lighting
fixtures must be installed; the ceiling can be literally covered
with fixtures.

Why not produce lamps that will produce more lumens per
foot of length?   This has been done in comparatively recent
kinds of lamps.   Lamps called "high-output" type produce from
800 to 900 lumens per foot; another type called "power groove"

in one brand and "very high output" or "super high output" in other brands produces from 1,500 to 1,600 lumens per foot. (Note that "high output" does not refer to lumens *per watt* but to lumens *per foot of length*.) Such lamps are available in 48-, 72-, and 96-in. lengths. Using such lamps will not result in an installation consuming fewer watts for any given footcandle level of lighting, but will permit a smaller number of fixtures and lamps to be used. This leads to a definite saving in the installation cost, less maintenance, and higher footcandle levels of lighting.

The output per foot of length is controlled by varying the amperage flowing through the lamp. The current in most of the ordinary type lamps is about 0.430 amp. In the high-output type it is about 0.800 amp, while in the very-high-output type it is about 1.500 amp. The current is controlled by the proper selection of ballasts.

Effect of Voltage on Fluorescent Lamps. Ordinary incandescent lamps must be selected for the circuit voltage on which they are to be operated. For maximum efficiency a 115-volt lamp should not be operated on a 110- or 120-volt circuit. Chapter 14 outlined the very considerable effect that off-voltage has on the life and efficiency of such lamps.

Fluorescent lamps on the other hand are not rated in volts; the same lamp is used on a 115-volt circuit as on a 230-volt circuit. However, the ballast used must be carefully selected to match the voltage of the circuit on which the ballast and the lamp are to be used. Suppose the proper ballast has been selected and is used with a lamp on a 120-volt circuit. What is the effect on the lamp if the circuit voltage changes? No precise data can be given because the effect is dependent on the size of the lamp, the kind of lamp, and the particular ballast used.

On a 40-watt lamp, however, a 10% overvoltage will increase the light output about 10% and reduce the efficiency about 5%, but affect the life of the lamp very little. A 10% undervoltage will have the opposite effect. In other words, fluorescent lamps are not so radically affected by incorrect voltages as are incandescent lamps.

Color of Light from Fluorescent Lamps. As already mentioned in Chap. 14, there are many kinds of "white" fluorescent lamps.   The "de luxe" varieties of white are about 25% less efficient than the other kinds of white.   The cool-white lamp represents about 75% of all the fluorescent lamps sold and is quite satisfactory where color discrimination is not overly important.

In general the cool white and de luxe cool white produce light that simulates natural light; the warm white and de luxe warm white produce light that is more nearly like the light produced by incandescent lamps and emphasizes the red, orange, and brown colors.

For lighting merchandise displays in stores, the de luxe cool white probably gives the best over-all effect, more or less simulating natural daylight.   But if the merchandise on display tends toward the red, orange, and brown colors, the de luxe warm white is preferred by many.

For decorative purposes and specialized lighting, some fluorescent lamps are available in colors such as blue, green, gold, pink, and red.   Ordinary incandescent lamps in color are most inefficient, for they are ordinary lamps with color on the glass that absorbs most of the light, allowing only the desired color to pass through.   Fluorescent lamps on the other hand have the proper phosphor on the inside of the tube, which creates primarily the color desired.   For that reason they are many times as efficient as colored incandescent lamps.

Tabulation of Characteristics of Fluorescent Lamps.   The table on the next page shows the characteristics of the more common types of lamps.   Necessarily this must be an abbreviated table, and those who need more information about a particular lamp or about lamps not shown can obtain it from the manufacturers of lamps.

Mercury-vapor Lighting.   Like fluorescent lamps, mercury lamps are arc lamps.   Whereas the fluorescent lamp has a long, low-density arc, the mercury lamp has a short, high-density arc. Being arc lamps, they cannot be connected directly into a circuit but require auxiliary equipment for proper starting and control. While they are available in many sizes, only the 400- and the 1,000-watt are in common use.   Figure 30-3 shows two kinds of the 400-watt size and one of the 1,000-watt.

The mercury lamp is made by using a bulb within a bulb. The inner bulb contains the light-producing source: the arc.   It

Variety	Watts	Bulb type	Diam- eter, inches	Length, inches	Type of starting	Lumens*		Type of base
						Total	Per watt	
Ordinary........	15	T-8	1	18	Preheat	750	50	Medium bi-pin
	30	T-8	1	36	Preheat	1,900	63	Medium bi-pin
	15	T-12	1½	18	Preheat	680	45	Medium bi-pin
	20	T-12	1½	24	Preheat	1,030	52	Medium bi-pin
	40	T-12	1½	48	Preheat	2,800	70	Medium bi-pin
"Premium"†.....	40	T-12	1½	48	Preheat	3,100	77†	Medium bi-pin
Slimline.........	38	T-12	1½	48	Instant	2,600	68	Single-pin
	55	T-12	1½	72	Instant	4,100	75	Single-pin
	74	T-12	1½	96	Instant	5,060	76	Single-pin
High output.....	60	T-12	1½	48	Rapid	3,500	58	Recessed dou-
	85	T-12	1½	72	Rapid	5,550	65	ble contact
	105	T-12	1½	96	Rapid	7,600	72	
Extra-high output	107	PG-17	2⅛	48	Rapid	6,900	65	Recessed dou-
	155	PG-17	2⅛	72	Rapid	10,900	70	ble contact
	200	PG-17	2⅛	96	Rapid	15,000	75	

* Total lumens and lumens per watt are for cool-white lamps after 100 hr of use. The average during the useful life of the lamps will be about 15% less. The figures are based on watts consumed by the lamps, not including power consumed by the ballasts.

† The higher efficiency of this lamp is accomplished at the expense of some reduction in the life of the lamp. It can also be used in fixtures designed for rapid-start lamps, but not in those designed for instant-start.

is made of quartz to withstand the intense heat produced by the arc. The outer bulb is made of glass.

The efficiency of mercury lamps is much higher than that of incandescent (filament-type) lamps but less than that of fluorescent lamps. In the 400- and 1,000-watt sizes they produce from 50 to 57 lumens per watt. The efficiency of mercury lamps drops off comparatively little, about 16% during their useful life of about 9,000 hr. Mercury lamps are used mostly for lighting of factories and for street lighting. Their comparatively high output coupled with relatively small size makes them especially suitable in areas with very high ceilings, where it would be difficult and costly to install the necessary fluorescent fixtures to provide a high footcandle level of light. Since in such areas it is usually expensive to change a lamp, the long life of the mercury type suggests their use in these locations.

One drawback to the use of mercury lighting has been the color of the light produced, very deficient in the red end of the spectrum. While an ordinary white object may appear quite white under ordinary mercury lighting, any object with color has an unnatural appearance. Blue, green, and yellow are emphasized, while orange and red are distorted to look brownish or black. Under this light people have a corpselike appearance.

FIG. 30-3. Three different kinds of mercury lamps. (*General Electric Co.*)

In the past, this color deficiency has been corrected by using a combination of mercury lamps (deficient in red) and incandescent lamps (strong in red). Recently, however, "color-improved" mercury lamps have become available. In the mercury lamp, the arc produces the red-poor light already described; it also produces a good deal of invisible ultraviolet light, which in the ordinary lamp is wasted. In the color-improved lamp, the inside of the outer bulb is coated with a layer of the "phosphor" or chemical used on the inside of fluorescent-lamp tubes, specifically the kind of phosphor that produces reddish light. Just as in the fluorescent lamp the invisible ultraviolet light produced in the lamp makes the phosphor glow, so also in the mercury type: The ultraviolet light from the arc makes the phosphor glow, producing a generous quantity of red-rich light. This, combined with the red-poor light produced by the mercury arc itself, results in a light which is acceptable for most purposes. However, color-improved mercury lamps are a little less efficient than the ordinary ones.

Figure 30-4 shows a typical wiring diagram of the simplest variety for a mercury lamp. When first turned on, the lamp does not light immediately. At first there is only a slight glow which comes from a small arc from a special starting electrode. This small arc leads to a gradual heating which in turn gradually vaporizes the mercury in the lamp; the lamp becomes brighter. Finally the lamp operates at full brilliancy. All this requires from

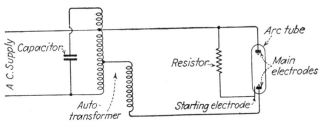

FIG. 30-4. Wiring diagram for the mercury-vapor type of lamp.

5 to 10 min, depending on temperature, voltage, and similar factors.

If a mercury lamp is operating in normal fashion and the power is turned off, the lamp, of course, goes out, but it *stays out* even if the power is turned on again immediately. It must go through its starting cycle, and only after 5 to 10 min will it light

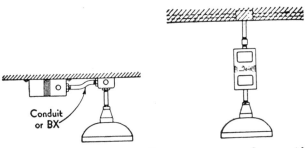

FIG. 30-5. Typical methods of installing mercury-vapor lamps with their transformers. (*General Electric Co.*)

again. If used on a circuit where there are frequent and severe fluctuations in voltage, mercury lamps will be found to be impractical, for they will go out during the voltage dips and not relight without going through the complete starting cycle. Moreover, if they are used with voltages considerably in excess of their rated voltages, their life will be reduced.

Good Lighting. Chapter 14 outlined the fundamental fact that one lumen of light falling on one square foot of area always produces one footcandle of illumination. From this statement it is easy to jump to some very wrong conclusions. For example if a room with 100 sq ft of floor area is lighted by a lamp producing 5,000 lumens, obviously there are 50 lumens for every square foot of floor area, but the illumination will be very much less than 50 footcandles. That is because only a part of the light that is generated reaches the place where it is to be used.

In calculating the lighting of a room, the problem is to determine how much of the light that is generated falls on the area to be lighted. The subject is much too large to be fully covered in a book of this type, and this chapter will be devoted only to a brief study of the factors that are involved. Detailed technical data can be obtained from manufacturers of lamps and fixtures.

Utilization Factor. The ratio of the number of lumens of light reaching the area where it is wanted, to the total lumens generated, is called the "utilization factor," or "coefficient of utilization." It may be as little as 10% or even less and rarely exceeds 70%. Many things affect the utilization factor. Important factors are the particular type of fixture (direct or indirect lighting), the color of the walls and ceilings, the size and shape of the room. These will be discussed separately, not necessarily in order of their importance, for what is the most important factor in one installation may not be so important in the next.

Room Index. In any room, we want the light on our desks or on our machinery. Black walls would be very dreary, so light-colored walls are used. Of the light that falls on the walls, some is reflected into the room, but some is absorbed and lost. Naturally we want to lose as little as possible, so let us consider the influence of walls. A room 10 × 10 ft has a floor area of 100 sq ft. If the ceiling height is also 10 ft, the wall area is 400 sq ft, or *four* square feet of wall per square foot of floor. If the room is 20 × 20 ft, the floor area is 400 sq ft, and if the ceiling height remains 10 ft, the total wall area is 800 sq ft, or *two* square feet of wall per square foot of floor. The ratio is twice as good as in the case of the smaller room. Stating it another way, the larger room has less light-absorbing *wall* area per square foot of *floor* area than the smaller room. Therefore, as the size of a room increases, more and more of the light that is produced is usefully used, and less and less of it is wasted by absorption on walls. Likewise, the higher the mounting height of the lighting fixture, the more the light produced will fall on the walls, and a greater portion of it will be lost. Therefore, in general, low mounting heights produce the greater efficiency if all other factors are properly considered.

The room index or room ratio was formerly expressed by letters from A to J; A was the best, and J the poorest. Today the ratio is often numerically expressed by numbers ranging approximately from 5.0 to 0.5; the higher the number, the better the factor. As a matter of fact, the ratio is based on a simple formula $(W \times L)/[H \times (W + L)]$ in which W is the width of the room, L is the length, and H is the height of the fixtures above the floor (except when, in the case of the particular fixtures to be used, less than 40% of the light output goes downward, in which case H becomes the ceiling height).

A table showing the room index or room ratio is given in Fig. 30-6. You will note that the index improves with the size of the room but deteriorates as the mounting height (or ceiling height) increases. More complete information can be found in technical literature available from manufacturers of lighting equipment.

Color of Ceilings. If no light is reflected from the ceiling, in other words if good reflectors direct all the light downward, the reflecting ability of the ceiling is of no importance. Whether it is a clean white or a dirty black makes little difference.

If, however, a totally indirect lighting system is used, in which all the light is directed to the ceiling from which it is reflected downward, the reflecting power of the ceiling is all-important. A dirty ceiling regardless of color will absorb a very large part of the light thrown on it. The ceiling must have good reflecting power and so must be of an appropriate color (see Chap. 14), and it must be kept clean.

The color (and cleanliness) of the ceiling are important to the extent that light falls on it, to be reflected downward. However, it is little affected by room index.

Color of Walls. What has been said about the ceiling also holds true for the walls, although to a lesser extent. The better the room index, the less important the color of the walls (for the ratio of wall area to floor area is a large factor in determining room index in the first place).

Type of Fixture Used. Regardless of the type of fixture used,

ROOM W ft.	L ft.	Height of Light Source** above Floor (feet)										
		7	8	9	10	11	12	13	15	17	19	23
8	10	1.0	0.8	0.7	0.6	0.5						
	14	1.1	0.9	0.8	0.7	0.6	0.5					
	18	1.2	1.0	0.9	0.7	0.7	0.6	0.5				
	24	1.3	1.1	0.9	0.8	0.7	0.6	0.6	0.5			
	30	1.4	1.2	1.0	0.8	0.7	0.7	0.6	0.5			
	40	1.5	1.2	1.0	0.9	0.8	0.7	0.6	0.5			
	50	1.5	1.3	1.1	0.9	0.8	0.7	0.7	0.6	0.5		
10	10	1.1	0.9	0.8	0.7	0.6	0.5					
	14	1.3	1.1	0.9	0.8	0.7	0.6	0.6				
	18	1.4	1.2	1.0	0.9	0.8	0.7	0.6	0.5			
	24	1.6	1.3	1.1	0.9	0.8	0.7	0.6	0.5			
	30	1.7	1.4	1.2	1.0	0.9	0.8	0.7	0.6	0.5		
	40	1.8	1.5	1.2	1.1	0.9	0.8	0.6	0.6	0.5		
	60	1.9	1.6	1.3	1.1	1.0	0.9	0.8	0.7	-0.6	0.5	
12	12	1.3	1.1	0.9	0.8	0.7	0.6	0.6	0.5			
	16	1.5	1.2	1.1	0.9	0.8	0.7	0.7	0.5			
	20	1.7	1.4	1.2	1.0	0.9	0.8	0.7	0.6	0.5		
	30	1.9	1.6	1.3	1.1	1.0	0.9	0.8	0.7	0.6	0.5	
	50	2.1	1.8	1.5	1.3	1.1	1.0	0.9	0.8	0.7	0.6	
	70	2.3	1.9	1.6	1.4	1.2	1.1	1.0	0.8	0.7	0.6	0.5
	100	2.4	1.9	1.6	1.4	1.3	1.1	1.0	0.9	0.7	0.7	0.5
14	14	1.6	1.3	1.1	0.9	0.8	0.7	0.7	0.6	0.5		
	20	1.8	1.5	1.3	1.1	1.0	0.9	0.8	0.7	0.6	0.5	
	30	2.1	1.7	1.5	1.3	1.1	1.0	0.9	0.7	0.6	0.5	
	40	2.3	1.9	1.6	1.4	1.2	1.1	1.0	0.8	0.7	0.6	0.5
	60	2.5	2.1	1.8	1.5	1.3	1.2	1.1	0.9	0.7	0.6	0.5
	80	2.6	2.2	1.8	1.6	1.4	1.2	1.1	1.0	0.8	0.7	0.6
	100	2.7	2.2	1.9	1.6	1.5	1.3	1.2	1.0	0.8	0.8	0.6
16	16	1.8	1.5	1.2	1.1	0.9	0.8	0.8	0.6	0.5		
	20	2.0	1.6	1.4	1.2	1.0	0.9	0.8	0.7	0.6	0.5	
	30	2.3	1.9	1.6	1.4	1.2	1.1	1.0	0.8	0.7	0.6	0.5
	40	2.5	2.1	1.8	1.5	1.3	1.2	1.1	0.9	0.7	0.6	0.5
	60	2.8	2.3	1.9	1.7	1.5	1.3	1.2	1.0	0.8	0.7	0.6
	80	3.0	2.4	2.0	1.8	1.6	1.4	1.3	1.1	0.9	0.8	0.7
	100	3.1	2.5	2.1	1.8	1.6	1.4	1.3	1.1	1.0	0.8	0.7
18	20	2.1	1.7	1.5	1.3	1.1	1.0	0.9	0.8	0.7	0.6	0.5
	30	2.5	2.0	1.7	1.5	1.3	1.2	1.1	0.9	0.8	0.7	0.5
	40	2.8	2.3	1.9	1.6	1.5	1.3	1.2	1.0	0.8	0.8	0.6
	60	3.1	2.5	2.1	1.8	1.6	1.4	1.3	1.1	1.0	0.8	0.7
	80	3.3	2.7	2.3	2.0	1.7	1.5	1.4	1.2	1.0	0.9	0.7
	100	3.4	2.8	2.4	2.0	1.8	1.6	1.5	1.2	1.1	0.9	0.7
	120	3.5	2.9	2.4	2.1	1.9	1.6	1.5	1.3	1.1	1.0	0.8
20	20	2.2	1.8	1.5	1.3	1.2	1.0	1.0	0.8	0.7	0.6	0.5
	30	2.7	2.2	1.8	1.6	1.4	1.3	1.1	1.0	0.8	0.7	0.6
	40	3.0	2.4	2.0	1.8	1.6	1.4	1.3	1.1	0.9	0.8	0.7
	60	3.3	2.7	2.3	2.0	1.8	1.6	1.4	1.2	1.0	0.8	0.7
	80	3.6	2.9	2.5	2.1	1.9	1.7	1.5	1.3	1.1	1.0	0.8
	100	3.7	3.0	2.6	2.2	2.0	1.8	1.6	1.3	1.2	1.0	0.8
	120	3.8	3.1	2.6	2.3	2.0	1.8	1.6	1.4	1.2	1.0	0.8
25	30	3.0	2.5	2.1	1.8	1.6	1.4	1.3	1.1	0.9	0.8	0.7
	40	3.4	2.8	2.4	2.1	1.8	1.6	1.5	1.2	1.1	0.9	0.8
	60	3.9	3.2	2.7	2.4	2.1	1.9	1.7	1.4	1.2	1.1	0.9
	80	4.2	3.5	2.9	2.5	2.2	2.0	1.8	1.5	1.3	1.2	0.9
	100	4.4	3.6	3.1	2.7	2.4	2.1	1.9	1.6	1.4	1.2	1.0
	120	4.6	3.8	3.2	2.8	2.4	2.2	2.0	1.7	1.4	1.3	1.0
	140	4.7	3.9	3.3	2.8	2.5	2.2	2.0	1.7	1.5	1.3	1.0
30	30	3.3	2.7	2.3	2.0	1.8	1.6	1.4	1.2	1.0	0.9	0.7
	40	3.8	3.1	2.6	2.3	2.0	1.8	1.6	1.4	1.2	1.0	0.8
	60	4.4	3.6	3.1	2.7	2.4	2.1	1.9	1.6	1.4	1.3	1.0
	80	4.8	4.0	3.4	2.9	2.6	2.3	2.1	1.7	1.5	1.3	1.1
	100	5.1	4.2	3.6	3.1	2.7	2.4	2.2	1.8	1.6	1.4	1.1
	120	5.3	4.4	3.7	3.2	2.8	2.5	2.3	1.9	1.7	1.5	1.2
	140	5.5	4.5	3.8	3.3	2.9	2.6	2.3	2.0	1.7	1.5	1.2
35	40	4.2	3.4	2.9	2.5	2.2	2.0	1.8	1.5	1.3	1.1	0.9
	60	4.9	4.0	3.4	2.9	2.6	2.3	2.1	1.8	1.5	1.3	1.1
	80	5.4	4.4	3.7	3.2	2.9	2.6	2.3	1.9	1.7	1.5	1.2
	100		4.7	4.0	3.4	3.1	2.7	2.5	2.1	1.8	1.6	1.3
	120		4.9	4.2	3.6	3.2	2.8	2.6	2.2	1.9	1.7	1.3
	140		5.1	4.3	3.7	3.3	2.9	2.7	2.2	1.9	1.7	1.4

Fig. 30-6. A partial table of room indexes. (*General Electric Co.*)

a goodly share of the light produced is lost right in the fixture, being absorbed by glassware and by the reflecting surfaces. Losses range from 20 to 40%. This is mentioned merely as a factor in helping you understand why most installations have what appear to be relatively low utilization factors.

The type of fixture will be determined by the kind of lighting wanted. Direct-lighting fixtures direct 100% of the useful light downward; indirect-lighting fixtures direct 100% of the useful light upward. In between are endless variations. The type of fixtures selected will greatly affect the over-all efficiency or utilization factor of the installation. The type of room, its purpose (foundry or style-show) will usually determine the type of lighting that is suitable and proper.

Maintenance Factor. A lighting installation using brand-new fixtures, new lamps, and freshly painted walls, and providing, for example, 50 footcandles when installed, will probably produce only 35 footcandles after six months of operation. This is due to quite a variety of causes. First of all, all lamps produce fewer lumens per watt after a period of use, as compared with the lumens per watt produced when new. Fixtures gather dust which absorbs light. Walls and ceilings darken, which means that they absorb more light. For these reasons, every lighting job must be calculated for a higher level of illumination than is expected during average use. A maintenance factor of 70% is probably average; in other words, an installation which will provide 50 footcandles in a brand-new building will later provide more nearly 35 footcandles on the average. Therefore if 50 footcandles are wanted during normal usage, figure the job for about 70 footcandles.

Utilization Factors. Complete and elaborate tables can be obtained from manufacturers of lighting equipment, showing the utilization factor to be expected in any given room using any one of dozens of different types of lighting equipment. An abbreviated table is shown in Fig. 30-7, showing what factor to expect with six different types of fixtures, ranging from totally indirect to totally direct. (The percentages shown at the heads of the several columns represent the reflecting value of ceiling and walls.)

You will note that with direct lighting, the utilization factor varies from 25 to 60%. With indirect lighting, it varies from 7 to 45%. What is the significance of this utilization factor? When you know this factor for any given room, you can quite accurately predict how many watts will be required to produce a given level of illumination, using fixtures of the type used in determining the factor.

Assume that you have determined that, for a particular room

TYPICAL DISTRIBUTION	LUMINAIRE	Ceiling	80%			70%			50%			30%		
		Walls	50%	30%	10%	50%	30%	10%	50%	30%	10%	50%	30%	10%
	INDIRECT*	Floor	10%			10%			10%			10%		
		Room Ratio												
M.F.=.70		0.6	.27	.21	.16	.24	.19	.14	.17	.14	.11	.12	.09	.07
		0.8	.34	.28	.22	.30	.25	.20	.22	.18	.15	.15	.12	.09
		1.0	.39	.33	.28	.35	.30	.25	.26	.22	.18	.17	.14	.12
		1.25	.45	.39	.33	.40	.34	.29	.30	.26	.22	.20	.17	.14
		1.5	.49	.43	.38	.43	.38	.33	.32	.28	.24	.22	.19	.16
		2.0	.55	.49	.44	.48	.43	.39	.36	.32	.29	.24	.22	.19
		2.5	.58	.53	.48	.52	.47	.43	.38	.35	.32	.26	.23	.21
		3.0	.61	.56	.52	.54	.50	.46	.40	.37	.34	.27	.25	.23
		4.0	.65	.61	.57	.57	.54	.50	.43	.40	.37	.28	.26	.25
		5.0	.68	.64	.61	.59	.56	.53	.44	.42	.39	.29	.27	.26
M.F.=.65	SEMI-INDIRECT	0.6	.24	.19	.15	.22	.17	.13	.17	.14	.11	.13	.11	.08
		0.8	.30	.25	.20	.27	.23	.19	.22	.18	.15	.17	.14	.12
		1.0	.35	.30	.25	.32	.27	.23	.26	.22	.19	.20	.17	.14
		1.25	.40	.35	.30	.36	.32	.28	.29	.26	.22	.22	.20	.18
		1.5	.44	.38	.34	.40	.35	.31	.32	.28	.25	.24	.22	.20
		2.0	.49	.44	.40	.44	.40	.36	.36	.32	.29	.27	.25	.23
		2.5	.52	.48	.44	.48	.44	.40	.38	.35	.32	.29	.27	.25
		3.0	.55	.50	.47	.50	.46	.42	.40	.37	.34	.30	.28	.27
		4.0	.58	.54	.51	.53	.49	.46	.43	.40	.37	.32	.30	.29
		5.0	.60	.57	.54	.55	.52	.49	.45	.42	.39	.34	.32	.31
M.F.=.70	GENERAL DIFFUSING	0.6	.26	.21	.18	.25	.21	.17	.23	.19	.16	.20	.17	.15
		0.8	.32	.27	.23	.31	.26	.22	.28	.24	.21	.25	.22	.19
		1.0	.38	.33	.29	.36	.32	.28	.33	.29	.26	.29	.26	.23
		1.25	.43	.38	.34	.41	.36	.33	.37	.33	.30	.33	.30	.27
		1.5	.47	.42	.38	.45	.40	.36	.40	.36	.33	.35	.32	.30
		2.0	.53	.48	.44	.50	.46	.42	.44	.41	.38	.39	.36	.34
		2.5	.56	.52	.48	.53	.49	.46	.47	.44	.41	.41	.39	.37
		3.0	.59	.55	.51	.55	.52	.49	.49	.46	.44	.43	.41	.39
		4.0	.62	.58	.55	.58	.55	.53	.52	.49	.47	.45	.43	.42
		5.0	.64	.61	.59	.61	.58	.55	.54	.51	.49	.46	.45	.44
M.F.=.70	SEMI-DIRECT	0.6	.34	.28	.24	.33	.28	.24	.31	.26	.24	.30	.25	.22
		0.8	.42	.36	.32	.40	.35	.31	.38	.33	.30	.36	.32	.29
		1.0	.48	.42	.38	.47	.41	.37	.44	.39	.36	.41	.37	.34
		1.25	.54	.48	.44	.52	.47	.43	.49	.45	.41	.46	.42	.39
		1.5	.58	.53	.48	.56	.51	.47	.53	.49	.45	.49	.46	.43
		2.0	.64	.59	.55	.62	.57	.54	.58	.54	.51	.54	.51	.48
		2.5	.67	.63	.59	.65	.61	.58	.61	.57	.54	.56	.54	.52
		3.0	.70	.66	.62	.68	.64	.61	.63	.60	.57	.58	.56	.54
		4.0	.73	.70	.67	.70	.67	.65	.66	.63	.61	.61	.59	.57
		5.0	.75	.72	.70	.72	.70	.68	.68	.65	.63	.62	.61	.60
M.F.=.65	DIRECT	0.6	.34	.28	.24	.34	.28	.23	.33	.27	.24	.32	.27	.23
		0.8	.43	.36	.31	.42	.36	.31	.41	.35	.31	.40	.35	.31
		1.0	.49	.42	.38	.48	.42	.38	.47	.42	.37	.46	.41	.37
		1.25	.55	.49	.44	.54	.49	.44	.53	.48	.44	.52	.47	.44
		1.5	.60	.54	.49	.59	.53	.49	.57	.52	.48	.56	.52	.48
		2.0	.65	.60	.56	.64	.60	.55	.63	.59	.55	.61	.58	.55
		2.5	.69	.64	.60	.68	.64	.60	.66	.63	.59	.65	.62	.59
		3.0	.72	.67	.64	.71	.67	.63	.69	.66	.63	.67	.65	.62
		4.0	.76	.72	.69	.75	.71	.69	.73	.70	.68	.67	.65	.67
		5.0	.78	.75	.72	.77	.74	.72	.75	.73	.71	.74	.72	.70
M.F.=.70	DIRECT	0.6	.53	.46	.42	.53	.46	.42	.52	.46	.42	.51	.46	.42
		0.8	.64	.57	.52	.63	.57	.52	.62	.56	.52	.61	.56	.52
		1.0	.72	.65	.60	.71	.65	.60	.70	.64	.60	.68	.64	.60
		1.25	.78	.72	.68	.78	.72	.68	.76	.71	.68	.75	.70	.67
		1.5	.83	.77	.73	.82	.77	.73	.81	.76	.72	.80	.76	.72
		2.0	.89	.84	.80	.88	.84	.80	.87	.83	.80	.85	.82	.79
		2.5	.93	.88	.85	.92	.88	.84	.90	.86	.84	.88	.86	.83
		3.0	.95	.92	.88	.94	.91	.88	.92	.90	.87	.91	.88	.86
		4.0	.99	.95	.93	.97	.94	.92	.95	.93	.91	.94	.92	.90
		5.0	1.01	.98	.96	1.00	.97	.95	.98	.96	.94	.96	.94	.92

Fig. 30-7. An abbreviated table of typical utilization factors under varying conditions. (*General Electric Co.*)

using direct lighting, the utilization factor will be 45%. Also assume that the maintenance factor is 70%. Since 70% of 45% is 31½%, use the nearest even number of 30%. Now be arbitrary and say that 300-watt incandescent lamps will be used for lighting. The table on page 211 shows that this lamp produces 6,000 lumens. But you can utilize only 30% of that total, and 30% of 6,000 is 1,800 lumens. If you want 50 footcandles, 1,800/50 gives an answer of about 36; therefore you must provide one 300-watt lamp for every 36 sq ft of floor area, or about 9 watts per sq ft. Such an installation will provide more nearly 70 footcandles when new but only about 50 footcandles after a period of time.

An ordinary 40-watt fluorescent lamp produces about 2,800 lumens; 30% of 2,800 gives us 840 lumens. Since 840/50 gives us about 17, we must provide one 40-watt fluorescent lamp for every 17 sq ft of floor area in this particular room in order to provide a maintained 50-footcandle level of illumination.

Formula for Determining Total Lumens Required. From the known factors it is fairly easy to calculate the lumens required for any particular lighting problem. The formula is

$$\text{Lumens} = \frac{\text{footcandles} \times \text{square feet}}{\text{utilization factor} \times \text{maintenance factor}}$$

Assume that an office 20 ft square, floor area 400 sq ft, is to be lighted to 50 footcandles.

Assume that fluorescent fixtures each with two ordinary 40-watt lamps are to be used. The ceiling will probably be relatively low, so the fixtures will be mounted directly on the ceiling. The walls and ceiling will probably be a light color giving good reflective values. The combination of all these things suggests a utilization factor of 50%. A maintenance factor of 70% may be assumed. The formula above then becomes

$$\text{Lumens} = \frac{50 \times 400}{0.50 \times 0.70} = \frac{20,000}{0.35} = 57,000 \ (\text{approx})$$

A 40-watt fluorescent lamp produces about 2,800 lumens, so you will need 57,000/2,800, or 20 lamps, making a total of 1C two-lamp fixtures.

Using the same formula, it is quite simple to estimate the total lumens required for any given area, with any type of lighting fixture, for any number of footcandles desired.

Comparative Lumen Output of Various Kinds of Lamps. The output of each kind of lamp in lumens per watt has already been outlined in other parts of this chapter in considerable detail. Remember that for fluorescent and mercury lamps the figures given were for lamps after 100 hr of use and were based on the watts of the lamps only, not including the power consumed by ballasts or other auxiliary equipment. A brief comparison of the various types follows:

Incandescent (filament type) .... 14 to 23 lumens
Fluorescent .... 58 to 75 lumens
Mercury .... 50 to 57 lumens

Future Lighting. When you enter a room lighted to 100 footcandles, it will appear well lighted; if you move from there into another room lighted to 500 footcandles, that room will appear very brightly lighted. But if you move from outdoor sunlight into a room lighted to 500 footcandles, this room will *not* appear very bright. As a matter of fact few people (even those who are in the lighting business) moving from sunlight into such a 500-footcandle lighted area will estimate the lighting at more than 200 footcandles.

Since people in general are quite accustomed to outdoor light which ranges from 500 to 10,000 footcandles, it would seem only normal that the trend toward higher and higher footcandle levels of lighting will continue. Who knows what level will be demanded 10 or 20 years from now? But as the demand for a higher level increases, how is the additional light to be provided? There is a limit to the number of lighting fixtures that can be installed in a given area. The answer can only be new light-producing sources. Lamp manufacturers are, of course, working on the problem and have many ideas under development. A few that are now coming out of the confidential stage can be mentioned.

Flat fluorescent panels perhaps a foot square are among these. Instead of round tubes installed in rectangular fixtures, these panels can be used to cover an entire ceiling if desired.

Fluorescent lamps of the usual tubular shape but with *very* much higher output in lumens per foot of length (and probably more lumens per watt) are in sight and should appear on the market in due course of time.

Incandescent (filament-type) lamps of a radically new type

have been on the market only a short time. Ordinary lamps have a tungsten filament enclosed in a glass bulb with a screw-shell base. The new lamps have the tungsten filament enclosed in a short, round quartz tube; glass would melt in the heat concentrated in such a small area. The lamps have clamp-type terminals at each end. A 500-watt lamp of this type is only $\frac{3}{8}$ in. in diameter, only $4\frac{1}{2}$ in. long. Such lamps have much longer life than ordinary lamps, will not blacken in use, and will make small, compact, and lightweight fixtures and other lighting equipment such as floodlights quite practical. The light from such lamps is very intense and concentrated, requiring fixtures so designed that the lamps themselves cannot be seen.

Selection of Lighting System. In choosing the type of lighting fixtures for any job, you will meet an endless variety of fixtures for the purpose. At one extreme is the direct-lighting variety in which all the light is directed downward, with no intention of letting any of it fall on the ceiling. At the other extreme is the indirect-lighting variety in which all the light is directed upward against the ceiling, to be reflected downward. In between are all possible combinations of the two. Which is most suitable for a particular installation? That question has no direct answer; only general principles can be outlined here.

Indirect lighting is possible when ceilings and walls have good and permanent reflecting ability. Sometimes it is used for special lighting effects. Usually the utilization factor is low with indirect lighting, making the operating cost higher than with other methods.

Direct lighting becomes the only choice in any location where ceilings and walls do not have permanently good reflecting power. This includes heavy manufacturing areas, foundries, and similar locations. Direct lighting usually provides the best utilization factors.

Except for locations where only direct lighting may be used, most installations are a combination of direct and indirect. Of the useful light produced, in one installation it may be 90% direct, 10% indirect; in another it may be 10% direct, 90% indirect. A combination is usually considered a logical system. Especially in offices or any other location where close attention to detail is required, a 100% direct-lighting system will prove quite unsatisfactory, for it will lead to uneven lighting including glare, shadows, and a generally cramped feeling. This has led to a trend toward fixtures so designed that, even if the fixture is mounted directly on the ceiling, a generous portion of the light falls on

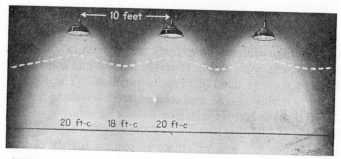

FIG. 30-8. Reflectors properly spaced produce even illumination. (*General Electric Co.*)

the ceiling, to be reflected downward. This produces a pleasing, comfortable, diffused light, which is essential to efficiency.

Location of Reflectors. Especially in direct-lighting installations, the spacing and location of reflectors become very important.

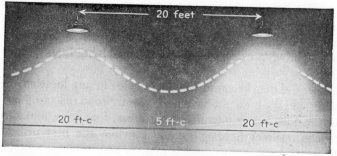

FIG. 30-9. Reflectors improperly spaced produce dark spots. (*General Electric Co.*)

Usually it is sound practice to mount them as far apart as their height above the floor. This results in a reasonably even level of illumination at the work level of tables or benches, as shown in Fig. 30-8. If such reflectors are mounted too far apart, dark areas will result, as shown in Fig. 30-9.

Point-of-work Lighting. It is quite customary to provide additional localized lighting at the point where work of a very exacting nature is performed. This might include inspection stations, watchmakers' benches, toolmakers' work stations, and similar locations. Special reflectors or reflector-type lamps described earlier in this chapter may be used.

The illumination in the concentrated area, however, should not be too great as compared with surrounding areas, for otherwise the contrast will be too great, glare will become a factor, and much of the advantage will be offset.

Lighting of Athletic Fields. The lighting of an athletic field is a bigger project than is usually realized. For example, to light a baseball field in a fashion that is acceptable for major-league contests requires 750 to 1,000 kw of power, and even for semiprofessional games anything under 200 kw would probably not be considered acceptable. It should be interesting to know that Yankee Stadium in New York and Briggs Stadium in Detroit each consumes well over 2,000 kw of lighting power, developing about 200 footcandles of illumination.

For football even a high-school game should have 75 kw as a minimum, while college football requires 150 to 500 kw. Even a tennis court should have a minimum of 8 kw for ordinary playing, and 20 kw or more would be correct for more serious games.

From this it should be apparent that the lighting of athletic fields in general involves problems much greater than those who are only casually interested would ever suspect.

One "trick of the trade" should be borne in mind when considering the lighting of athletic fields or of other areas where the light is needed for relatively few hours per year. As was pointed out in Chap. 14, when a lamp designed for any specific voltage is connected to a circuit delivering a higher voltage, the wattage consumed by the lamp increases to more than is marked on the lamp, the life of the lamp is greatly reduced, but the light output increases rapidly. In other words, when a lamp is burned at a voltage considerably higher than that for which it was designed, the light as measured in lumens *per watt* increases rapidly. Therefore, for maximum light per watt of power consumed, use lamps designed for a voltage considerably below the actual voltage of the circuit.

If the circuit voltage is 10% greater than the rated voltage of the lamp, each lamp will consume about 16% more than its rated watts, but its light output in lumens will increase 35%. The fact that the lamp will last only 200 to 300 hr (instead of the normal 1,000 hr) becomes very unimportant, for that is equivalent to probably a year's usage. Using voltages higher than normal means smaller lamps, smaller reflectors, less expensive supporting towers, all leading to more footcandles of illumination with a given number of dollars to spend on an installation.

Because more and more athletic fields are being lighted each year, one precaution should be noted: Do provide a switching arrangement so that each tower can be separately disconnected. If the power is not disconnected, the servicing of an installation on a tower becomes a dangerous business, especially after rainstorms.

Chapter 31

WIRING FOR MOTORS

Chapter 15 covered the wiring of ordinary types of motors as used in residential and farm applications. This chapter will cover the wiring of commercial and industrial motors in considerable detail, so that the motor when installed will have proper operating characteristics, proper protection, and proper control.

Sections 430-1 to 430-153 of the Code cover all phases of this work. This portion of the Code is decidedly complicated and involved but can be broken down to be relatively simple, although the wiring of motors from a fraction of a horsepower to hundreds of horsepower can never be condensed to a few simple rules.

In studying this chapter, you can make it easier for yourself if you will think in terms of a particular motor as you read the chapter; then think of a much larger or much smaller motor, or a different type, as you read it again.

This chapter does not pretend to cover every last detail defined in the Code. Rather it is intended to pertain to the more ordinary installations, which should include a very large proportion of motors being installed. Only installations operating at 600 volts or less will be discussed.

Sealed (Hermetic-type) Refrigeration Motors. Motors of this kind must be treated differently from ordinary motors. They will be discussed in a separate section toward the end of this chapter.

Switches. Various types of switches will be mentioned here as in the Code. A good understanding of these various types is essential; study the following definitions, which are quoted from the Code:

497

General-use Switch. A switch intended for use as a switch in general distribution and branch circuits. It is *rated in amperes* and is capable of interrupting its rated current at its rated voltage.

Motor-circuit Switch. A switch, *rated in horsepower,* capable of interrupting the maximum operating overload current of a motor of the same horsepower rating as the switch at the rated voltage.

Isolating Switch. A switch intended for isolating a circuit from its source of power. It has no interrupting rating and is intended to be operated only after the circuit has been opened by some other means.

Circuit Breaker. A device designed to open under abnormal conditions a current-carrying circuit without injury to itself. The term as used in this Code applies only to the automatic type designed to trip on a predetermined overload of current.

Motor Branch Circuit. The elements that make up a motor branch circuit are as follows:

A. Motor-branch-circuit conductors—the wires from the panel-board to the motor.

B. Motor-branch-circuit overcurrent protection—to protect the wires, the controls, and the motor against overloads *due to short circuits and grounds only.*

C. Disconnecting means—totally to isolate the motor and its controls when necessary to work on the motor or its controls or the driven machinery.

D. Motor-running overcurrent protection—to protect the motor, the overcurrent device itself, and the wires against damage caused by overloads *other than short circuits or grounds.* Such devices are *not* capable of opening short-circuit currents.

E. Controller—to start and stop the motor, or reverse it, possibly control its speed, etc.

Figure 31-1 shows all the elements involved. In practice several of these elements often are combined into a single device; these cases will be considered one at a time. The first part of this chapter will cover these elements under the simplest possible conditions: one motor, and nothing except that motor, on a branch circuit. Many of the answers can be found in Code Table 430-146 (see Appendix). Nevertheless it will be well to discuss the various factors so that they may be understood rather than learned by rule of thumb.

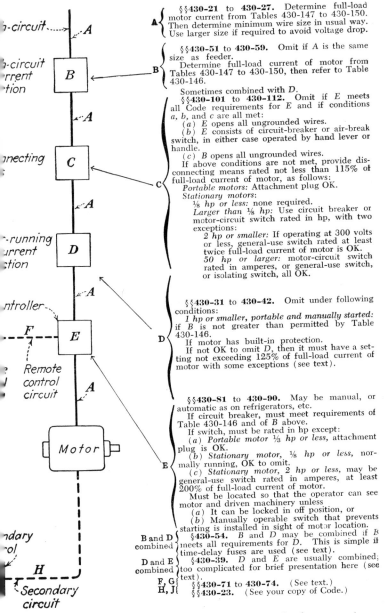

ग-circuit ⟶ *A*

ग-circuit
rrent
tion
B

A

gnecting
C

A

-running
urrent
ttion
D

A

ntroller
F
E

Remote
control
circuit
A

Motor

ndary
ol

H

Secondary
circuit

A ⟨ §§**430-21** to **430-27**. Determine full-load motor current from Tables 430-147 to 430-150. Then determine minimum wire size in usual way. Use larger size if required to avoid voltage drop.

B ⟨ §§**430-51** to **430-59**. Omit if A is the same size as feeder. Determine full-load current of motor from Tables 430-147 to 430-150, then refer to Table 430-146. Sometimes combined with D.

C ⟨ §§**430-101** to **430-112**. Omit if E meets all Code requirements for E and if conditions a, b, and c are all met:
(a) E opens all ungrounded wires.
(b) E consists of circuit-breaker or air-break switch, in either case operated by hand lever or handle.
(c) B opens all ungrounded wires.
If above conditions are not met, provide disconnecting means rated not less than 115% of full-load current of motor, as follows:
Portable motors: Attachment plug OK.
Stationary motors:
⅛ hp or less: none required.
Larger than ⅛ hp: Use circuit breaker or motor-circuit switch rated in hp, with two exceptions:
2 hp or smaller: If operating at 300 volts or less, general-use switch rated at least twice full-load current of motor is OK.
50 hp or larger: motor-circuit switch rated in amperes, or general-use switch, or isolating switch, all OK.

D ⟨ §§**430-31** to **430-42**. Omit under following conditions:
1 hp or smaller, portable and manually started: if B is not greater than permitted by Table 430-146.
If motor has built-in protection.
If not OK to omit D, then it must have a setting not exceeding 125% of full-load current of motor with some exceptions (see text).

E ⟨ §§**430-81** to **430-90**. May be manual, or automatic as on refrigerators, etc.
If circuit breaker, must meet requirements of Table 430-146 and of B above.
If switch, must be rated in hp except:
(a) Portable motor ⅓ hp or less, attachment plug is OK.
(b) Stationary motor, ⅛ hp or less, normally running, OK to omit.
(c) Stationary motor, 2 hp or less, may be general-use switch rated in amperes, at least 200% of full-load current of motor.
Must be located so that the operator can see motor and driven machinery unless
(a) It can be locked in off position, or
(b) Manually operable switch that prevents starting is installed in sight of motor location.

B and D combined ⟨ §**430-54**. B and D may be combined if B meets all requirements for D. This is simple if time-delay fuses are used (see text).

D and E combined ⟨ §**430-39**. D and E are usually combined; too complicated for brief presentation here (see text).

F, G ⟨ §§**430-71** to **430-74**. (See text.)
H, J ⟨ §**430-23**. (See your copy of Code.)

ग. 31-1. Elements of a motor branch circuit; the details shown are in abbreviated form.

Motor Current. The amperage consumed by a motor varies greatly with the circumstances. In most motors it is very high while starting, drops to a normal value as the motor reaches full speed, but increases if the motor is overloaded. That introduces many problems in overcurrent protection. It will be wise to review this topic.

Full-load Current. This is the amperage consumed by the motor while it is delivering its rated horsepower. It is also the amperage stamped on its name-plate. However, when a motor installation is planned, the motor itself usually has not yet been obtained. Therefore consult Code Tables 430-147 to 430-150 which specify the amperage to be used in calculations, for different kinds of motors at various voltages. The table pertaining to the more ordinary kinds of motors will be found in the Appendix of this book.

Overload Current. As already discussed in Chap. 15, a motor should not be installed with the expectation that it will deliver more than its rated horsepower *continuously*. But when called upon to do so, the motor will deliver much more than its rated horsepower but will consume an increased amperage. If that higher amperage is permitted to flow indefinitely, in other words if the motor is overloaded continuously, it will overheat, thus reducing the life of the insulation. If the overload is large enough, the motor will burn out. The purpose of what the Code calls "motor-running overcurrent protection" is to disconnect the motor from the line if the overload continues long enough to damage the motor.

Starting Current. When a motor is first connected to the line, the amperage consumed is very much higher than after the motor comes up to speed. The ratio of starting current to running current varies greatly with the size and type of motor and may be as high as 600%. An ordinary washing-machine motor consuming only 5 amp while running at full load may require as much as 30 amp for a second or two when first started. For larger motors the ratio is usually much lower, but the starting current nevertheless is always higher than the running current.

Any AC motor of ½ hp or more manufactured since 1940 carries on its name-plate a "Code letter" that indicates the approximate number of kilovolt-amperes consumed *per horsepower* with the motor in a locked-rotor condition. Locked-rotor means that the motor is locked so that the rotor cannot turn. Of course, a motor is never operated that way, but when a motor is first connected to the power line, it is not turning, so that locked-rotor condition does exist until the motor starts to turn. The amperage consumed by the motor until it starts to turn is very high. Then the amperage drops off until the motor reaches full speed, at which time normal amperage is established. From the Code letter you can determine the maximum amperage required by a motor while starting, which is useful information in establishing the size of the various components in a motor circuit. The table in Code Sec. 430-7(b) covering the Code letters is as follows:

Code letter	Kilovolt-amperes per horsepower with locked rotor	Code letter	Kilovolt-amperes per horsepower with locked rotor
A	Under 3.14	L	9.00 to 9.99
B	3.15 to 3.54	M	10.00 to 11.19
C	3.55 to 3.99	N	11.20 to 12.49
D	4.00 to 4.49	P	12.50 to 13.99
E	4.50 to 4.99	R	14.00 to 15.99
F	5.00 to 5.59	S	16.00 to 17.99
G	5.60 to 6.29	T	18.00 to 19.99
H	6.30 to 7.00	U	20.00 to 22.39
J	7.10 to 7.99	V	22.4 and up
K	8.00 to 8.99		

Generally speaking, the larger the motor, the lower the locked-rotor current per horsepower. For example, in general-purpose 60-cycle 1,800 rpm 3-phase motors, the 1-hp size in most brands has a Code letter L; the 2-hp has K; the 5-hp has H; the 7½- and 10-hp have G; 15- to 100-hp have F. Single-phase capacitor motors range from L in the case of ½-hp size to E, F, or G on the 5-hp size. Single-phase repulsion-start induction-run motors range from H on the ½- and 1-hp sizes to E on the 5-hp size.

To establish the approximate maximum amperes required by a specific motor while starting, first determine the actual Code letter on the name-plate of the motor; assume that it is J and that the motor is 3 hp. Refer to the table and you will find that J

shows from 7.10 to 7.99 kva per horsepower. Call the average
7.55 kva, or 7,550 volt-amp. For 3 hp the total is 7,550 × 3 or
22,650 volt-amp. If the motor is single-phase, divide by the
voltage. This (22,650/230) produces a result of about 98 amp.
In other words as the motor is first thrown on the line, there is a
momentary inrush of about 98 amp, diminishing gradually to
about 17 amp (Table 430-148) when the motor is running at full
speed and delivering its rated 3 hp.

If the motor is a 3-phase motor, first multiply the volts by 1.73
(see Chap. 3); in the case of a 230-volt motor, the result is 397.9.
Use the number 400, which is easy to remember. Then divide
22,650 by 400, giving about 57 amp, which is the inrush when the
motor is first turned on, diminishing to about 9 amp when the
motor reaches full speed.

MOTOR-BRANCH-CIRCUIT WIRES
(Code Secs. 430-21 to 430-27)

Must Carry 125% of Running Current. The Code in Sec.
430-22 specifies that these wires must have a carrying capacity of
at least 125% of the full-load current of the motor, as set forth in
Code Tables 430-147 to 430-150. There are a number of exceptions when the wire must be larger and a few where it may be
smaller. The exceptions pertain to types of motors that are not
very common and for that reason will not be discussed here,
especially since Code Sec. 430-22 quite clearly defines the exceptions.

Voltage Drop. The Code specifies only the *minimum* size
wires that may be used in a motor circuit. It does not take into
consideration the voltage drop that always occurs. Measure or
figure the distance from the motor back to the panelboard, measured along the wire; then calculate the voltage drop for the
minimum size wire (how to do this was covered in Chap. 7), and
if it exceeds 2½% of the voltage at which the motor operates, use
larger wire. Remember, if the voltage drop as calculated is 5%, in
order to reduce it to 2½%, wire with double the cross-sectional
area (twice the circular mils) must be used. It is not ordinarily
considered good practice to permit voltage drop greater than
2½%, for this simply means that a substantial percentage of the

power paid for is wasted, which may mean a considerable sum during the life of the motor. Too great voltage drop also means the motor will not develop full power, start heavy loads, or accelerate so rapidly as under full voltage. Remember that there is additional voltage drop ahead of the panelboard.

MOTOR-BRANCH-CIRCUIT OVERCURRENT PROTECTION
(Code Secs. 430-51 to 430-59)

This branch-circuit overcurrent protection is necessary to protect the wires of the circuit against overloads greater than the starting amperage, in other words, against short circuits and grounds. At the same time, it protects the motor controller, which ordinarily is designed to handle only the amperage consumed by the motor and which would be damaged by a short circuit or ground if branch-circuit protection were not separately provided. Grounds are often practically equivalent to short circuits.

As in other branch circuits, the protection in a motor branch circuit may take the form of either fuses or circuit breakers. The maximum amperage rating permitted by Code for the overcurrent device in a *motor* branch circuit is higher when fuses are used than when circuit breakers are used.

Maximum Rating. First refer to Code Tables 430-147 to 430-150 in the Appendix to determine the full-load current of the motor in question. Then refer to Table 430-146, columns 4, 5, 6, or 7 (see Appendix). This will give you the *maximum* rating of the fuse or circuit breaker. However, if an overcurrent device of this maximum rating will not carry the starting current of the motor, the rating may be increased up to 400% of the full-load current of the motor.

An alternate approach is to refer to Tables 430-147 to 430-150 as before, then refer to Table 430-152 if the motor is marked with a Code letter and to Table 430-153 if not so marked. (These two tables will be found in your copy of the Code.) One of these two tables, whichever applies in your particular case, will then give you a percentage that is to be applied to the full-load current rating of the motor to arrive at the maximum rating of the fuse or circuit breaker. If the answer comes out to a nonstandard rating, use the next larger standard rating. Actually using this method is "the long way around," and the use of Table 430-146 is the usual method.

If a circuit breaker is used, per Sec. 430-57, it must be rated *at least* 115% of the full-load motor current, and the maximum permissible rating can be determined from the Code, as already outlined.

Since Sec. 430-22 requires that the motor-branch-circuit wires must have a carrying capacity of *at least* 125% *of the motor* full-load current, and since Sec. 430-52 permits overcurrent protection in some cases up to 400% of the motor full-load current, it is evident that the branch-circuit overcurrent protection may be as much as 400/125, or 320% of the carrying capacity of the wire. This is contrary to general practice; hence it should be well understood that this is permitted only in the case of wires serving motors.

All the foregoing has reference to the maximum setting permitted for the overcurrent device. In practice it should be set as low as possible and still carry the maximum current required by the motor while starting or running. However, Sec. 430-56 requires that when fuses are used, the fuseholder must be capable of holding the *largest* fuse permitted by Table 430-146. Occasionally this will necessitate using an adapter to permit, for example, 60-amp fuses to be used in fuseholders designed for the larger 70- to 100-amp fuses. However, if time-delay fuses are used, this requirement is waived.

Motor-branch-circuit Overcurrent Device Omitted. If branch-circuit wires are the same size as the feeder, all the way up to the motor-running overcurrent device, the branch-circuit overcurrent device may be omitted entirely. Obviously the branch-circuit wires are protected by the feeder overcurrent protection. It would be more correct to say that there is no feeder and that what was considered the feeder becomes the motor branch circuit.

Motor-feeder Overcurrent Protection. Before discussing this topic, which is covered by Secs. 430-61 to 430-63 of the Code, it is important to understand just what a feeder is. The Code defines feeders as "any conductors of a wiring system between the service equipment, or the generator switchboard of an isolated plant, and the branch-circuit overcurrent device." The overcurrent device used to protect the motor for *running protection,* which will be covered later in this chapter, is not the overcurrent device referred to; the feeder ends at the *branch-circuit* overcurrent device.

In large installations the requirements for power are usually such that each individual branch circuit cannot possibly be run back to a common point at the service entrance. Instead, there are feeders to panelboards at various locations, and the individual branch circuits start from these panelboards.

The feeders are subject to certain requirements as covered in the Code. These requirements are simple. A feeder that supplies only one motor and nothing else must be provided with overcurrent protection no greater than that calculated as just outlined for the motor-branch-circuit protection.

If the feeder serves the one motor in addition to supplying power for lighting or appliances, add the amperage required for lighting or appliances to the maximum amperage permitted for the branch-circuit protection of the motor only; this is, then, the maximum setting of the feeder overcurrent device.

Feeder Taps in Inaccessible Locations. At times it is necessary to tap the motor-branch-circuit wires to a feeder at a location not readily accessible. To locate the branch-circuit overcurrent protective device at such a point would render it equally inaccessible, which would be impractical. The simplest way of getting around this difficulty is to make the branch-circuit wires of the same size as the feeder, up to a convenient location, where the overcurrent device is then located. Obviously no overcurrent protection is then required at the point of the tap; beyond the overcurrent device wherever located, up to the motor, the size wire to be used is determined in the usual way.

If the distance between the tap and the location of the overcurrent device is not over 25 ft, and if the wires are protected against mechanical injury, then the Code in Sec. 430-58 permits wires to be used which are smaller than the feeder, but they must have a carrying capacity in amperes at least one-third that of the feeder; obviously they must be no smaller than the minimum required for the motor branch circuit in question.

DISCONNECTING MEANS, RUNNING OVERCURRENT PROTECTION, AND CONTROLLER

These three components in a motor circuit may be three separate devices, but more often two are combined into a single device, and sometimes all three are combined into a single device. In some cases one or more of the components may be omitted. We shall first discuss the requirements of each component separately, as if each were a separate device; this will automatically lead to a discussion of how some of the components can be combined with others. Later we shall discuss other situations that permit such combining.

"Out of Sight. . . ." The Code in many cases requires that the motor may not be out of sight of the controller and the controller in turn may not be out of sight of the disconnecting means. These statements are self-explanatory, but do note that a distance of 50 ft or more means "out of sight" regardless of circumstances.

DISCONNECTING MEANS
(Code Secs. 430-101 to 430-112)

The purpose of the disconnecting means is totally to isolate the motor and its controller, when, for example, it is necessary to work on the motor, the controller, or the machinery driven by the motor.

Requirements for Disconnecting Means. The Code requires that the disconnecting means must have a capacity of at least 115% of the running current of the motor. It must plainly indicate whether it is in the open or closed position. It must be located within sight of the controller unless it can be locked in the off position. It must open all the ungrounded wires simultaneously (it may also open a grounded wire provided it opens all the ungrounded wires at the same time). It must disconnect the motor and the controller; it may be in the same case with the controller.

The disconnecting means must be a manually operated switch *rated in horsepower* or a circuit breaker, with the following exceptions:

1. For stationary motors of ⅛ hp or less, the branch-circuit overcurrent device is sufficient, no separate disconnecting means being required.

2. For stationary motors of 2 hp or less and 300 volts or less, a general-use switch, *rated only in amperes,* may be used if it has an amperage rating at least *twice* the full-load current rating of the motor.

3. For stationary motors of more than 50 hp, a motor-circuit switch rated also in amperes, a general-use switch, or an isolating switch may be used.

4. For portable motors, the attachment plug and receptacle are sufficient.

Types of Disconnecting Means. Any kind of circuit breaker may be used. If a switch is used, it may be the general type shown in Fig. 31-2; similar but larger switches are suitable for larger motors. These switches do not need to be fused. However, if properly fused, they may also serve as the running overcurrent protection under conditions that will be outlined later. Sometimes the switch will also serve as a controller as will also be discussed later.

FIG. 31-2. This switch may be used as the disconnecting means for small motors. Larger motors require larger switches. (*Clark Controller Co.*)

Service Switch as Disconnecting Means. In the rare instance when an installation consists of a single motor and nothing else, the service switch, per Code Sec. 430-106, serves as the disconnecting means, provided that it is within sight of the controller and can be locked in the open position.

MOTOR-RUNNING OVERCURRENT PROTECTION
(Code Secs. 430-31 to 430-43)

Need for Running Protection. A motor that requires, for example, 10 amp while delivering its rated horsepower may require

as much as 40 amp while starting.   Once the motor has come up
to speed, there will probably be times when the machine which
the motor drives will require more power than the rated horsepower of the motor; the motor may be entirely capable of delivering more horsepower for a nominal period of time, consuming a
correspondingly greater amperage while doing so.   Under overload this motor usually drawing 10 amp may require 15 amp, or
more.   If permitted to draw 15 amp continuously, the motor will
probably be damaged.

So far in this discussion only the motor-branch-circuit overcurrent device has been under consideration, and that may under
certain conditions be rated as high as 400% of the full-load current,
or 40 amp in this case.   Obviously a 40-amp overcurrent device
will protect the 10-amp motor against short circuits and grounds,
but it will in no way protect the motor against an overload which
makes the motor consume 15 instead of 10 amp.

Therefore the Code requires (in addition to the motor-branch-
circuit overcurrent protection) a separate overcurrent device that
protects the motor against nominal increase in amperage, which
if continued long enough will damage the motor.

Types of Running Overcurrent Devices.   The motor-running
overcurrent device may consist of fuses.   The fuses must carry
the starting current for a short period, must carry the normal running current indefinitely, but must blow if an overload current
occurs and is maintained long enough to damage the motor.
Ordinary fuses will seldom serve the purpose, but time-delay fuses
are suitable for most purposes.

A circuit breaker may be used in place of fuses and serves the
purpose in approximately the same way as time-delay fuses.

Quite often the motor-running overcurrent protection is combined with the controller in a single device which most people
simply call a motor starter.   The overcurrent portion of the
starter can be called an overcurrent *device*; the device contains
one or more overcurrent *units*.   For example, a 3-phase starter
may have two or three contacts to close the circuits in as many
wires when the motor is started.   It will also contain two or more
overcurrent *units*, each in a separate wire, although the device
collectively is only one overcurrent *device*.   However, no matter
if only one overcurrent *unit* operates, due to an overcurrent, it

will by virtue of the mechanical design open all the contacts of the starter, stopping the motor. The operating principle will be discussed later in this chapter.

The Code requirements as to the number of overcurrent *units* and their location in the several wires running up to a motor can be found in Sec. 430-37 of your copy of the Code. The requirements of this table are of more interest to manufacturers of motor protective and control devices than to the general public. Approved devices will have proper construction.

"Continuous Duty." The Code in Sec. 430-33 defines this as follows: "Any motor is considered to be for continuous duty unless the nature of the apparatus which it drives is such that the motor cannot operate continuously *with load* under any condition of use." That seems to leave some room for debate as to when a motor is *not* continuous duty. One might argue that a motor on a home water system with an automatic controller that stops the motor when the pressure in the water tank reaches its proper value is not a continuous-duty type. However, if a sprinkler is left on accidentally for a day, the motor will probably run continuously. If in doubt, protect the motor as specified for a continuous-duty type.

Continuous-duty Motors. The motor-running overcurrent device required is defined in Code Secs. 430-31 to 430-43 and depends on many factors, as follows:

More than 1 *hp.* Whether manually started or automatically, as on refrigerators, water pumps, etc., the overcurrent device must be rated at not over 125% of the full-load current of the motor if the motor is of the ordinary type designed for a temperature rise not exceeding 40°C. If it is of a different type, the maximum rating is 115%. However, if applying the 125% factor results in an odd amperage rating for which there is no standard overcurrent device, the next higher standard rating may be used provided that it is not more than 140% of the full-load current of the motor. For those motors where the normal maximum is 115%, the next higher standard rating not exceeding 130% of the full-load current of the motor may be used.

Some motors have inherent overcurrent protection. This is a built-in device, a component part of the motor which operates not only by the heat created by the current flowing through it but usually also by heat conducted to it from the frame and windings of the motor. If the motor is already hot from operating for a long time at full load, then the device will disconnect the motor more quickly when an overload arises than if the motor started cold and immediately overloaded to the same degree. In this respect such built-in devices as "Thermotrons" and "Thermoguards" provide better protection than separate devices.

One horsepower or less, portable, *manually started.* If the motor is out of sight of the starter location, it must be protected as will be explained below for *automatically* started motors. If, however, it is in sight from the starter location, the branch-circuit overcurrent protection is considered adequate if it does not exceed the value shown in Table 430-146. However, it is permissible to operate any motor at 125 volts or less on any branch circuit protected by 20-amp overcurrent protection.

One horsepower or less, not portable, *manually started.* Protect such motors in the way described in the next paragraph for automatically started motors.

One horsepower or less, automatically started. For protecting such motors, a choice of several methods is available, as follows:

1. A separate overcurrent device rated at not over 125% of the full-load current for 40°C motors, 115% for all other motors. If this results in a nonstandard amperage, use the next higher standard provided that it does not exceed 140% of the full-load current where 125% is the normal limit or 130% where 115% is the normal limit.

2. Inherent overcurrent protection. This has already been discussed in connection with motors over 1 hp.

3. The motor shall be considered as being properly protected where it is part of an approved assembly which does not normally subject the motor to overloads and which is also equipped with other safety controls (such as the safety combustion controls of a domestic oil burner) which protect the motor against damage due to stalled-rotor current. Where such protective equipment is used, it shall be indicated on the name-plate of the assembly where it will be visible after installation.

4. Motors of the general type of clock motors are not harmed if they do not start and are considered protected by the branch-circuit overcurrent device.

MOTOR CONTROLLERS
(Code Secs. 430-81 to 430-90)

A motor controller according to Code definition is "any switch or device normally used to start and stop the motor." The controller may be a manually operable device, or it may be an automatic device as found on refrigerators, oil burners, and similar appliances.

Requirements for Controllers. In general the controller "shall be capable of starting and stopping the motor which it controls, and for an alternating-current motor shall be capable of interrupting the stalled-rotor current of the motor." These basic requirements are of chief interest to manufacturers. Users and contractors will find that approved controllers furnished by manufacturers will automatically meet these requirements if the proper selection is made by the user. Nevertheless it will be well to be familiar with them.

The Code requirements for controllers are as follows:

The controller shall have a horsepower rating which shall not be lower than the horsepower rating of the motor, except as follows:

1. Stationary motor of $\frac{1}{8}$ hp or less: For a stationary motor rated at $\frac{1}{8}$ hp or less that is normally left running and is so constructed that it cannot be damaged by overload or failure to start, such as clock motors and the like, the branch-circuit overcurrent device may serve as the controller.

2. Portable motor of $\frac{1}{3}$ hp or less: For a portable motor rated at $\frac{1}{3}$ hp or less, the controller may be an attachment plug and receptacle.

3. Stationary motor of 2 hp or less: For a stationary motor rated at 2 hp or less, and 300 volts or less, the controller *may* be a general-use switch having an ampere rating at least twice the full-load current rating of the motor.

4. Circuit breaker as controller: A branch-circuit circuit breaker, rated in amperes only, may be used as a controller. When this circuit breaker is also used for running overcurrent protection, it shall conform to the appropriate provisions of this article governing overcurrent protection.

The controller need open only enough conductors to start and stop the motor. If, however, it serves also as the disconnecting means as will be discussed shortly, then it must meet certain other requirements. In this connection note that it is permissible that the grounded wire be opened by the controller provided only that the device is so constructed that all the ungrounded wires are opened simultaneously with the grounded wire.

In general the controller must be located so that the motor and its driven machinery shall be within sight of the point from which the motor is controlled unless *one* of the following points is complied with:

1. The controller or its disconnecting means is capable of being locked in the open position.

2. A manually operable switch, which shall prevent the starting of the motor, is placed within sight of the motor location. Obviously this provision is included to make it safe to work on the motor or its driven machinery without the danger of having the motor started from some remote point by some person who does not know that the motor or its machinery is being worked on. This switch may be directly in the motor circuit or it may be a very simple toggle switch such as is used for lighting purposes, in the remote-control circuit of the motor, in a wire to the push-button starting station controlling the motor.

3. Special permission is given by the inspector.

How Motor Starter Operates. A typical controller or starter is shown in Fig. 31-3. Note the push buttons in the cover to start and stop the motor. Such controllers usually have the motor-running overcurrent protection built into them.

Fig. 31-3. A typical motor starter. It serves the purpose of both controller and running overcurrent protection. (*Allen-Bradley Co.*)

Careful study of the wiring diagram shown in Fig. 31-4 will show the principle of operation, both as a controller and as a motor-running overcurrent device. The diagram is for a 3-phase motor. The wires shown as heavy lines carry the full motor current; the light lines represent small wires carrying only a very small current flowing through the start-stop buttons. Note the difference between the two buttons: The start button is a normally-open type, and pushing the button *closes* a circuit; the stop button is of the normally-closed type, and pushing the button *opens* a circuit.

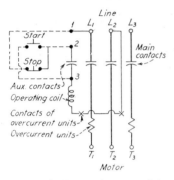

Fig. 31-4. Circuit diagram of the starter shown in Fig. 31-3.

The starter is an electrically operated switch. When the operating coil is energized, it closes the three main contacts and starts the motor. It also closes a small auxiliary contact at the same time. In the diagram the operating coil is not energized and the motor is not running. Study the circuit and you will see that pushing the start button lets current flow through the operating coil, which energizes it; it then closes all four contacts. That starts the motor, and as you remove your finger from the start button, the circuit opens but the coil remains energized because the circuit to the coil, at first energized by current flowing through the start button, now remains energized by current flowing through the auxiliary contacts. Do note that the current that energizes the coil at all times flows through the stop button, which is normally closed.

When the time comes to stop the motor, push the stop button; this interrupts the current flowing through the coil, deenergizing it, and all contacts open, stopping the motor. When the motor has stopped, remove your finger from the stop button; the motor is then ready for the next start.

Should the voltage fail or drop to a very low value while the motor is running, the coil will not have enough power to keep the contacts closed. The contactor will "drop out," stopping the motor, just as if the stop button had been pushed. This is a safety feature, for a motor running at greatly reduced voltage will probably burn out.

Now consider the motor-running overcurrent protection built

into the starter. The starter incorporates several overcurrent units already discussed; the number required varies, but in this particular case two are used, as shown in the diagram. These overcurrent units carry the full amperage of the motor and are basically heating elements. Near each of these overcurrent units is a small, normally closed contact sensitive to heat. These contacts are in series with the coil. While the motor is consuming only its normal amperage, the heat developed in the overcurrent units is not enough to trip these contacts, but when the motor for any reason consumes more than its normal amperage, the heat in the overcurrent unit makes the contact near it open. The contact is in series with the coil, so when the contact opens, it is the same as pushing the stop button, and the motor stops.

The starter may have two or three overcurrent units, but all of them are in series with the coil. No matter which one opens, it stops the motor. Note that when the motor stops because of overload, it cannot be started again until the contacts are manually closed by pushing a "reset" button in the cover of the starter.

COMBINING SEVERAL COMPONENTS OF MOTOR BRANCH CIRCUIT

In order to combine several components or omit one or more components, specific Code requirements must be met. If these cases have not already been discussed in the several sections concerning individual components, they will be discussed here.

Disconnecting Means Omitted. All permissible cases have already been discussed.

Running Overcurrent Protection Omitted. In addition to the cases already discussed, it is permissible, per Sec. 430-31(b) of the Code, to omit it "where it might introduce additional or increased hazards as in the case of fire pumps."

Controller Omitted. All permissible cases have already been discussed.

Branch-circuit and Running Overcurrent Protection Combined. As already discussed, the branch-circuit overcurrent protection *may* have an ampere rating several times as great as that of the running overcurrent protection. It is, however, required that its ampere rating be as low as possible. Some motors start so readily that their starting current is not greatly in excess of the running current. In that case, per Sec. 430-54, if the branch-circuit over-current protection has an amperage *not higher than* that permitted for the running overcurrent protection, the running over-current protection may be omitted. In practice this means that a circuit breaker or time-delay fuses must be used for the motor-branch-circuit overcurrent protection; ordinary fuses will not serve the purpose.

Running Overcurrent Protection and Controller Combined. If the conventional type of motor starter shown in Fig. 31-3 is used, you will find that most of them combine the functions of controller and running overcurrent protection. If a fused switch of the general type shown in Fig. 31-2 is used as a controller, and if the fuses are of the time-delay type with an ampere rating not greater than permitted for running overcurrent protection, then per Sec. 430-90 the switch serves the purpose of controller and running overcurrent protection.

Disconnect, Running Overcurrent Protection, and Controller Combined. The switch discussed in the preceding paragraph will, per Sec. 430-111, serve the purpose of all three components provided it opens all ungrounded conductors. A circuit breaker of an amperage rating not exceeding that permitted for the running overcurrent protection and opening all ungrounded conductors will also serve the same purpose. In each case the switch or breaker must be of a type operated by applying the hand to a handle, and in each case the branch-circuit overcurrent protection must open all ungrounded conductors in the circuit. Fuses are acceptable for the purpose.

Branch-circuit Overcurrent Protection and Controller Combined. Per Sec. 430-83 (Exception No. 2) when a circuit breaker is used as the motor-branch-circuit overcurrent protection, it may also be used as the controller for the motor.

Branch-circuit Overcurrent Protection, Running Overcurrent Protection, and Controller Combined. If the circuit breaker just discussed has an ampere rating not greater than permitted for separate running overcurrent protection, it will serve the purpose of all three components.

Disconnect and Controller Combined. If the controller takes the form of a motor starter of the general type of Fig. 31-3 (which then usually includes the running overcurrent protection), the disconnecting means, which may be a circuit breaker or a switch, is often installed in the same cabinet with the controller. This, then, is not really a case of combining several components in the sense of having one serve the purpose of the other, but rather a case of locating several separate components in a single enclosure.

REMOTE-CONTROL CIRCUITS
(Code Secs. 430-71 to 430-74)

Often a motor must be started and stopped from a point some distance from the motor. You can locate the controller at that point, run the motor wires first to the controller, then to the motor. If the controller is a hand-operated switch, or a starter of the type shown in Fig. 31-3 with push buttons in the cover, there is no choice.

If the controller must be located at some distance from the motor, this leads to extra cost of running heavy wires farther than in a direct line to the motor. Because of that fact the controller is often of the remote-control type. A remote-control starter is the same device shown in Figs. 31-3 and 31-4 except that the start and stop buttons, instead of being installed on the cover of the starter, are located at a distance. A typical start-stop station is shown in Fig. 31-5. Then the wires carrying the full motor

Fig. 31-5. Push buttons for starters can be located wherever convenient. (*Allen-Bradley Co.*)

current run directly to the starter located near the motor, and then to the motor. Only small wires run from the starter to the start-stop push-button stations, which may be located any distance from the starter. These wires carry only a few amperes even in the case of a very large motor. This method saves much material and labor, adds greatly to convenience, and is commonly used.

The wiring from the control station to the controller proper is known as "remote-control wiring" and is covered by Code Secs. 430-71 to 430-74. Overcurrent protection for them is subject to the following conditions:

1. No overcurrent protection is necessary provided that the setting of the branch-circuit overcurrent device in the circuit serving the motor in question is not over 500% of the carrying capacity, per Table 310-12, of the wires connecting the push-button control station with the controller proper.

2. No overcurrent protection is necessary if the controller device and the point of control (start and stop buttons, pressure switch, thermostatic switch, etc.) are both located on the same machine and the control circuit does not extend beyond the machine.

3. No overcurrent protection is necessary if the opening of the control circuit would create a hazard, as, for example, the control circuit of a fire-pump motor.

4. In the absence of any of the above three points, protect the wires of the control circuit with overcurrent devices rated at not over 500% of their carrying capacity per Table 310-12. The overcurrent device, however, must *not* be of the time-delay type (Sec. 430-72).

If damage to the remote-control circuit would constitute a hazard, the wires of the remote-control circuit must be installed in conduit or otherwise suitably protected against mechanical injury.

The control device must be so wired that it is disconnected automatically whenever the motor is disconnected by the disconnecting means as defined in the Code and as covered in a previous portion of this chapter.

MISCELLANEOUS

Protection of Live Parts. Most motors in common use and built today do not have exposed live parts. Some motors constructed years ago and still in use may have exposed live parts. If there are such parts, then the motor must be guarded against accidental contact by a guardrail or some similar device.

Grounding.   Controller cases must always be grounded unless attached to portable motors.   The frames of the motors themselves must be grounded if they operate at a voltage in excess of 150 volts to ground,[1] if in a hazardous location, or if in a continuously wet place.   If the wires to the motor are inside armor, conduit, or other metallic raceways, then the motor must also be grounded, but the armor or conduit itself serves as the ground. It is doubly necessary that all joints in the armor or conduit be particularly secure mechanically in order to provide a good ground.   Where wiring is by a different scheme, ground the motor as directed in Chap. 9.   It is good practice to ground the frames of all motors, whether required or not.

Portable motors must be grounded if they operate at voltage in excess of 150 volts to ground.   The simplest way is to use an extra conductor in the cord serving the motor, this extra conductor in turn contacting a terminal in the receptacle to which the grounded supply wire is connected.

SEALED (HERMETIC-TYPE) REFRIGERATION COMPRESSOR MOTORS

Motors of the ordinary type are cooled by radiating the heat that develops during operation, into the surrounding air of the area in which they operate. Motors which the Code calls "sealed (hermetic-type) refrigeration compressor motors" are closely coupled to the compressor and sealed in a common case with the compressor (see Fig. 31-6). The refrigerant in the case is in a gaseous state, and that motor runs in that refrigerant. As the refrigerant comes into the compressor, it is at a temperature *below* room temperature and, of course, cools the motor.

Because of that unusually efficient cooling, a relatively small motor can consume more amperes (and deliver more horsepower) than an ordinary motor of the same physical size, cooled in the usual way. But when such a motor is started after a period of idleness, the refrigerant is at room temperature and provides relatively poor cooling; the motor then heats up faster

---

[1] In the case of a 230-volt single-phase motor connected to the outside two wires of a 3-wire system, with a grounded neutral, the voltage to ground is not 230 but 115 volts.

than an ordinary motor of the same physical size. For that reason, overcurrent protection on hermetic motors must be somewhat different from that on ordinary motors if full protection is to be expected.

Hermetic motors are used specifically on compressors of refrigeration units, including those used for air conditioning.

On an ordinary motor, the name-plate shows the horsepower of the motor, also the number of amperes it consumes while delivering that horsepower. On a hermetic-type motor the name-plate does not show a horsepower rating at all. It shows two

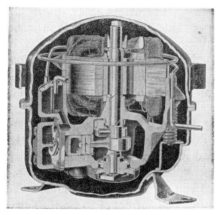

Fig. 31-6. A typical hermetic-type motor, in same case with refrigeration compressor. (*Tecumseh Products Co.*)

amperage ratings: first, the number of amperes consumed by the motor while driving its compressor at its rated output and, second, the locked-rotor current of that motor.

All the Code rules discussed so far regarding motor-running overcurrent protection, controllers, and disconnecting means correlate these components to the horsepower rating of the motor. But hermetic-type motors have no horsepower ratings. How then is an intelligent selection of these components to be made? The Code covers the situation.

First of all, on ordinary motors, you do not need to see the name-plate of the motor as long as you know its general characteristics. The Code Tables 430-146 to 430-153 provide the

answer.   But if you are dealing with a hermetic-type motor, you
must have the name-plate information of the particular motor
to be installed: its full-load amperage and its locked-rotor amperage.

With these two figures before you, proceed as outlined below.
Assume that the motor is a 60-cycle 230-volt 3-phase motor with
name-plate ratings of 25 amp full-load current and 125 amp
locked-rotor current.

Motor-branch-circuit Wires.   Instead of using Code Tables
430-146 to 430-150, use the actual name-plate full-load amperes
and add 25%.   For the 25-amp motor under discussion, that makes
a total of 31.25 amp.   Use wire with a carrying capacity of 31.25
amp or more, per Code Table 310-12.   You may wish to use a
larger wire to minimize voltage drop.

Motor-branch-circuit Overcurrent Protection.   Use Code
Table 430-146.   Begin with the actual name-plate full-load amperage in column 1, then obtain the answer from columns 4, 5, 6,
or 7.

Disconnecting Means.   Follow Code Sec. 430-83.   For ordinary motors, as discussed earlier in this chapter, the starting point
is the horsepower rating of the motor and the switch usually is
rated in horsepower.   But the hermetic-type motor has no horsepower rating, so you must work backwards.   The motor under
discussion has a full-load current of 25 amp.   Turn to Code Table
430-150; look in the "220-volt" column.   You won't find a motor
with a 25-amp rating, but you will find that a 7½-hp motor of
the ordinary type has a 22-amp rating and a 10-hp size has a
27-amp rating.   You will then have to call the 25-amp hermetic-
type motor temporarily a "10-hp" motor, based on its 25-amp full-
load rating.

Turn to Code Table 430-151, which is concerned with the
locked-rotor amperage.   Go to the 3-phase 220-volt column and
find the 125-amp figure that you originally determined from the
name-plate of the motor.   There won't be a 125-amp figure, so
use the next larger one, 132 amp.   From there go left to the first
column, and there you will find the figure 7½ hp.   So now you
call the motor temporarily a "7½-hp."

When Tables 430-150 and 430-151 give two different answers,
use the larger one of the two; in this case provide a disconnecting

means which is suitable for an ordinary 10-hp motor, as discussed earlier in this chapter.

Controller. When you have determined the answer for the disconnecting means, you also have the answer for the controller. For this motor, provide the same controller that you would provide for an ordinary 10-hp motor. In almost every case, the controller will come with the air-conditioning equipment, so the problem is solved in advance.

Motor-running Overcurrent Protection. Proceed as with ordinary motors, but base your conclusions on the actual full-load amperage found on the name-plate of the motor, not on the theoretical amperage derived from Code tables. The maximum rating is 125% of full-load amperage for hermetic-type motors, but if the answer comes out to a nonstandard rating of overcurrent device, use the next larger size, but never more than 140% under any circumstances. (Exception: if the *locked-rotor* amperage of the motor is over 160 amp and a nonstandard overcurrent device is indicated, use next larger size, but never more than 130% of full-load current.)

TWO OR MORE MOTORS ON ONE CIRCUIT
(Code Secs. 430-42 and 430-53)

The Code differentiates between one or more motors connected to a *general-purpose* branch circuit (an ordinary circuit in a home) and two or more motors connected to a single *motor* branch circuit.

Several Motors on *General-purpose* Branch Circuit. If each motor is 1 hp or smaller and has a full-load current of 6 amp or less, per Sec. 430-42 two or more of them may be connected to a general-purpose circuit protected by 20-amp or smaller overcurrent protection if the circuit operates at 125 volts or less, or if protected at 15 amp at higher voltages but not over 600 volts. Each motor still requires individual overcurrent protection if it is one of the kinds discussed in the section of this book dealing with running overcurrent in general. Since that section concerned *continuous-duty* motors, it follows that motors of the kind described in this paragraph, if they are *not* continuous duty, do not require the running overcurrent protection. But do remember the Code definition in Sec. 430-22: "Any motor is considered to be for continuous duty unless the nature of the apparatus which it drives is such that the motor will not operate continuously *with load* under any condition of use."

Motors larger than discussed above may still be connected to general-purpose branch circuits, but each must have a controller and running overcurrent protection of a type "approved for group installation." This will be defined later in this chapter.

If the motor is connected to the circuit by means of a plug and receptacle, *and* individual running overcurrent protection is omitted, the plug and receptacle may have a rating not over 15 amp at 125 volts or 10 amp at 250 volts. If the motor does have individual running overcurrent protection, it must be part of the motor or appliance, and the plug and receptacle then may have a rating permissible for the particular circuit involved, as outlined in Chap. 5.

Several Motors on One *Motor* Branch Circuit. It is best to provide an individual circuit for each motor. When several motors are to be used in the same location, it is a simple matter to provide a feeder to that location to serve a number of individual branch circuits, one for each motor.

Nevertheless the Code, in Sec. 430-53, permits several motors on one circuit, but certain factors change considerably. These will be discussed here in the same sequence in which these elements appeared in the first part of this chapter, where a single motor on a branch circuit was discussed.

The general requirements for two or more motors on one motor branch circuit are as follows:

If each motor is not over 1 hp, if each motor has a full-load current of 6 amp or less, and if the circuit is protected at not over 20 amp when operating at 125 volts (or 15 amp at higher voltages not exceeding 600 volts), then the requirements are the same as when these motors are connected to a general-purpose circuit. In all other cases, *all* the following conditions must be complied with:

1. Each motor must be provided with motor-running overcurrent protection, and the device must be a special type "approved for group installation."

2. Each controller must be "approved for group installation."

3. The branch circuit must be protected by *fuses* (not other overcurrent devices) having a rating as specified in Tables 430-152 and 430-153 of the Code for the largest motor, plus an additional amperage equivalent to the full-load currents of all the other motors.

4. The branch-circuit fuses must not be larger than permitted for thermal cutouts or other similar devices used for motor-running protection.

Motor-branch-circuit Wires. When more than one motor is involved, first determine the minimum required carrying capacity in amperes of the wires (whether branch or feeder) if only the largest motor were involved. Then add the full-load current (Tables 430-147 to 430-150) for each of the other motors in the group. Finally, add amperage required for the lighting and appliance load, if any. This gives the total minimum amperage carrying capacity required, from which it is easy, with the aid of Table 310-12, to determine the size wire required as a minimum.

For example, consider one each 3-, 1½-, and ½-hp single-phase 230-volt motors. In Table 430-148 the full-load currents for these three motors are, respectively, 17, 10, and 4.9 amp. If only the 3-hp motor were connected, the minimum carrying capacity of the wires would be 125% of 17 amp, or 21.2 amp. Add 10 and 4.9 amp, making a total of 36.1 amp. The minimum carrying capacity of the wires must be 36.1 amp.

If two of the motors are of the *same* size, consider one of them the "largest" and the others as the smaller motors.

Motor-feeder Overcurrent Protection. The feeder for a group of motors is to be protected by an overcurrent device of an amperage rating no greater than the *branch-circuit* overcurrent device for the largest motor served by the feeder, plus the full-load current for each of the other motors in the group. If two motors are of the same size, consider one of them as the "largest," the other as the smaller. There will be times when several motors must be started at the same time. In that case both feeder wires and feeder overcurrent may have to be increased; this is a case for consultation with the local inspector.

If a lighting or appliance load is also served by the same feeder, simply add the amperage required for this purpose to the amperage determined by the preceding paragraph.

Motor-branch-circuit Overcurrent Protection. In the case of a motor branch circuit serving several motors, proceed as follows:

Determine the maximum rating permitted (Table 430-146, column 4, 5, 6 or 7) if only the largest motor were on the circuit. Add the full-load current (Tables 430-147 to 430-150) for each of the other motors in question. The total adjusted upward to the next standard size of overcurrent device (if the total comes out to a nonstandard size) is the maximum rating of the branch-circuit overcurrent device, provided that fuses or other devices capable of interrupting short circuits are used for the individual *motor-running* overcurrent devices. If, however, for this pur-

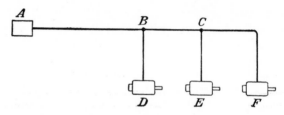

Fig. 31-7. Problem in several motors in one circuit.

pose thermal cutouts or other devices are used, approved for group installation but still not capable of interrupting short circuits, then make sure that the rating of the branch-circuit overcurrent device, as determined above, does not exceed the maximum current-interrupting ability of the *smallest* device used on the group of motors for motor-running overcurrent protection.

Problems will arise as to the size of the wires and protection for the wires from the point where they branch off from the branch-circuit wires proper (see Fig. 31-7). The wire from A to B to C is the branch-circuit wire, the size of which is determined as already outlined. A is the branch-circuit overcurrent device, also determined as already outlined. From B to D, from C to E, and from C to F are the taps supplying the individual motors. If these taps are the same size as the branch-circuit wires, no overcurrent protection is required at points B and C. If the tap is the minimum size, as outlined in the first part of this chapter covering a single motor, if it has an amperage carrying capacity at least one-third that of the branch-circuit wire A-B-C, and if it is not over 25 ft long and is protected against mechanical injury, then no overcurrent protection is required at points B and C. Under all other conditions overcurrent protection is required at these points; determine the size just as if you were considering a single motor on a branch circuit, as outlined in the first part of this chapter.

As a matter of fact, installing overcurrent protection at the points B and C completely changes the complexion of the picture, for then the wire A-B-C is no longer a branch-circuit wire but becomes a feeder; A becomes the feeder overcurrent protection; the wires B to D and C to E, also C to F, become branch-circuit wires. The overcurrent protectors at points B and C become branch-circuit overcurrent devices, and, instead of a group of motors on a single branch circuit, we now have individual motors on individual branch circuits, fed by a common feeder A-B-C.

Disconnecting Means. Each motor may have its own disconnecting means, but the Code permits a group to be handled by a single disconnecting means under one of three conditions:

1. If several motors drive different parts of a single machine, as, for example, metal- or woodworking machines, cranes, hoists, etc.

2. If several motors are in a single room within sight of the disconnecting means.

3. If several motors are protected by a single branch-circuit overcurrent device.

The rating of such a common disconnecting means must not be smaller than would be required for a single motor of a horsepower equal to the sum of the horsepowers of all the individual motors (or a full-load amperage equal to the sum of the full-load amperages of all the individual motors).

Running Overcurrent Protection. The first Code requirement is that each motor must be provided with individual *motor-running* overcurrent protection of a rating determined exactly as if the motor were alone on a circuit, but it must be a type that is "approved for group installation." The ordinary devices used for motor-running overcurrent protection are not designed to be able to interrupt short circuits and would be damaged should they be subjected to short-circuit currents. Since the Code requires, in the case of a single motor on a branch circuit, that the branch-circuit overcurrent protection not exceed 400% of the full-load current, the *motor-running* overcurrent device is, of course, protected against short circuits by the *branch-circuit* overcurrent device.

When, however, a *group* of motors is connected to a branch circuit, if the branch-circuit overcurrent device is of a rating heavy enough to permit all the motors to run at one time or perhaps to start at the same time, the branch-circuit overcurrent device would have to be many times greater than 400% of the full-load current of the *smallest* motor in the group. The motor-running overcurrent device for that motor would not then be adequately protected by the branch-circuit overcurrent device. Consequently, the motor-running overcurrent device for each motor must be of the type approved for group installation, which tests have shown is capable of interrupting currents much heavier than merely normal motor overloads.

Such devices may be "thermal cutouts," devices something like fuses. They are capable of interrupting quite heavy currents but not capable of opening short circuits. Such devices have stamped on them two amperages. The smaller rating is their normal rating, just as a fuse is rated in amperes. The larger rating represents the maximum permissible rating of the overcurrent device protecting the branch circuit. The rating of the branch-circuit overcurrent device must be no greater than this second or larger rating stamped on the *smallest* thermal cutout on the circuit.

Such overcurrent devices "approved for group installation" are not at all common. However, some types are shown in the Underwriters' "List of Inspected Electrical Equipment" as being so approved.

Controllers. Each controller must be of a type "approved for group installation." The comments already made with respect to running overcurrent devices of that type apply also to controllers.

Several motors may be handled by a single controller under the same conditions as already outlined for disconnecting means.

Chapter 32

WIRING SCHOOLS AND CHURCHES

Statistics show that 9% of all students in the elementary grades of school have defective vision. In high schools the figure is 24%, and in colleges it is 31%. It is a well-established fact that, if good lighting is provided from the first grade onward, the percentages of students with defective vision are greatly reduced. Moreover it is equally well established that good lighting contributes materially toward raising the average grades of the students. Many of those who have been lagging behind respond when proper illumination is provided; the number of failures drops. Good lighting is therefore a tremendous asset for the students themselves and likewise has been found to pay good dividends in the form of reduced over-all cost of providing education on a "per student per year" basis.

Footcandles Required. For class and study rooms 30 footcandles is usually accepted as the absolute minimum. In drawing rooms 50 footcandles is acceptable, and 80 footcandles is not too high. Double these values would not be too high and would be truly modern. In auditoriums 10 footcandles is sufficient, and for corridors 5 footcandles is ample. These are definite minimum standards that should be met. It is safe to say that only a small percentage of schools today are lighted to a point even remotely approaching these figures; too many installations even today are of the type shown in Fig. 32-1. Installations made many years ago have not been changed even if woefully inadequate according to the standards of today. Here is a fertile field for modernization, and Fig. 32-2 shows what can be done. This shows a schoolroom equipped with really modern glare-free lighting, combined with acoustical treatment to reduce the noise level. It is safe to

FIG. 32-1. Lighting of the type shown here is not unusual in schools even today. Efficient work under such conditions is not possible. (*Curtis Lighting, Inc.*)

FIG. 32-2. A schoolroom equipped with really modern lighting. Lighting of this type makes for highest pupil efficiency. (*Curtis Lighting, Inc.*)

say that the students of this school will progress further than before, with less effort.

Types of Fixtures Recommended. A modern installation will automatically be of the fluorescent type, furnishing an abundance of light with minimum surface brightness and glare. If the ceiling height is sufficient, a type of fixture which lets a good deal of the light fall on the ceiling will probably furnish most acceptable lighting. Special attention, of course, must be paid to the ceilings, walls, and all reflecting surfaces. Ceilings and walls must be clean, of a light color to reflect light well, but with a flat finish to avoid glare and to provide well-diffused light.

FIG. 32-3. The footcandle level of illumination drops very rapidly as the distance from the window increases. (*General Electric Co.*)

Switch Control. In a fairly large classroom, the level of illumination from natural light will vary greatly in different parts of the room. See Fig. 32-3, which shows how the footcandle level drops as the distance from the windows increases. The row of desks next to the windows may have 100 footcandles of light; the row on the opposite side of the room may have only 5 footcandles.

Considering this fact, it may be well to consider having switches that control each row of lights separately, so that the row farthest from the window can be turned on independently of the rest. The more usual custom, however, is to have all the lights on most of the time.

Code Requirements for Schools. For lighting purposes the Code requires 3 watts per sq ft of area, except in assembly halls and auditoriums, where 1 watt is sufficient, and in corridors, where ½ watt is required. The demand factor is 100% for the entire load.

To the wattage determined by the area must be added the wattage for specific loads other than lighting. Take into consideration any motors that may be in operation, motion-picture equipment, appliances in the domestic science department, special loads that may develop in laboratories, and similar loads. A calculation based on the 3 watts per sq ft required by the Code as a minimum for safety will result in a total wattage insufficient to provide the footcandles suggested above for the various parts of the building. It will be wise to check the total specific lighting load that is to be connected and, if it is greater in watts than the figure reached by the first method, to take it into consideration in calculating feeders and similar factors.

Churches. The Code requires 1 watt per sq ft for churches. The demand factor is 100% regardless of the size of the installation.

Proper attention should, however, be given to what may be considered good lighting for churches. Illumination below 8 to 10 footcandles would in most cases be considered inadequate for the church proper. To provide this level may require 4 to 7 watts per sq ft, depending on a wide assortment of factors such as the reflecting ability of the ceiling and walls, the type of fixtures selected, ceiling height, and many others.

In many churches the lighting fixtures in use seem to have been designed to conform to the architectural scheme, with less thought given to the matter of proper illumination. Sometimes fixtures are selected which use many small lamps, and since a dozen 25-watt lamps consuming altogether 300 watts produce only about half the light produced by a single 300-watt lamp, the lighting suffers.

In many churches indirect lighting will be found to be practical. In others, it may be found more desirable to install fixtures which have substantial decorative value and which contribute toward the general decorative and architectural scheme. For that purpose fixtures have been designed which outwardly seem to be the direct-lighting type; actually concealed within the fixture is the more important indirect component which provides the

FIG. 32-4. This church is equipped with direct lighting which was installed many years ago. Note the extreme glare. (*Curtis Lighting, Inc.*)

FIG. 32-5. The church of Fig. 32-4, reequipped with modern lighting. Note how the beauty and dignity of the church have been emphasized. (*Curtis Lighting, Inc.*)

greater part of the total illumination. Figure 32-4 shows St. Rose of Lima church at Kankakee, Ill., with the original lighting, and Fig. 32-5 shows the same church after the installation of modern lighting.

The nave or auditorium of the church having been properly lighted, the fact that in a great majority of all churches the sanctuary and the altar constitute the focal point of the worshipers must not be overlooked. This portion of the church should be lighted to a level considerably above that of the rest of the church; levels of 20 to 30 footcandles or higher are the rule. This illumination is usually provided through the medium of spotlights, concealed from the view of the congregation. This may require a minimum of 1,500 watts upward to a much higher wattage, depending entirely on the area to be illuminated and the intensity desired. Statuary should be specially lighted. Each church will present an individual problem, and the method of lighting should be left to one well versed in the art of church lighting.

If the church has a choir loft, adequate illumination of a minimum of 30 footcandles should be provided. The organ motor may require a special circuit. The heating plant, if it is of the oil-burning type, will require a special circuit for the motor. Throughout the church, miscellaneous loads also exist. Conveniently located receptacle outlets should not be overlooked; too often unsightly and dangerous extension cords are used to operate fans, pulpit lights, loud-speaking apparatus, and similar equipment. Outdoor receptacle outlets are most desirable, for example to permit lighted displays during festival seasons.

Chapter 33

WIRING OFFICES

An office may be a single room with a desk and chair and one lighting fixture, or a modern well-appointed office with really adequate lighting, an assortment of electrical devices including dictating machines, fans, water coolers, and similar equipment. It is therefore difficult to cover the subject adequately in a single chapter, and suggestions given here must be of necessity quite general.

Code Requirements. For lighting purpose the Code now requires 5 watts per sq ft, with 100% demand factor for the entire area. (Codes earlier than 1959 required fewer than 5 watts and also permitted a demand factor.)

Even under the best of conditions it is not likely that the 5 watts per sq ft will provide the footcandles of illumination today considered acceptable for modern offices. It would probably not produce more than 25 footcandles. The absolute minimum should be considered 30 footcandles, and the alert office manager knows that the extra cost of equipment required to provide a much higher level is soon offset by the increased efficiency of the personnel. For regular office work a level of 100 footcandles is now considered more or less standard. For accounting work or similar work where prolonged attention to detailed figures is necessary, the recommendation is 150 footcandles, and for drafting, it is 200 footcandles.

The specific load which is planned, rather than the Code 5-watts-per-sq-ft minimum, will in all probability determine the total wattage. Once the wattage and the amperage have been determined, feeder sizes and similar data can easily be figured as in other cases that have already been discussed.

In planning an office installation of some significant size, do consider the advantages of 277-volt lighting as already discussed in another chapter.

Receptacle Outlets. Most offices have entirely too few receptacle outlets. Every individual office space, no matter how small, should have a minimum of one outlet; one such outlet for each 10 linear feet of wall space is more nearly correct. In offices larger than 400 sq ft there should be a minimum of four for the first 400 sq ft of area, and at least two additional outlets for each additional 400 sq ft of area.

Special outlets should be provided for fans; receptacles are available with a stud or bolt on which the fan is supported, making unsightly shelves unnecessary. There should be at least two such outlets for every 400 sq ft of floor area, and they should be located about 7 ft above floor level.

Types of Fixtures. Office work is usually of a continuous and exacting nature. Besides a sufficient quantity of light there is needed the right kind of lighting—freedom from glare, low surface brightness, avoidance of shadows. The factors that make good lighting must be considered.

Flexibility. If a sizable floor area is involved, which will accommodate a considerable number of people, it is not likely that original arrangement of the individual office space will long remain unchanged. Large office space is often subdivided into many individual offices by movable partitions about 7 ft high. These partitions are shifted as the need arises, and, as the individual office spaces change, the lighting equipment must be moved. This is frequently accomplished by originally providing flush ceiling outlet boxes on which the original lighting equipment is installed. When it becomes necessary to move this equipment, surface metal raceway of the type described in Chap. 29 is used in the way there described. Similar material is used to provide receptacle outlets for dictaphones and other equipment at the exact point needed.

Signaling Equipment. In larger offices it will be necessary to provide a raceway, usually concealed, for low-voltage wires for telephones, buzzer systems, call systems, and similar purposes. This raceway, which usually is conduit, must never contain wires that are part of the regular electrical system operating at the usual voltages.   A review of this subject in Chap. 26 would be advisable.   To bring such low-voltage wires to the individual desks in an office, surface metal raceway of the floor type which was shown in Fig. 29-14 in Chap. 29 is used.

Control Equipment.   In relatively small offices, a single panel-board or fuse cabinet with switches in the individual circuits will probably serve the purpose.   In larger installations it is often necessary to install more elaborate equipment so that an entire group of fixtures can be controlled by a single switch.   Many fixtures such as those located in individual offices, of course, must be provided with individual switches.

Chapter 34

WIRING STORES

Wiring in stores may vary from a simple installation in a small store to a complicated and highly specialized installation in a large department store. The latter type of job is entirely beyond the scope of this book, which will cover only the wiring of small stores.

Footcandle Recommendations. The minimum illumination in the average store in a neighborhood location must be at least 50 footcandles in areas open to the shopping public if a good selling display is to be obtained. In larger stores and in better locations the minimum is higher, never less than 100 footcandles. If self-service counters are involved, 150 to 200 footcandles will be necessary. For showcases, wall cases, and feature displays, double the figures.

If these levels of illumination at first seem high, remember that mediocre lighting may be sufficient to sell the customer the things that he has decided to buy before he comes into the store. No merchant, however, will be a great success if he depends only on that type of business, if he sells only the specific things his customers ask for. Good lighting draws the customer's attention to the merchandise on display, emphasizes the points which lead to a wish for ownership and an urge to buy. Additional sales of customers' "wants" rather than "needs" will result, and good lighting will prove to be a good investment rather than expense. See Fig. 34-1, which shows the furniture department of a well-lighted store.

In show windows 100 footcandles is usually considered a minimum, and in larger cities 200 to 500 footcandles is not unusual. On a dark street a window that is lighted to 100 footcandles will appear very bright and well lighted, but if the street is itself well lighted, a window with 200 footcandles may appear very ordinary indeed, especially if another window next door is provided with a still higher level of illumination.

In order to light a show window to the point where it will attract attention in the daytime, it is necessary to provide sufficient light inside the window to minimize the reflections that arise from the natural outdoor light. This requires an unusual level of illumination, for 300 to 1,000 footcandles must be provided.

Fig. 34-1. A well-lighted furniture department in a store.

Code Requirements. For lighting purposes the Code requires a minimum of 3 watts per sq ft for the store proper; naturally for warehouse space, storerooms, and similar locations this is not required. To this must be added the further load required for show windows. For each linear foot measured horizontally along the base of the window, allow 200 watts. Regardless of the size of the store the demand factor is always 100%; in other words no deduction may be made regardless of the number of square feet involved.

As in the case of all other occupancies, specific loads such as motors, appliances, and similar equipment must be added. The demand for electric power in the average store will certainly grow rather than decrease, so it is well to leave a very generous margin for future expansion when figuring service entrance, feeders, number of spare circuits on panelboards, and all similar factors. Do not overlook probable future load for air conditioning.

Considering the suggestions regarding proper footcandle levels of illumination, it is not likely that 3 watts per sq ft, plus the special loads for show windows, will be sufficient to provide the illumination needed. Check the actual load, as determined from the footcandle level selected and the particular fixtures and sizes of lamps involved, to determine whether the 3-watt minimum is

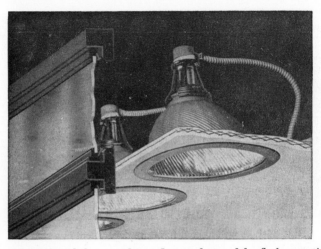

FIG. 34-2. Typical show-window reflectors designed for flush mounting.

sufficient or not. In accordance with the very general formula shown in Chap. 30, 6 watts per sq ft might provide 25 footcandles of illumination, and that is not enough.

Type of Lighting Equipment. For a most modern store located in perhaps the most competitive area of a large city, there is little choice except to design the lighting system specifically to suit the exact size, structure, and layout of the building; the type of merchandise sold; the effects desired; and many other factors. Only the most general rules can be given in a book of this kind, and final selection of the equipment must be left to one competent to analyze the dozens of factors involved.

No general rules can be given concerning the types of fixtures to be used. They might be fluorescent or incandescent or a combination thereof. They might be suspended from the ceiling, mounted on the ceiling, or flush in the ceiling. With a low ceiling and fixtures mounted directly on the ceiling, select fixtures that direct most of the light downward. With higher ceilings and fixtures suspended some distance below the ceiling, select fixtures that let a considerable portion of light go upward to light the ceiling. In any event let some light fall on the ceiling in order to avoid a somewhat cavernous appearance that would be the result of dark ceilings.

Fig. 34-3. Automatic time switches control show-window lights. (*Paragon Electric Co.*)

Often it is desirable to direct extra light upon some particular feature item on display. This cannot be accomplished by using fluorescent lamps. Often flush ceiling fixtures with incandescent lamps are used for the purpose.

In general, store lighting should be installed based on the recommendations of a lighting specialist well versed in the subject.

Types of Fluorescent Lamps. For general lighting and for the most light per watt of power consumed, use cool white lamps. On the other hand, the kind of merchandise on display will also be a major factor in the proper selection of lamps. For light that is most nearly like natural light, use de luxe cool white; if the merchandise happens to have mostly "warm" colors such as red, brown, orange, or tan, the de luxe warm white will enhance its appearance. In food stores the de luxe cool white emphasizes the crisp appearance of green vegetables and gives good appearance to meats, both lean and fat. Prepared foods have acceptable appearance under either de luxe cool white or de luxe warm white.

Show-window Lighting. Since the Code requires 200 watts per running foot of show window, obviously a rather elaborate installation is needed. The light source must not be visible to the shopper on the street if good display of merchandise is to be obtained. The reflectors may be the flush type shown in Fig. 34-2 or many other available types.

A time switch, such as that shown in Fig. 34-3, is very frequently installed to control the show-window circuit, automatically turning off the show-window lighting at any desired time after closing hours.

Chapter 35

WIRING MISCELLANEOUS OCCUPANCIES

In determining the service entrance, feeders, panelboards, and switchboards for any type of occupancy, it is necessary only to estimate the lighting load, to which must be added the appliance load, if any, and the motor load. The Code in Sec. 220-2(a) (see Appendix) specifies the watts per square foot that must be allowed for the lighting load. The calculation then is relatively simple, but the answer based on the Code minimum requirements is not likely to provide the footcandles of light now considered acceptable.

For such factors as are not covered by Sec. 220-2(a), the load must be estimated from the specifications. Do not overlook future loads, including air conditioning.

Factories. It is impossible to specify the power that will be required for lighting purposes without knowing exactly what kind of project is involved. A factory may be anything from a foundry where 30 footcandles might be considered good lighting to a watchmaking establishment where 200 footcandles would be considered too little. Furthermore, the complete operation must be broken down into smaller parts. The lighting in the boiler room need not be so good as that in the office. In very few cases, however, will less than 30 footcandles be considered sufficient.

The motor load can be determined from the specification of the building. The demand factor that is to be used with the motors will depend entirely upon the type of installation involved, and good common sense will be far more valuable than any number of printed pages in a book.

Theaters and Assembly Halls. The Code in Art. 520 outlines the requirements for electrical installations in theaters and assembly halls, which are defined as "buildings, or part of a building, designed, intended, or used for dramatic, operatic, motion-picture, or other shows, and night clubs, dance halls, armories, sporting arenas, bowling alleys, public auditoriums, television studios, and like buildings used for public assembly."

Code requirements are rigid and severe, but simply covered in Art. 520, which should be studied in detail by those who intend to design or install an electrical installation in a theater. Only the most essential of the requirements can be covered here.

If there are over 200 seats, the wiring must be in conduit or MI cable. The projector must be operated in an approved booth, and the circuit serving it must have wire No. 8, or heavier if required by the specific load.

If the theater is equipped for sound, the wiring for the sound system must be considered as an entirely separate system, and its wires must not run through the raceways containing the usual wiring for light and power.

Receptacles for portable arc lamps must have a rated capacity of at least 35 amp and must be wired with No. 6 or larger wire. Receptacles for portable incandescent lamps may be rated as little as 15 amp but must be wired with No. 12 or heavier wire. All portable cord must be heavy-duty type such as, for example, Type S.

In dressing rooms all lights and receptacles must be controlled by switches. All lights within 8 ft of the floor must be provided with guards. Each switch controlling a receptacle must have a pilot light to indicate when the receptacle is turned on.

The requirements outlined by no means constitute all Code requirements for theaters. Study Art. 520 well if you intend to do theater work.

Signs. This topic is covered by Art. 600 of the Code. The switch that controls a sign must open all ungrounded wires to the sign and must be located within sight of the sign unless it is a type that can be locked in the "off" position. Obviously this provision is intended to protect people working on the sign. All controls, including flashers, must be enclosed in metal cases.

All signs must be grounded, except that they may be completely insulated from the ground if "inaccessible to unauthorized persons." This does not apply to small portable signs supplied from a circuit operating at a voltage of less than 150 volts to ground. The maximum current permitted is 15 amp per circuit.

The wiring in signs may be open wiring on insulators, in conduit, or in troughs formed by the construction of the sign, or armored cable. Wires must be of the lead-covered type, unless the wire is in conduit, so arranged as to be raintight and to drain in case moisture penetrates. The wiring may be no lighter than No. 14 and, in case of those signs operating in excess of 600 volts, which includes all neon signs, must be selected with an insulation heavy enough for the voltage involved. These details constitute but a small part of the Code requirements with respect to signs. If you intend to do sign work, study Art. 600.

Signal Systems. Ordinary installations for the operation of doorbells, door openers, buzzers, telephones, call systems, and the like are classified by the Code, Art. 725, into four groups, as follows:

A. Those limited to not over 15 volts, 5 amp.
B. Those limited to 15 to 30 volts, 3.2 amp.
C. Those limited to 30 to 60 volts, 1.6 amp.
D. Those limited to 60 to 150 volts, 1 amp.

The usual source of power is a small transformer so designed that even if the secondary is short-circuited, not more than 100 volt-amp will flow in the transformer, thus automatically limiting its temperature and the danger of fire. In the case of a Class D system, a 1-amp fuse must be provided in the secondary of the transformer. In Class A, B, and C systems no overcurrent protection is required. If the system is fed by a battery other than a storage battery, no overcurrent protection is required.

Hazardous Locations. This topic is covered by Art. 500 of the Code. A location may be considered hazardous for a variety of reasons. If explosive vapors, such as those formed by gasoline, lacquers, or other similar volatile products, are present, obviously an explosion hazard exists. The same is true where explosive dusts such as coal or grain dusts are present, as also is the case where there is a considerable amount of easily ignitible fibers such as in a cotton mill.

Such materials can easily cause an explosion if ignited by electric sparks caused by switches, motors, pulling a plug out of a receptacle, or excessive heating.

In most of such locations only conduit may be used for wiring. Ordinary outlet boxes may not be used, and special cast fittings which enclose all wires, switches, and similar devices are required. The purpose of these explosion-proof fittings is not to prevent explosive gases from reaching the device, for that has been found impossible, but rather to enclose all such devices in fittings sufficiently sturdy so as not to be harmed by an explosion, and to confine the explosion to the interior of the fittings. In other words the small amounts of explosive vapors that do find their way into these fittings do explode occasionally, but the explosion stays inside, not getting out where it might set off a major explosion in a room filled with an explosive mixture.

Instead of outlet boxes, explosion-proof conduit fittings are required, similar to that shown in Fig. 35-1. The hubs on these fittings must engage at least five full threads of conduit. The covers either are screwed on with a suffi-

FIG. 35-1. A typical explosion-proof fitting. (*Killark Electric Mfg. Co.*)

cient number of threads engaged to make them explosion-proof or have a machined fit with a tolerance of 0.002 in. and at least ⅜ in. wide, either of which experience has shown will confine the explosion. For switches, use a Type FS conduit fitting which was shown in Fig. 29-2 but of the explosion-proof type. Where portable devices must be used, special types of explosion-proof outlet and plug are required. Both are shown in Fig. 35-2, and the combination is so designed that with the first pull the plug can be withdrawn only a part of the way. This breaks the connection, and an arc, if it forms, will explode the small amount of vapor present in the interior. This takes place during the brief period of time required to give the plug the twist that is necessary before it can be completely withdrawn.

Fixtures of the explosion-proof type are designed so that the lamp is enclosed in a sturdy glass globe. A typical unit of this type is shown in Fig. 35-3.

When a number of fittings or enclosures are installed using conduit, explosive gases or other materials can pass from one fitting or enclosure to another, through the conduit. The conduit itself can also contain a substantial amount of such explosive material. To minimize the quantity of explosive material that can accumulate in any one place, the Code in Sec. 501-5 requires that seals of the general type shown in Fig. 35-4 be installed, under many conditions there outlined. The seal is installed in the run of conduit, and after the wires are pulled into place, is filled with a sealing compound that effectively prevents explosive materials from passing from one portion of the electrical installation, to another, through the conduit.

Fig. 35-2. For portable devices used in hazardous locations, an explosion-proof fitting of this type is used. (*Crouse-Hinds Co.*)

Code Classifications. In its treatment of hazardous locations, the Code in Art. 500 at first appears to be very complicated, but careful analysis reduces it to fairly simple proportions. The entire subject, however, is in no sense one which can be understood by casual reading, and careful study is necessary.

The Code divides different kinds of explosive *atmospheres* into seven different *groups,* depending on the nature of the explosive element.

Fig. 35-3. An explosion-proof fixture. (*Benjamin Electric Mfg. Co.*)

The Code divides different kinds of *locations* into three *classes,* each subdivided into two *divisions.*

Types of Hazardous Atmospheres. For exact definition, see Code Sec. 500-2. The following is an *abbreviated* recap:

Group A: Atmospheres containing acetylene.

Group B: Atmospheres containing hydrogen or gases or vapors of equivalent hazard such as manufactured gas.

Group C: Atmospheres containing ethyl ether vapor, ethylene, or cyclopropane.

Group D: Atmospheres containing gasoline, petroleum, naphtha, alcohols, acetone, lacquer solvent vapors, and natural gas.

Group E: Atmospheres containing metal dust.

Group F: Atmospheres containing carbon black, coal, or coke dust.

Group G: Atmospheres containing dust: flour, starch, grain.

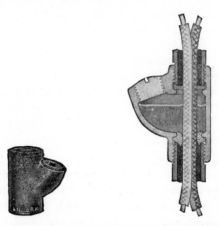

FIG. 35-4. By pouring sealing compound into a fitting of this kind, devices that might cause an explosion are sealed off from a run of conduit. (*Killark Electric Mfg. Co.*)

Types of Hazardous Locations. The various kinds of hazardous locations are defined in the Code. The following is an *abbreviated* recap:

Class 1, Div. 1. Locations in which explosive **gases** or **vapors** may be *regularly* expected (periodically, intermittently or continuously) under *normal operating conditions.* Examples: spray booths; locations with open tanks or vats of volatile flammable liquids; drying rooms or compartments for evaporation of flammable solvents; portions of cleaning and dyeing rooms where flammable liquids are used; many similar locations.

Class 1, Div. 2. Locations similar to Class 1, Div. 1, except that the explosive conditions are not present under normal operating conditions, but only under *abnormal* conditions such as exist, for example, during a period of breakdown. Details such as the amount of hazardous material that might escape in case of accident, the efficiency of the ventilating system, and similar factors will determine whether the location in question falls into Div. 1 or Div. 2. The local inspector is the judge.

Class 2, Div. 1. Locations where combustible and explosive **dust** may be *regularly* expected (periodically, intermittently or continuously) under *normal operating conditions*. Examples: grain-handling and -storage plants, flour mills, starch plants.

Class 2, Div. 2. Locations similar to Class 2, Div. 1, except that the explosive conditions are not present under normal operating conditions, but only under *abnormal* conditions such as exist during breakdown.

Class 3, Div. 1. Locations where **ignitible fibers or combustible flyings** are handled, manufactured, or used. Examples: rayon, cotton, and similar textile mills; clothing-manufacturing establishments; woodworking plants.

Class 3, Div. 2. Locations where such materials are stored or handled.

Wiring in Hazardous Locations. The subject of wiring in hazardous locations is a most important one, in which experience, good judgment, and "horse sense" all weigh heavily. The entire subject is much too complicated and too important to be covered completely by the scope of this book. Therefore the discussion here given as to atmospheres and locations and the wiring methods shown should be considered only in very general terms, and layouts and installations involving hazardous locations should be undertaken only by those entirely conversant with the subject. The electrical inspector should be freely consulted.

Residential Garages. If the garage is designed to hold no more than three cars, and if it is at or above ground level, it is not considered a hazardous area, and any wiring method acceptable for the house is also acceptable for the garage.

If, however, the floor of such a garage is below ground level, it is considered a hazardous area as far as the first 18 in. above floor level are concerned, and any wiring within 18 in. of the floor must then be handled as in any other Class 1, Div. 2, location. But if you keep all wiring above that 18-in. line, wire the garage using any method acceptable for the house.

Commercial Garages. Any locations where cars and similar vehicles are serviced and repaired, or where more than three such vehicles may be stored, are considered commercial garages. Only some of the more important details of the wiring of such buildings can be covered here, and careful study of Art. 510 is necessary before proceeding to work on such premises.

All floors at or above ground level are considered Class 1, Div. 2, locations as far as the first 18 in. above each floor are concerned. But for any floor below ground level, the entire floor is considered Class 1, Div. 2, up to a point which is 18 in. *above* the bottom of *outside* doors or similar openings. Pits and depressions below floor level are also considered Class 1, Div. 2, locations, except that a single depression may be called Class 1, Div. 1, by the inspector.

The wiring within the Class 1, Div. 2, areas must, of course, be as prescribed by the Code for such locations, but all wiring in the remainder of the garage must be in a metallic raceway, or it may be MI cable. Adjacent areas such as storerooms, offices, and so on are not considered hazardous areas provided their floors are at least 18 in. above the level of the garage floor.

Equipment of any type that is likely to produce sparks in ordinary operation (such as receptacles, switches, lighting fixtures, battery chargers, motors, and so on) if located more than 18 in. but less than 12 ft above the floor must have all openings screened or guarded to prevent escape of sparks or hot metal particles.

Filling Stations. The wiring to the island on which gasoline-dispensing pumps are found must be in rigid conduit, and all fittings within 4 ft of the ground level must be of the explosion-proof type. A sealing fitting must be installed where the conduit enters the pump or other equipment on the island. If the insulation on the wires is rubber or some other type which would be affected by gasoline spilled on it, the wires must be in lead-sheathed cable. Some brands of Type T or TW are also available in a special construction suitable for use in contact with gasoline. The label on the coil will read "Gasoline- and Oil-resistant." Such wire may be used without a lead sheath. Do note, however, that ordinary Type T or TW is not suitable for this purpose; it is suitable only if it is the special type with the special label.

All circuits feeding dispensing pumps on pump islands must be controlled by switches that disconnect every wire, including the neutral (which, however, does not change the requirement that there must be no fuse in the neutral wire); if a circuit breaker is used, it must break all wires simultaneously.

Motors in Hazardous Locations.   All motors for use in hazardous locations must be of the explosion-proof type.   Obviously such motors can have no opening into the motor but must be totally enclosed and also constructed with extremely close tolerances on the mechanical fit of all parts.

Paint-spray Booths.   No electrical devices of any kind are permitted within the booth.   Here there is danger of an explosion not only from sparks but also by vapors present, which may explode upon contact with the relatively high temperatures found on lamps and similar devices under ordinary operating conditions.

BIBLIOGRAPHY

ABBOTT, ARTHUR L., and FRANK STETKA: "National Electrical Code Handbook," McGraw-Hill Book Company, Inc., New York.

AMICK, CHARLES L.: "Fluorescent Lighting Manual," McGraw-Hill Book Company, Inc., New York.

HARRISON, WARD, and K. A. STALEY: "Fundamentals of Illumination," General Electric Co., Nela Park, Cleveland.

HARRISON, WARD, and C. E. WEIT: "Illumination Design Data," General Electric Co., Nela Park, Cleveland.

LUCKIESH, MATTHEW, and FRANK K. MOSS: "The Science of Seeing," D. Van Nostrand Company, Inc., New York.

VEINOTT, CYRIL G.: "Fractional Horsepower Electric Motors," McGraw-Hill Book Company, Inc., New York.

WRIGHT, FORREST B.: "Electricity in the Home and on the Farm," John Wiley & Sons, Inc., New York.

"Handbook of Interior Wiring Design," Industry Committee on Interior Wiring Design, New York.

"Illuminating Engineering Nomenclature and Photometric Standards," Illuminating Engineering Society, New York.

"National Electrical Code," National Fire Protection Association, Boston, Mass.

APPENDIX

This Appendix contains tables quoted from the National Electrical Code.[1] Some of the tables shown in the Code are not repeated here because they refer to subjects beyond the scope of this book. Others are omitted because they are rarely used and can be found in your copy of the Code. Portions of other tables are omitted for the same reason.

Certain sections of the Code are most important and specific, for which reason they are included here in full.

The Code contains some specific "examples" illustrating the application of Code requirements. They are included in this Appendix.

[1] Every student is urged to study the National Electrical Code.

Excerpts from the 1965 National Electrical Code are published with the permission of the National Fire Protection Association. Any further reproduction of this material is not authorized except with the permission of that association. Copies of the full text of the 1965 National Electrical Code are available from the National Fire Protection Association, 60 Batterymarch St., Boston, Mass. 02110 in a prepared bound edition at $2.00 per copy.

Table 220-2(a). General Lighting Loads by Occupancies

Type of Occupancy	Unit Load per Square Foot, Watts
Armories and auditoriums	1
Banks	2
Barbershops and beauty parlors	3
Churches	1
Clubs	2
Courtrooms	2
Dwellings (other than hotels)*	3
Garages—commercial (storage)	½
Hospitals	2
Hotels, including apartment houses without provisions for cooking by tenants*	2
Industrial commercial (loft) buildings	2
Lodge rooms	1½
Office buildings	5
Restaurants	2
Schools	3
Stores	3
Warehouses (storage)	¼
In any of the above occupancies except single-family dwellings and individual apartments of multifamily dwellings:	
Assembly halls and auditoriums	1
Halls, corridors, closets	½
Storage spaces	¼

* All receptacle outlets of 15-amp or less rating in single-family and multifamily dwellings and in guest rooms of hotels [except those connected to the receptacle circuits specified in Paragraph 220-3(b)] may be considered as outlets for general illumination, and no additional load need be included for such outlets. The provisions of Paragraph 220-2(b) shall apply to all other receptacle outlets.

Table 220-4(a). Calculation of Feeder Loads by Occupancies

Type of occupancy	Portion of lighting load to which demand factor applies, wattage	Feeder demand factor, per cent
Dwellings—other than hotels . .	First 3,000 or less at	100
	Next 3,001 to 120,000 at	35
	Remainder over 120,000 at	25
Hospitals*	First 50,000 or less at	40
	Remainder over 50,000 at	20
Hotels—including apartment houses without provision for cooking by tenants*	First 20,000 or less at	50
	Next 20,001 to 100,000 at	40
	Remainder over 100,000 at	30
Warehouses (storage)	First 12,500 or less at	100
	Remainder over 12,500 at	50
All others	Total wattage	100

* The demand factors of this table shall not apply to the computed load of subfeeders to areas in hospitals and hotels where entire lighting is likely to be used at one time, as in operating rooms, ballrooms, or dining rooms.

Table 220-5. Demand Loads for Household Electric Ranges, Wall-mounted Ovens, Counter-mounted Cooking Units, and Other Household Cooking Appliances over 1 3/4-kw Rating

(Column A to be used in all cases except as otherwise permitted in Note 4 on opposite page)

Number of appliances	Maximum demand, kilowatts (see notes)	Demand factors, per cent (see Note 4)	
	Column A (not over 12-kw rating)	Column B (less than $3\frac{1}{2}$-kw rating)	Column C ($3\frac{1}{2}$- to $8\frac{3}{4}$-kw rating)
1	8	80	80
2	11	75	65
3	14	70	55
4	17	66	50
5	20	62	45
6	21	59	43
7	22	56	40
8	23	53	36
9	24	51	35
10	25	49	34
11	26	47	32
12	27	45	32
13	28	43	32
14	29	41	32
15	30	40	32
16	31	39	28
17	32	38	28
18	33	37	28
19	34	36	28
20	35	35	28
21	36	34	26
22	37	33	26
23	38	32	26
24	39	31	26
25	40	30	26
26–30	⎰15 plus 1 for⎱	30	24
31–40	⎱ each range ⎰	30	22
41–50	⎰25 plus ¾ for⎱	30	20
51–60	⎱ each range ⎰	30	18
61 & over		30	16

Notes to Table 220-5

Note 1. Over 12- to 21-kw ranges all of same kilowatt rating. For ranges, individually rated more than 12 kw but not more than 21 kw, the maximum demand in column A shall be increased 5% for each additional kilowatt of rating or major fraction thereof by which the rating of individual ranges exceeds 12 kw.

Note 2. Over 12- to 21-kw ranges of unequal ratings. For ranges individually rated more than 12 kw and of different ratings but none exceeding 21 kw an average value of rating shall be calculated by adding together the ratings of all ranges to obtain the total connected load (using 12 kw for any range rated less than 12 kw) and dividing by the total number of ranges, and then the maximum demand in column A shall be increased 5% for each kw or major fraction thereof by which this average value exceeds 12 kw.

Note 3. Generally, the demand for commercial ranges should be based on the maximum name-plate rating.

Note 4. Over 1¾ to 8¾ kw. In lieu of the method provided in column A, loads rated more than 1¾ kw but not more than 8¾ kw may be considered as the sum of the name-plate ratings of all the loads, multiplied by the demand factors specified in columns B or C for the given number of loads.

Note 5. Branch-circuit load. Branch-circuit load for one range may be computed in accordance with Table 220-5. The branch-circuit load for one wall-mounted oven or one counter-mounted cooking unit shall be the name-plate rating of the appliance. The branch-circuit load for a counter-mounted cooking unit and not more than two wall-mounted ovens, all supplied from a single branch circuit and located in the same room shall be computed by adding the nameplate ratings of the individual appliances and treating this total as equivalent to one range.

Table 310-2(a). Conductor Application

Trade name	Type letter	Max operating temp	Application provisions
Rubber-covered fixture wire, solid or 7-strand	RF-1*	60°C 140°F	Fixture wiring. Limited to 300 volts
	RF-2*	60°C 140°F	Fixture wiring, and as permitted in Sec. 310-8
Rubber-covered fixture wire, flexible stranding	FF-1*	60°C 140°F	Fixture wiring. Limited to 300 volts
	FF-2*	60°C 140°F	Fixture wiring, and as permitted in Sec. 310-8
Heat-resistant, rubber-covered fixture wire, solid or 7-strand	RFH-*	75°C 167°F	Fixture wiring. Limited to 300 volts
	RFH-2*	75°C 167°F	Fixture wiring, and as permitted in Sec. 310-8
Heat-resistant, rubber-covered fixture wire, flexible stranding	FFH-1*	75°C 167°F	Fixture wiring. Limited to 300 volts
	FFH-2*	75°C 167°F	Fixture wiring, and as permitted in Sec. 310-8
Thermoplastic-covered fixture wire, solid or stranded	TF*	60°C 140°F	Fixture wiring, and as permitted in Sec. 310-8
Thermoplastic-covered fixture wire, flexible stranding	TFF*	60°C 140°F	Fixture wiring
Cotton-covered heat-resistant fixture wire	CF*	90°C 194°F	Fixture wiring. Limited to 300 volts
Asbestos-covered heat-resistant fixture wire	AF*	150°C 302°F	Fixture wiring. Limited to 300 volts and indoor dry location

* Fixture wires are not intended for installation as branch-circuit conductors or for the connection of portable or stationary appliances.

Table 310-2(a). Conductor Application (*Continued*)

Trade name	Type letter	Max operating temp	Application provisions
Silicone-rubber-insulated fixture wire, solid or 7-strand	SF-1*	200°C 392°F	Fixture wiring. Limited to 300 volts
	SF-2*	200°C 392°F	Fixture wiring, and as permitted in Sec. 310-8
Silicone-rubber-insulated fixture wire, flexible stranding	SFF-1*	150°C 302°F	Fixture wiring. Limited to 300 volts
	SFF-2*	150°C 302°F	Fixture wiring, and as permitted in Sec. 310-8
Code rubber	R	60°C 140°F	Dry locations
Heat-resistant rubber	RH	75°C 167°F	Dry locations
Heat-resistant rubber	RHH	90°C 194°F	Dry locations
Moisture-resistant rubber	RW	60°C 140°F	Dry and wet locations. For over 2,000 volts, insulation shall be ozone-resistant
Moisture- and heat-resistant rubber	RH-RW	60°C 140°F	Dry and wet locations. For over 2,000 volts, insulation shall be ozone-resistant
		75°C 167°F	Dry locations. For over 2,000 volts, insulation shall be ozone-resistant
Moisture- and heat-resistant rubber	RHW	75°C 167°F	Dry and wet locations. For over 2,000 volts, insulation shall be ozone-resistant
Latex rubber	RU	60°C 140°F	Dry locations

Table 310-2(a). Conductor Application (*Continued*)

Trade name	Type letter	Max operating temp	Application provisions
Heat-resistant latex rubber	RUH	75°C	Dry locations
Moisture-resistant latex rubber	RUW	60°C 140°F	Dry and wet locations
Thermoplastic	T	60°C 140°F	Dry locations
Moisture-resistant thermoplastic	TW	60°C 140°F	Dry and wet locations
Heat-resistant thermoplastic	THHN	90°C 194°F	Dry locations
Moisture and heat-resistant thermoplastic	THW	75°C 167°F	Dry and wet locations
Moisture and heat-resistant thermoplastic	THWN	75°C 167°F	Dry and wet locations
Thermoplastic and asbestos	TA	90°C 194°F	Switchboard wiring only
Thermoplastic and fibrous outer braid	TBS	90°C 194°F	Switchboard wiring only
Synthetic heat-resistant	SIS	90°C 194°F	Switchboard wiring only
Mineral insulation (metal sheathed)	MI	85°C 185°F	Dry and wet locations with Type O termination fittings. Maximum operating temperature for special applications 250°C
Silicone-asbestos	SA	90°C	Dry locations—maximum operating temperature for special application 125°C

Appendix

559

Table 310-2(a). Conductor Application (*Continued*)

Trade name	Type letter	Max operating temp	Application provisions
Fluorinated ethylene propylene	FEP or FEPB	90°C 194°F	Dry locations
		200°C 392°F	Dry locations—special applications
Varnished cambric	V	85°C 185°F	Dry locations only. Smaller than No. 6 by special permission
Asbestos and varnished cambric	AVA	110°C 230°F	Dry locations only
Asbestos and varnished cambric	AVL	110°C 230°F	Dry and wet locations
Asbestos and varnished cambric	AVB	90°C 194°F	Dry locations only
Asbestos	A	200°C 392°F	Dry locations only. In raceways, only for leads to or within apparatus. Limited to 300 volts
Asbestos	AA	200°C 392°F	Dry locations only. Open wiring. In raceways, only for leads to or within apparatus. Limited to 300 volts
Asbestos	AI	125°C 257°F	Dry locations only. In raceways, only for leads to or within apparatus. Limited to 300 volts
Asbestos	AIA	125°C 257°F	Dry locations only. Open wiring. In raceways, only for leads to or within apparatus
Paper		85°C 185°F	For underground service conductors, or by special permission

Table 310-12. Allowable Ampacities of Insulated Copper Conductors in Amperes

Not More than Three Conductors in Raceway or Cable or Direct Burial
(Based on room temperature of 30°C, 86°F)

Size	Temperature rating of conductor. See Table 310-2(a)					
AWG MCM	60°C (140°F)	75°C (167°F)	85°–90°C (185°F)	110°C (230°F)	125°C (257°F)	200°C (392°F)
14	15	15	25†	30	30	30
12	20	20	30†	35	40	40
10	30	30	40†	45	50	55
8	40	45	50	60	65	70
6	55	65	70	80	85	95
4	70	85	90	105	115	120
3	80	100	105	120	130	145
2	95	115	120	135	145	165
1	110	130	140	160	170	190
0	125	150	155	190	200	225
00	145	175	185	215	230	250
000	165	200	210	245	265	285
0000	195	230	235	275	310	340
250	215	255	270	315	335	
300	240	285	300	345	380	
350	260	310	325	390	420	
400	280	335	360	420	450	
500	320	380	405	470	500	
600	355	420	455	525	545	
700	385	460	490	560	600	
750	400	475	500	580	620	
800	410	490	515	600	640	
900	435	520	555			
1,000	455	545	585	680	730	
1,250	495	590	645			
1,500	520	625	700	785		
1,750	545	650	735			
2,000	560	665	775	840		

Correction factors, room temperatures over 30°C, 86°F

°C	°F					
40	104	0.82	0.88	0.90	0.94	0.95	
45	113	0.71	0.82	0.85	0.90	0.92	
50	122	0.58	0.75	0.80	0.87	0.89	
55	131	0.41	0.67	0.74	0.83	0.86	
60	140	....	0.58	0.67	0.79	0.83	0.91
70	158	...	0.35	0.52	0.71	0.76	0.87
75	167	...	....	0.43	0.66	0.72	0.86
80	176	...	....	0.30	0.61	0.69	0.84
90	194	..	....	....	0.50	0.61	0.80
100	212	.	....	...	....	0.51	0.77
120	248	...	....	....	....	....	0.69
140	284	....	....	....	....	....	0.59

These ampacities relate only to conductors described in Table 310-2(a).

† The ampacities for Types FEP, FEPB, RHH and THHN conductors for sizes AWG 14, 12 and 10 shall be the same as designated for 75°C conductors in this Table.

Author's note: The temperature ratings for the more ordinary kinds of wire are as follows:

60°C (140°F): Types R, RW, RH-RW in wet locations, T, TW

75°C (167°F): Types RH, RH-RW in dry locations, RHW, THW, THWN

85–90°C (185°F): Types RHH, TA, TBS, SA, AVB

For temperature ratings of other types, see Code Table 310-2(a) in this Appendix.

Be sure to read Code "Notes" on pages 562 and 563.

Table 310-13. Allowable Ampacities of Insulated Copper Conductors in Amperes

Single Conductor in Free Air
(Based on room temperature of 30°C, 86°F)

Size AWG MCM	Temperature rating of conductor. See Table 310-2(a)						Bare & Covered Conductor
	60°C (140°F)	75°C (167°F)	85–90°C (185°F)	110°C (230°F)	125°C (257°F)	200°C (392°F)	
14	20	20	30†	40	40	45	30
12	25	25	40†	50	50	55	40
10	40	40	55†	65	70	75	55
8	55	65	70	85	90	100	70
6	80	95	100	120	125	135	100
4	105	125	135	160	170	180	130
3	120	145	155	180	195	210	150
2	140	170	180	210	225	240	175
1	165	195	210	245	265	280	205
0	195	230	245	285	305	325	235
00	225	265	285	330	355	370	275
000	260	310	330	385	410	430	320
0000	300	360	385	445	475	510	370
250	340	405	425	495	530	. . .	410
300	375	445	480	555	590	. .	460
350	420	505	530	610	655	. . .	510
400	455	545	575	665	710	. .	555
500	515	620	660	765	815	. . .	630
600	575	690	740	855	910	. . .	710
700	630	755	815	940	1,005	. . .	780
750	655	785	845	980	1,045	. . .	810
800	680	815	880	1,020	1,085	. .	845
900	730	870	940	. .	. . . .	.	905
1,000	780	935	1,000	1,165	1,240	. .	965
1,250	890	1,065	1,130	. . . .	. . .	. . .	. . . .
1,500	980	1,175	1,260	1,450	. . .	. .	1,215
1,750	1,070	1,280	1,370	. . . .	. .	. . .	. . . .
2,000	1,155	1,385	1,470	1,715	. . .	. . .	1,405

Correction factors, room temperatures over 30°C, 86°F

°C	°F						
40	104	0.82	0.88	0.90	0.94	0.95	
45	113	0.71	0.82	0.85	0.90	0.92	
50	122	0.58	0.75	0.80	0.87	0.89	
55	131	0.41	0.67	0.74	0.83	0.86	
60	140	. . . .	0.58	0.67	0.79	0.83	0.91
70	158	. . . .	0.35	0.52	0.71	0.76	0.87
75	167	. . . .	. . . .	0.43	0.66	0.72	0.86
80	176	. . . .	. . . .	0.30	0.61	0.69	0.84
90	194	. . . .	. . . .	. .	0.50	0.61	0.80
100	212	. . . .	. . . .	. . . .	. . .	0.51	0.77
120	248	. . . .	. . . .	. . . .	. . .	. .	0.69
140	284	. . . .	. . . .	. . . .	. . . .	. . .	0.59

These ampacities relate only to conductors described in Table 310-2(a).

† The ampacities for Types FEP, FEPB, RHH and THHN conductors for sizes AWG 14, 12 and 10 shall be the same as designated for 75°C conductors in this Table.

Author's note: The temperature ratings for the more ordinary kinds of wire are as follows:

60°C (140°F): Types R, RW, RH-RW in wet locations, T, TW

75°C (167°F): Types RH, RH-RW in dry locations, RHW, THW, THWN

85–90°C (185°F): Types RHH, TA, TBS, SA, AVB

For temperature ratings of other types, see Code Table 310-2(a) in this Appendix.

Be sure to read Code "Notes" on pages 562 and 563.

Notes to Tables 310-12 through 310-15.

Ampacity. The maximum, continuous, ampacities of copper conductors are given in Tables 310-12 and 310-13. The ampacities of aluminum conductors are given in Tables 310-14 and 310-15.

1. Explanation of Tables. For explanation of Type Letters, and for recognized size of conductors for the various conductor insulations, see Sections 310-2 and 310-3. For installation requirements, see Section 310-1 through 310-7, and the various Articles of this Code. For flexible cords see Tables 400-9 and 400-11.

2. Application of Tables. For open wiring on insulators and for concealed knob-and-tube work, the allowable ampacities of Tables 310-13 and 310-15 shall be used. For all other recognized wiring methods, the allowable ampacities of Tables 310-12 and 310-14 shall be used, unless otherwise provided in this Code.

3. Aluminum Conductors. For aluminum conductors, the allowable ampacities shall be in accordance with Tables 310-14 and 310-15.

4. Bare Conductors. Where bare conductors are used with insulated conductors, their allowable ampacities shall be limited to that permitted for the insulated conductors of the same size.

5. Type MI Cable. The temperature limitation on which the ampacities of Type MI cable are based, is determined by the insulating materials used in the end seal. Termination fittings incorporating unimpregnated organic insulating materials are limited to 85°C operation.

6. Ultimate Insulation Temperature. In no case shall conductors be associated together in such a way with respect to the kind of circuit, the wiring method employed, or the number of conductors, that the limiting temperature of the conductors will be exceeded.

7. Use of Conductors with Higher Operating Temperatures. Where the room temperature is within 10 degrees C of the maximum allowable operating temperature of the insulation, it is desirable to use an insulation with a higher maximum allowable operating temperature; although insulation can be used in a room temperature approaching its maximum allowable operating temperature limit if the current is reduced in accordance with the Correction Factors for different room temperatures.

8. More Than Three Conductors in a Raceway or Cable. Tables 310-12 and 310-14 give the allowable ampacities for not more than three conductors in a raceway or cable. Where the number of conductors in a raceway or cable exceeds three, the allowable ampacity of each conductor shall be reduced as shown in the following Table:

Number of Conductors	Per cent of values in Tables 310–12 and 310–14
4 to 6	80
7 to 24	70
25 to 42	60
43 and above	50

Exception No. 1—When conductors of different systems, as provided in Section 300-3, are installed in a common raceway the derating factors shown above apply to the number of Power and Lighting (Articles 210, 215, 220 and 230) conductors only.

Where the number of conductors in a raceway or cable exceeds three, or where single conductors or multi-conductor cables are stacked or bundled without maintaining spacing as required in Article 318 and are not installed in raceways, the individual ampacity of each conductor shall be reduced as shown in the above table.

Exception No. 2—The derating factors of Sections 210-23(b) and 220-2 (second paragraph) do not apply when the above derating factors are also required.

9. Where Type RH-RW rubber insulated wire is used in wet locations the allowable ampacities shall be that of Column 2 in Tables 310-12 through 310-15. Where used in dry locations the allowable ampacities shall be that of Column 3 in Tables 310-12 through 310-15.

10. Overcurrent Protection. Where the standard ratings and settings of overcurrent devices do not correspond with the ratings and settings allowed for conductors, the next higher standard rating and setting may be used.

Exception—Except as limited in Section 240-5.

11. Neutral Conductor. A neutral conductor which carries only the un-balanced current from other conductors, as in the case of normally balanced circuits of three or more conductors, shall not be counted in determining ampacities as provided for in Note 8.

In a 3-wire circuit consisting of two phase wires and the neutral of a 4-wire, 3-phase WYE connected system, a common conductor carries approximately the same current as the other conductors and is not therefore considered as a neutral conductor.

12. Voltage Drop. The allowable ampacities in Tables 310-12 through 310-15 are based on temperature alone and do not take voltage drop into consideration.

13. Deterioration of Insulation. It should be noted that even the best grades of rubber insulation will deteriorate in time, so eventually will need to be replaced.

14. Aluminum Sheathed Cable. The ampacities of Type ALS cable are determined by the temperature limitation of the insulated conductors in-corporated within the cable. Hence the ampacities of aluminum sheathed cable may be determined from the columns in Tables 310-12 and 310-14 applicable to the type of insulated conductors employed within the cable. See Note 9.

Table 430-146. Overcurrent Protection for Motors

(See Tables 430-152 and 430-153)

These values are in accordance with Secs. 430-6, 430-22, 430-32, 430-34, 430-52, 430-59, except as follows: The current values in column 1 are to be taken from Tables 430-147 through 430-150, including footnotes, but the values shown for running protection in columns 2 and 3 must be modified if all motors other than open-type motors marked to have a temperature rise of not over 40°C as required by Sec. 430-32. The current values shown in columns 2 and 3 must be reduced by 8% for values in columns 4, 5, 6, and 7, see Secs. 430-52, and 430-59. See Sec. 430-53 for values to be used for several motors on one branch circuit. For running protection of motors, see Sec. 430-32. For setting of motor branch-circuit protective devices, see tables in Secs. 430-152 and 430-153. For group-ing of small motors under the protection of a single set of fuses, see Sec. 430-53.

Full-load-current rating of motor, amperes*	For running protection of motors		Maximum allowable rating or setting of branch-circuit protective devices							
	Maximum rating of non-adjustable protective devices, amperes	Maximum setting of adjustable protective devices, amperes	With Code letters Single-phase, squirrel-cage, and synchronous. Full-voltage, resistor, or reactor starting, Code letters F to V inclusive. Without Code letters — Same as above		With Code letters Single-phase, squirrel-cage, and synchronous. Full-voltage, resistor, or reactor start, Code letters B to E inclusive. Autotransformer start, Code letters F to V inclusive. Without Code letters (Not more than 30 amps) Squirrel-cage and synchronous, autotransformer start, high-reactance squirrel-cage†		With Code letters Squirrel-cage and synchronous autotransformer start, Code letters B to E inclusive. Without Code letters (More than 30 amps) Squirrel-cage and synchronous autotransformer start, high-reactance squirrel-cage†		With Code letters All motors code letter A. DC and wound-rotor motors. Without Code letters A	
			Fuses	Circuit breakers (non-adjustable overload trip)	Fuses	Circuit breakers (non-adjustable overload trip)	Fuses	Circuit breakers (non-adjustable overload trip)	Fuses	Circuit breakers (non-adjustable overload trip)
(1)	(2)	(3)	(4)		(5)		(6)			
1	2	1.25	15	15	15	15	15	15	15	15
2	3	2.50	15	15	15	15	15	15	15	15
3	4	3.75	15	15	15	15	15	15	15	15
4	6	5.0	15	15	15	15	15	15	15	15
5	8	6.25	15	15	15	15	15	15	15	15
6	8	7.50	20	15	15	15	15	15	15	15
7	10	8.75	25	20	20	20	15	15	15	15
8	10	10.0	25	20	20	20	20	20	15	15

9	12	11.25	30	30	25	20	20	20	15	15
10	15	12.50	30	30	25	20	20	20	15	15
11	15	13.75	35	30	30	30	25	30	20	20
12	15	15.00	40	30	30	30	25	30	20	20
13	20	16.25	40	40	35	30	30	30	20	20
14	20	17.50	45	40	35	30	30	30	25	30
15	20	18.75	45	40	40	30	30	30	25	30
16	20	20.00	50	40	40	40	35	40	25	30
17	25	21.25	60	50	45	40	35	40	30	30
18	25	22.50	60	50	45	40	40	40	30	30
19	25	23.75	60	50	50	40	40	40	30	30
20	25	25.00	60	50	50	40	40	40	30	30
22	30	27.50	70	70	60	50	45	50	35	40
24	30	30.00	80	70	60	50	50	50	40	40
26	35	32.50	80	70	70	70	60	70	40	40
28	35	35.00	90	70	70	70	60	70	45	50
30	40	37.50	90	100	80	70	60	70	45	50
32	40	40.00	100	100	80	70	70	70	50	50
34	45	42.50	110	100	90	70	70	70	60	70
36	45	45.00	110	100	90	100	80	100	60	70
38	50	47.50	125	100	100	100	80	100	60	70
40	50	50.00	125	100	100	100	80	100	70	70
42	50	52.50	125	125	110	100	90	100	70	70
44	60	55.00	125	125	110	100	90	100	80	70
46	60	57.50	150	125	125	100	100	100	70	70
48	60	60.00	150	125	125	100	100	100	80	100
50	60	62.50	150	125	125	100	100	100	80	100
52	70	65.00	175	150	150	125	110	125	80	100
54	70	67.50	175	150	150	125	110	125	90	100
56	70	70.00	175	150	150	125	125	125	90	100
58	70	72.50	175	150	150	125	125	125	90	100
60	80	75.00	200	150	150	125	125	125	90	100
62	80	77.50	200	175	175	125	125	125	100	100
64	80	80.00	200	175	175	150	150	150	100	100
66	80	82.50	200	175	175	150	150	150	100	100
68	90	85.00	225	175	175	150	150	150	110	125

* For motors with full-load-current rating greater than 68 amp, see your copy of the Code.
† High-reactance squirrel-cage motors are those designed to limit the starting current by means of deep-slot secondaries or double-wound secondaries and are generally started on full voltage.

Table 430-148.   Full-load Currents in Amperes
Singe-phase Alternating-current Motors

The following values of full-load currents are for motors running at usual speeds and motors with normal torque characteristics.   Motors built for especially low speeds or high torques may have higher full-load currents, in which case the name-plate current ratings should be used.

To obtain full-load currents of 208- and 200-volt motors, increase corresponding 230-volt motor full-load currents by 10 and 15%, respectively.

Horsepower	115 volts	230 volts	440 volts
⅙	4.4	2.2	
¼	5.8	2.9	
⅓	7.2	3.6	
½	9.8	4.9	
¾	13.8	6.9	
1	16	8	
1½	20	10	
2	24	12	
3	34	17	
5	56	28	
7½	80	40	21
10	100	50	26

Table 430-150. Full-load Current*
Three-phase Alternating-current Motors

	Induction-type squirrel-cage and wound-rotor, amperes					Synchronous-type unity power factor, amperes†			
Horse-power	110 volts	220 volts	440 volts	550 volts	2,300 volts	220 volts	440 volts	550 volts	2,300 volts
½	4	2	1	.8					
¾	5.6	2.8	1.4	1.1					
1	7	3.5	1.8	1.4					
1½	10	5	2.5	2.0					
2	13	6.5	3.3	2.6					
3	. . .	9	4.5	4					
5	. . .	15	7.5	6					
7½	. . .	22	11	9					
10	. . .	27	14	11					
15	. . .	40	20	16					
20	. . .	52	26	21					
25	. . .	64	32	26	7	54	27	22	5.4
30	. . .	78	39	31	8.5	65	33	26	6.5
40	. . .	104	52	41	10.5	86	43	35	8
50	. . .	125	63	50	13	108	54	44	10
60	. . .	150	75	60	16	128	64	51	12
75	. . .	185	93	74	19	161	81	65	15
100	. . .	246	123	98	25	211	106	85	20
125	. . .	310	155	124	31	264	132	106	25
150	. . .	360	180	144	37	. . .	158	127	30
200	. . .	480	240	192	48	. . .	210	168	40

For full-load currents of 208- and 200-volt motors, increase the corresponding 220-volt motor full-load current by 6 and 10%, respectively.

* These values of full-load current are for motors running at speeds usual for belted motors and motors with normal torque characteristics. Motors built for especially low speeds or high torques may require more running current, in which case the name-plate current rating should be used.

† For 90 and 80% power factor the above figures should be multiplied by 1.1 and 1.25, respectively.

Table 430-151. Locked-Rotor Current Conversion Table

As Determined from Horsepower and Voltage Rating
[For use only with Sec. 430-83, Exception No. 3, and 430-110(b)]

| Max horsepower rating | Max interrupting capacity, amperes | | | | | |
| | Single phase | | Two or three phase | | | |
	115 volts	230 volts	110 volts	220 volts	440 volts	550 volts
½	58.8	29.4	24	12	6	4.8
¾	82.8	41.4	33.6	16.8	8.4	6.6
1	96	48	42	21	10.8	8.4
1½	120	60	60	30	15	12
2	144	72	78	39	19.8	15.6
3	204	102	. . .	54	27	24
5	336	168	. . .	90	45	36
7½	480	240	. . .	132	66	54
10	600	300	. . .	162	84	66
15	. . .	. . .	. . .	240	120	96
20	. . .	. . .	. . .	312	156	126
25	. . .	. . .	. . .	384	192	156
30	. . .	. . .	. . .	468	234	186
40	. . .	. . .	. . .	624	312	246
50	. . .	. . .	. . .	750	378	300
60	. . .	. . .	. . .	900	450	360
75	. . .	. . .	. . .	1,110	558	444
100	. . .	. . .	. . .	1,476	738	588
125	. . .	. . .	. . .	1,860	930	744
150	. . .	. . .	. . .	2,160	1,080	864
200	. . .	. . .	. . .	2,880	1,440	1,152

CODE CHAPTER 9

Code Chapter 9 consists of two parts:

A. Tables not shown elsewhere in the Code. Only Tables 1, 1A, 1B, and 8 are of sufficient general interest to warrant repeating here. The others are of minor interest or concern projects beyond the scope of this book. However, *parts* of some of these tables have already been shown in the text of this book.

B. Examples. These show how to apply Code rules and will be repeated in the pages following.

Table 1.   Maximum Number of Conductors in Trade Sizes of Conduit or Tubing

New Work or Rewiring—Types RF-2, RFH-2, R, RH, RW, RHH, RHW, RH-RW

New Work—FEP, FEPB, RUH, RUW, T, TF, THHN, THW, THWN, TW

Derating factors for more than three conductors in raceways, see Note 8, Tables 310–12 through 310–15.

(See Section 300–17, 300–18, 346–6 and 348–6)

New Work or Rewiring

Size AWG or MCM	Maximum number of conductors in conduit or tubing (Based upon % conductor fill, Table 3, Chap. 9, for new work)											
	½ Inch	¾ Inch	1 Inch	1¼ Inch	1½ Inch	2 Inch	2½ Inch	3 Inch	3½ Inch	4 Inch	5 Inch	6 Inch
18	7	12	20	35	49	80	115	176				
16	6	10	17	30	41	68	98	150				
14	4	6	10	18	25	41	58	90	121	155		
12	3	5	8	15	21	34	50	76	103	132	208	
10	1	4	7	13	17	29	41	64	86	110	173	
8	1	3	4	7	10	17	25	38	52	67	105	152
6	1	1	3	4	6	10	15	23	32	41	64	93
4	1	1	1	3*	5	8	12	18	24	31	49	72
3		1	1	3	4	7	10	16	21	28	44	63
2		1	1	3	3	6	9	14	19	24	38	55
1		1	1	1	3	4	7	10	14	18	29	42
0			1	1	2	4	6	9	12	16	25	37
00			1	1	1	3	5	8	11	14	22	32
000			1	1	1	3	4	7	9	12	19	27
0000				1	1	2	3	6	8	10	16	23

* Where an existing service run of conduit or electrical metallic tubing does not exceed 50 ft in length and does not contain more than the equivalent of two quarter bends from end to end, two No. 4 insulated and one No. 4 bare conductors may be installed in 1-inch conduit or tubing.

Table 1A. Maximum Number of Conductors in Trade Sizes of Conduit or Tubing

Rewiring—Types TF, T, THW, TW, RUH, RUW

Derating factors for more than three conductors in raceways
See Note 8, Tables 310–12 through 310–15

(See Section 300–17, 300–18, 346–6 and 348–6)

Rewiring

Size AWG or MCM	Maximum number of conductors in conduit or tubing (Based upon % conductor-fill, Table 3, Chapter 9, for new work)											
	½ Inch	¾ Inch	1 Inch	1¼ Inch	1½ Inch	2 Inch	2½ Inch	3 Inch	3½ Inch	4 Inch	5 Inch	6 Inch
18	13	24	38	68	93	152	—	—	—	—	—	—
16	11	19	31	55	75	123	176	270	—	—	—	—
14	5	10	16	29	40	65	93	143	192	—	—	—
12	4	8	13	24	32	53	76	117	157	202	—	—
10	4	6	11	19	26	43	61	95	127	163	257	—
8	1	4	6	11	15	25	36	56	75	96	152	219
6	1	2	4	7	10	16	23	36	48	62	97	141
4	1	1	3	5	7	12	17	27	36	46	73	106
3	1	1	2	4	6	10	15	23	31	40	63	91
2	1	1	1	4	5	9	13	20	27	34	54	78
1	—	1	1	2	4	6	9	14	19	25	39	57
0	—	1	1	2	3	5	8	12	16	21	33	48
00	—	1	1	1	3	4	7	10	14	18	28	41
000	—	—	1	1	2	4	5	9	12	15	24	35
0000	—	—	1	1	1	3	5	7	10	13	20	29

Table 1B. Maximum Number of Conductors in Trade Sizes of Conduit or Tubing

Rewiring—Types FEP, FEPB, THHN, THWN

Derating factors for more than three conductors in raceways
See Note 8, Tables 310–12 through 310–15

(See Section 300–17, 300–18, 346–6 and 348–6)

Rewiring

Size AWG or MCM	Maximum number of conductors in conduit or tubing (Based upon % conductor-fill, Table 3, Chapter 9, for new work)											
	½ Inch	¾ Inch	1 Inch	1¼ Inch	1½ Inch	2 Inch	2½ Inch	3 Inch	3½ Inch	4 Inch	5 Inch	6 Inch
14	13	24	39	69	94	154	220	—	—	—	—	—
12	10	18	29	51	70	114	164	252	—	—	—	—
10	6	11	18	32	44	72	104	160	215	276	—	—
8	3	6	10	19	26	42	60	93	125	160	252	—
6	1	4	6	11	15	25	37	56	76	98	154	222
4	1	2	4	7	9	16	22	35	47	60	94	136
3	1	1	3	6	8	13	19	29	39	51	80	116
2	1	1	3	5	7	11	16	25	33	43	67	97
1	1	1	1	3	5	8	12	18	25	32	50	72
0	—	1	1	3	4	7	10	15	21	27	42	61
00	—	1	1	2	3	6	8	13	17	22	35	51
000	—	1	1	1	3	5	7	11	14	18	29	42
0000	—	—	1	1	2	4	6	9	12	15	24	35

Table 8. Properties of Conductors

Size, AWG	Area, circular mils	Concentric lay stranded conductors		Bare conductors		DC resistance, ohms per 1,000 feet at 25°C, 77°F		
						Copper		Aluminum
		No. wires	Diam each wire, inches	Diam, inches	Area, square inches*	Bare cond.	Tin'd. cond.	
18	1,624	Solid	0.0403	0.0403	0.0013	6.510	6.77	10.9
16	2,583	Solid	0.0508	0.0508	0.0020	4.094	4.25	6.85
14	4,107	Solid	0.0641	0.0641	0.0032	2.575	2.68	4.31
12	6,530	Solid	0.0808	0.0808	0.0051	1.619	1.69	2.71
10	10,380	Solid	0.1019	0.1019	0.0081	1.018	1.06	1.70
8	16,510	Solid	0.1285	0.1285	0.0130	0.641	0.660	1.07
6	26,250	7	0.0612	0.184	0.027	0.410	0.426	0.674
4	41,740	7	0.0772	0.232	0.042	0.259	0.269	0.423
3	52,640	7	0.0867	0.260	0.053	0.205	0.213	0.336
2	66,370	7	0.0974	0.292	0.067	0.162	0.169	0.266
1	83,690	19	0.0664	0.332	0.087	0.129	0.134	0.211
0	105,500	19	0.0745	0.373	0.109	0.102	0.106	0.168
00	133,100	19	0.0837	0.418	0.137	0.0811	0.0844	0.134
000	167,800	19	0.0940	0.470	0.173	0.0642	0.0668	0.105
0000	211,600	19	0.1055	0.528	0.219	0.0509	0.0524	0.0837
	250,000	37	0.0822	0.575	0.260	0.0431	0.0444	0.0708
	300,000	37	0.0900	0.630	0.312	0.0360	0.0371	0.0590
	350,000	37	0.0973	0.681	0.364	0.0308	0.0318	0.0506
	400,000	37	0.1040	0.728	0.416	0.0270	0.0278	0.0443
	500,000	37	0.1162	0.814	0.520	0.0216	0.0225	0.0354
	600,000	61	0.0992	0.893	0.626	0.0180	0.0185	0.0295
	700,000	61	0.1071	0.964	0.730	0.0154	0.0159	0.0253
	750,000	61	0.1109	0.998	0.782	0.0144	0.0148	0.0236
	800,000	61	0.1145	1.031	0.835	0.0135	0.0139	0.0221
	900,000	61	0.1215	1.093	0.938	0.0120	0.0124	0.0197
	1,000,000	61	0.1280	1.152	1.042	0.0108	0.0111	0.0176
	1,250,000	91	0.1172	1.289	1.305	0.00864	0.00890	0.0142
	1,500,000	91	0.1284	1.412	1.566	0.00719	0.00740	0.0118
	1,750,000	127	0.1174	1.526	1.829	0.00617	0.00636	0.0101
	2,000,000	127	0.1255	1.631	2.089	0.00539	0.00555	0.00884

* Area given is that of a circle having a diameter equal to the over-all diameter of a stranded conductor.

The values given in the table are those given in Circular 31 of the National Bureau of Standards except that those shown in the eighth column are those given in Specification B33 of the American Society for Testing Materials.

The resistance values given in the table are applicable only to direct current. When conductors larger than No. 4/0 are used with alternating current, the multiplying factors in Table 9, Chap. 9, of the Code should be used to compensate for skin effect.

EXAMPLES

Selection of Conductors. In the following examples, the size of conductor has been selected on the basis of the allowable current-carrying capacities tabulated in the second column of Table 310-12. If other types of insulated conductors are used, or if the conductors are run open or with more than three conductors in a raceway, the size of conductor may vary from those shown. Tables 310-12 through 310-15 and notes thereto should be consulted in selecting the size of conductor for a particular installation.

Voltage. For uniform application of the provisions of Art. 210, 215, and 220 a nominal voltage of 115 and 230 volts shall be used in computing the ampere load on the conductor.

Fractions of an Ampere. Where the computations result in a fraction of an ampere, such fractions may be dropped.

Ranges. For the computation of the range loads in these examples column A of Table 220-5 has been used. For optional methods, see columns B and C of Table 220-5.

EXAMPLE NO. 1.   SINGLE-FAMILY DWELLING

Dwelling has a floor area of 1,500 sq ft exclusive of unoccupied cellar, unfinished attic, and open porches.   It has a 12-kw range.

Computed Load (see Sec. 220-4):
   General lighting load:
      1500 sq ft at 3 watts per sq ft ....   4,500 watts

Minimum Number of Branch Circuits Required (see Sec. 220-3):
   General lighting load:
      4,500 ÷ 115 = 39.1 amp or three 15-amp 2-wire circuits or two 20-amp 2-wire circuits
   Small appliance load: two 2-wire 20-amp circuits [Sec. 220-3(b)].

Minimum Size Feeders Required (see Sec. 220-4):
   Computed load:
      General lighting ....   4,500 watts
      Small appliance load ....   3,000 watts
            Total (without range) ....   7,500 watts

      3,000 watts at 100% ....   3,000 watts
      7,500 − 3,000 = 4,500 watts at 35% = ...   1,575 watts
            Net computed (without range) ....   4,575 watts
      Range load (see Table 220-5) ....   8,000 watts
            Net computed (with range) .... 12,575 watts

For 115/230-volt 3-wire system feeders:

$$12,575 ÷ 230 = 55 \text{ amp}$$

Therefore, feeder size for total load may be selected on basis of 55-amp load (see Sec. 215-2).

Net computed load exceeds 10 kw, so service conductors shall be 100 amp (see Sec. 230-41, Exception No. 1).

EXAMPLE NO. 1(a). SINGLE-FAMILY DWELLING

Same conditions as Example No. 1, plus addition of one 6-amp 230-volt room air-conditioning unit and three 12-amp 115-volt room air-conditioning units. See Art. 422, Part F.

From Example No. 1, feeder current is 55 amp (3-wire, 230-volt)

Line A	Neutral	Line B	
55		55	amp from Example No. 1
6		6	one 230-volt air-conditioning motor
12		12	two 115-volt air-conditioning motors
—		12	one 115-volt air-conditioning motor
3		3	25% of largest motor (see Sec. 430-24)
76		88	amp per line

Therefore, feeder size for total load may be selected on basis of 88-amp load. For feeder overcurrent protection see Secs. 215-4 and 430-63.

EXAMPLE NO. 1(b). SINGLE-FAMILY DWELLING

Optional Calculation for One-family Dwelling (Sec. 220-7)

Dwelling has a floor area of 1,500 sq ft exclusive of unoccupied cellar, unfinished attic, and open porches. It has a 12-kw range, a 2.5-kw water heater, a 1.2-kw dishwasher, 9 kw of electric space heating installed in five rooms, a 4.5-kw clothes dryer, and a 6-amp 230-volt room air-conditioning unit.

Air conditioner kw is $6 \times 230 \div 1,000 = 1.38$ kw

1.38 kw is less than the connected load of 9 kw of space heating; therefore, the air-conditioner load need not be included in the service calculation [see Sec. 220-4(k)].

1,500 sq ft at 3 watts	4.5 kw
Two 20-amp appliance outlet circuits at 1,500 watts each	3.0 kw
Range (at name-plate rating)	12.0 kw
Water heater	2.5 kw
Dishwasher	1.2 kw
Space heating	9.0 kw
Clothes dryer	4.5 kw
	36.7 kw

First 10 kw at 100% = 10.00 kw
Remainder at 40% (26.7 kw × .4) = 10.68 kw
Calculated load for service size .... 20.68 kw = 20,680 watts

$$20,680 \div 230 = 90 \text{ amp}$$

Therefore, this dwelling may be served by a 100-amp service.

EXAMPLE NO. 1(c).   SINGLE-FAMILY DWELLING

Optional Calculation for One-family Dwelling (See Sec. 220-7)

Dwelling has a floor area of 1,500 sq ft exclusive of unoccupied cellar, unfinished attic, and open porches.   It has three 20-amp small appliance circuits, two 4-kw wall-mounted ovens, one 5.1-kw counter-mounted cooking unit, a 4.5-kw water heater, 1.2-kw dishwasher, a 4.2-kw combination clothes washer and dryer, six 7-amp 230-volt room air-conditioning units, and a 1.5-kw permanently installed bathroom space heater.

Air-conditioning kw calculation:

$$\text{Total amperes } 6 \times 7 = 42.00 \text{ amp}$$
$$25\% \text{ of largest motor } 0.25 \times 7 = \underline{\quad 1.75 \text{ amp}}$$
$$43.75 \text{ amp}$$
$$43.75 \times 230 \div 1,000 = 10.1 \text{ kw of air-conditioner load}$$

Load included at 100%:

Air conditioning	10.1 kw
Space heater [omit, see Sec. 220-4(k)]	

Other Load:

1,500 sq ft at 3 watts	4.5
Three 20-amp small appliance circuits	
at 1,500 watts	4.5
2 ovens	8.
1 cooking unit	5.1
Water heater	4.5
Dishwasher	1.2
Washer/dryer	4.2
Total other load	32.0
First 10 kw at 100%	10.0 kw
Remainder at 40% (22 kw × 0.4)	8.8 kw
Total calculated load	28.9 kw = 28,900 watts

$$28,900 \div 230 = 126 \text{ amp (service rating)}$$

EXAMPLE NO. 2.   SMALL ROADSIDE FRUITSTAND
WITH NO SHOW WINDOWS

A small roadside fruitstand with no show windows has a floor area of 150 sq ft.   The electrical load consists of general lighting and a 1,000-watt floodlight.   There are no other outlets.

Computed Load (Sec. 220-4):
General lighting:*
150 sq ft at 3 watts per sq ft $\times$ 1.25 = 562 watts
(3 watts per sq ft for stores)
562 watts $\div$ 115 = 4.88 amp

One 15-amp 2 wire branch circuit required (Section 220-3)

Minimum Size Service Conductor Required (Sec. 230-41 Exception No. 2):
Computed load .... 562 watts
Floodlight load .... 1,000 watts
Total load .... 1,562 watts

1,562 $\div$ 115 = 13.6 amp

Use No. 8 service conductor (Sec. 230-41 Exception No. 2)
Use a 30-amp service switch or breaker (Sec. 230-71)

* See Footnote on next page.

EXAMPLE NO. 3. STORE BUILDING

A store 50 by 60 ft, or 3,000 sq ft, has 30 ft of show window.

Computed Load (Sec. 220-4):
General lighting load:*
3,000 sq ft at 3 watts per sq ft × 1.25 . . . .   11,250 watts
Show-window lighting load:†
30 ft at 200 watts per ft . . . .   6,000 watts

Minimum Number of Branch Circuits Required (Sec. 220-3):
General lighting load:‡ 11,250 ÷ 230 = 49 amp for 3-wire, 115/230 volts; or 98 amp for 2-wire, 115 volts:
Three 30-amp, 2-wire; and one 15-amp, 2-wire circuits; or
Five 20-amp, 2-wire circuits; or
Three 20-amp, 2-wire, and three 15-amp, 2-wire circuits; or
Seven 15-amp, 2-wire circuits; or
Three 15-amp, 3-wire, and one 15-amp, 2-wire circuits.

Special lighting load (show window): [Secs. 220-2 Exception No. 2 and 220-4(b)]: 6,000 ÷ 230 = 26 amp for 3-wire, 115/230 volts; or 52 amp for 2-wire, 115 volts:
Four 15-amp, 2-wire circuits; or
Three 20-amp, 2-wire circuits; or
Two 15-amp, 3-wire circuits.

Minimum Size Feeders (or Service Conductors) Required (Section 215-2):
For 115/230-volts, 3-wire system:
Ampere load: 49 plus 26 = 75 amp (Sec. 220-2):
Size of each feeder, No. 3

For 115-volt system:
Ampere load: 98 plus 52 = 150 amp (Sec. 220-2):
Size of each feeder, No. 3/0

* The above examples assume that the entire general lighting load is likely to be used for long periods of time and the load is therefore increased by 25% in accordance with Sec. 220-2. The 25% increase is not applicable to any portion of the load not used for long periods.

† If show-window load computed as per Sec. 220-2, the unit load per outlet to be increased 25%.

‡ The load on individual branch circuits not to exceed 80% of the branch-circuit rating [Sec. 210-23(b)].

EXAMPLE NO. 4. MULTIFAMILY DWELLING

Multifamily dwelling having a total floor area of 32,000 sq ft with 40 apartments.

Meters in two banks of 20 each and individual subfeeders to each apartment.

One-half of the apartments are equipped with electric ranges of not exceeding 12 kw each.

Area of each apartment is 800 sq ft.

Computed Load for Each Apartment (Art. 220):

General lighting load:
800 sq ft at 3 watts per sq ft .... 2,400 watts
Special appliance load:
Electric range .... 8,000 watts

Minimum Number of Branch Circuits Required for Each Apartment (Sec. 220-3):

General lighting load: 2,400 ÷ 115 = 21 amp or two 15-amp, 2-wire circuits or two 20-amp, 2-wire circuits.

Small appliance load: Two 2-wire circuits of No. 12 wire [see Sec. 220-3(b)].

Range circuit: 8,000 ÷ 230 = 34 amp or a circuit of two No. 8's and one No. 10 as permitted by Sec. 210-9(c).

Minimum Size Subfeeder Required for Each Apartment (Sec. 215-2):

Computed load (Art. 220):
General lighting load .... 2,400 watts
Small appliance load, two 20-amp circuits .... 3,000 watts
Total computed load (without ranges) ..... 5,400 watts

Application of demand factor:
3,000 watts at 100% .... 3,000 watts
2,400 watts at 35% .... 840 watts
Net computed load (without ranges) ...... 3,840 watts
Range load .... 8,000 watts
Net computed load (with ranges) .... 11,840 watts

For 115/230-volt, 3-wire system (without ranges):
Net computed load, 3,840 ÷ 230 = 16.7 amp
Size of each subfeeder (see Sec. 215-2).

For 115/230-volt, 3-wire system (with ranges):
Net computed load, 11,840 ÷ 230 = 51.5 amp
Size of each ungrounded subfeeder, No. 6.

Neutral subfeeder:

Lighting and small appliance load	3,840 watts
Range load, 8,000 watts at 70% [see Sec. 220-4(f)]	5,600 watts
Net computed load (neutral)	9,440 watts

9,440 ÷ 230 = 41 amp

Size of neutral subfeeder, No. 6.

Minimum Size Feeders Required from Service Equipment to Meter Bank

(for 20 apartments—10 with ranges):

Total computed load:

Lighting and small appliance load, 20 × 5,400	108,000 watts

Application of demand factor:

3,000 watts at 100%	3,000 watts
105,000 watts at 35%	36,750 watts
Net computed lighting and small appliance load	39,750 watts
Range load, 10 ranges (less than 12 kw; column A, Table 220-5)	25,000 watts
Net computed load (with ranges)	64,750 watts

For 115/230-volt, 3-wire system:

Net computed load, 64,750 ÷ 230 = 282 amp

Size of each ungrounded feeder to each meter bank: 500,000 c.m.

Neutral feeder:

Lighting and small appliance load	39,750 watts
Range load: 25,000 watts at 70% [see Sec. 220-4(f)]	17,500 watts
Computed load (neutral)	57,250 watts

57,250 ÷ 230 = 249 amp

Further demand factor [Sec. 220-4(f)]:

200 amp at 100%	= 200 amp
49 amp at 70%	= 34 amp
Net computed load (neutral)	234 amp

Size of neutral feeder to each meter bank: 300,000 c.m.

Minimum Size Main Feeder (or Service Conductors) Required
(for 40 apartments—20 with ranges):

Total computed load:

Lighting and small appliance load, 40 × 5,400 ...   216,000 watts

Application of demand factor:

3,000 watts at 100%	3,000 watts
117,000 watts at 35%	40,950 watts
96,000 watts at 25%	24,000 watts
Net computed lighting and small appliance load	67,950 watts
Range load, 20 ranges (less than 12 kw, column A, Table 220-5)	35,000 watts
Net computed load	102,950 watts

For 115/230-volt, 3-wire system:

Net computed load, 102,950 ÷ 230 = 448 amp

Size of each ungrounded main feeder: 1,000,000 c.m.

Neutral feeder:

Lighting and small appliance load	67,950 watts
Range load, 35,000 watts at 70% [see Sec. 220-4(f)]	24,500 watts
Computed load (neutral)	92,450 watts
92,450 ÷ 230 = 402 amp	

Further demand factor [see Section 220-4(f)]:

200 amp at 100%	= 200 amp
202 amp at 70%	= 141 amp
Net computed load (neutral)	341 amp

Size of neutral main feeder: 600,000 c.m.

See Tables 310-12 through 310-15, Notes 8 and 12.

EXAMPLE NO. 5. CALCULATION OF NEUTRAL FEEDER
(See Sec. 220-4)

The following example illustrates the method of calculating size of neutral feeder for the computed load of a 5-wire, 2-phase system where it is desired to modify the load in accordance with provisions of Sec. 220-4.

An installation consisting of a computed load of 250 amp connected between neutral feeder and each underground feeder.

Neutral Feeder (maximum unbalance of load 250 amp $\times$ 140% = 350 amp):

200 amp (first)	at 100% =	200 amp
150 amp (excess)	at 70% =	105 amp
Computed load		305 amp

Size of neutral feeder: 500,000 c.m.

EXAMPLE NO. 6. MAXIMUM DEMAND FOR RANGE LOADS

Table 220-5, column A, applies to ranges not over 12 kw. The application of Note 1 to ranges over 12 kw (and not over 21 kw) is illustrated in the following examples:

A. Ranges all of same rating:

Assume 24 ranges each rated 16 kw.

From column A the maximum demand for 24 ranges of 12-kw rating is 39 kw.

16 kw exceeds 12 kw by 4.

5% $\times$ 4 = 20% (5% increase for each kw in excess of 12).

30 kw $\times$ 20% = 7.8 kw increase.

39 + 7.8 = 46.8 kw: value to be used in selection of feeders.

B. Ranges of unequal rating:

Assume 5 ranges each rated 11 kw.

2 ranges each rated 12 kw.

20 ranges each rated 13.5 kw.

3 ranges each rated 18 kw.

5 $\times$ 12	=	60	Use 12 kw for range rated less than 12.
2 $\times$ 12	=	24	
20 $\times$ 13.5	=	270	
3 $\times$ 18	=	54	
		408 kw	

408 $\div$ 30 = 13.6 kw (average to be used for computation)

From column A the demand for 30 ranges of 12 kw rating is 15 + 30 = 45 kw.

13.6 exceeds 12 by 1.6 (use 2).

5% $\times$ 2 = 10% (5% increase for each kw in excess of 12).

45 kw $\times$ 10% = 4.5 kw increase.

45 + 4.5 = 49.5 kw = value to be used in selection of feeders.

EXAMPLE NO. 7. RANGES ON A 3-PHASE SYSTEM
[Sec. 220-4(d)]

Thirty ranges rated at 12 kw each are supplied by a 3-phase, 4-wire, 120/208-volt feeder, 10 ranges on each phase.

As there are 20 ranges connected to each ungrounded conductor, the load should be calculated on the basis of 20 ranges (or in case of unbalance, twice the maximum number between any two phase wires) since diversity applies only to the number of ranges connected to adjacent phases and not the total.

The current in any one conductor will be one-half the total watt load of two adjacent phases divided by the line-to-neutral voltage. In this case, 20 ranges, from Table 220-5, will have a total watt load of 35,000 watts for two phases; therefore, the current in the feeder conductor would be:

$$17,500 \div 120 = 146 \text{ amp}$$

On a three-phases basis the load would be:

$$3 \times 17,500 = 52,500 \text{ watts}$$

and the current in each feeder conductor—

$$\frac{52,500}{208 \times 1.73} = 146 \text{ amp}$$

EXAMPLE NO. 8. MOTORS, CONDUCTORS, AND OVERCURRENT PROTECTION
(See Secs. 430-22, 430-24, 430-32, and 430-52)

Determine the size of conductors, the motor-running overcurrent protection, the branch-circuit protection, and the feeder protection for one 25-hp squirrel-cage induction motor (full-voltage starting) and two 30-hp wound-rotor induction motors on a 440-volt 3-phase 60-cycle supply.

Conductor Sizes

The full-load current of the 25-hp motor is 32 amp (Table 430-150). A full-load current of 32 amp × 1.25 (Sec. 430-22) requires a No. 8, Type R, rubber-covered conductor (Table 310-12). The full-load current of the 30-hp motor is 39 amp (Table 410-150). A full-load current of 39 amp × 1.25 (Sec. 430-22) requires a No. 6, Type R, rubber-covered conductor (Table 310-12).

The feeder conductor capacity will be 125 per cent of 39, plus 39, plus 32, or 120 amp (Sec. 430-24). In accordance with Table 310-12, this would require a No. 0, Type R, rubber-covered feeder.

Note. For Type R conductors run open in air, or for conductors with insulations other than Type R, see Tables 310-12 through 310-15.

Overcurrent Protection

Running. The 25-hp motor, with full-load current of 32 amp, must have running overcurrent protection of not over 40 amp (columns 2 and 3, Table 430-146). The 30-hp motor with full-load current of 39 amp must have running overcurrent protection of not over 50 amp (columns 2 and 3, Table 430-146).

Branch Circuit. The branch circuit of the 25-hp motor must have branch-circuit overcurrent protection of not over 100 amp (column 4, Table 430-146). The branch circuit of the 30-hp motor must have branch-circuit overcurrent protection of not over 60 amp (column 7, Table 430-146).

Feeder Circuit. The rating of the branch-circuit fuse for a 25-hp squirrel-cage motor is 300% of 32 amp, or 96 amp, which necessitates the use of a 100-amp standard-size fuse (Table 430-153), and for a 30-hp wound-rotor motor is 150% of 39 amp, or 59 amp (Table 430-153). The rating of the feeder fuse is, therefore, 100 plus 39 plus 39 which equals 178 amp, and a 200-amp fuse is the maximum size which may be used (see Sec. 430-62).

The setting of a motor-branch-circuit circuit breaker for a 25-hp squirrel-cage motor is 250% of 32 amp or 80 amp (Table 430-153); for a 30-hp wound-rotor motor is 150% of 39 amp or 59 amp (Table 430-153). The maximum setting of a feeder circuit breaker is 80 + 39 + 39 = 158 amp (see Sec. 430-62).

INDEX